HIGH-TEMPERATURE
INORGANIC COATINGS

Edited by

JOHN HUMINIK, JR.

Vice President and Senior Scientist
Value Engineering Company
Alexandria, Virginia

REINHOLD PUBLISHING CORPORATION
NEW YORK
CHAPMAN & HALL, LTD., LONDON

FOREWORD

At the root of all scientific progress is the simple fact that knowledge builds on knowledge; hence, rapid progress is a function not only of the effort expended as measured by time and dollars but also of how well and widely current information is disseminated to workers in a particular field. The bulk of research investigations are composed of methodical sifting of facts, reading of others' efforts on similar problems, and planning and conducting experiments. As thrilling as a spectacular advance may be to a scientist or engineer, actually such events are a rarity, and research of accumulated knowledge using new tools and fresh problem approaches in an orderly manner constitute the greatest part of scientific advancement.

"Protective Coatings for Metals" by Burns and Schuh was a monumental work when it appeared in 1939. At that time no one could have envisaged a time when we would seek means of protecting the ultimate high-temperature material, graphite, from deterioration, or ask for containers resistant to the passage of high velocity gases containing molten alumina. The present book on high-temperature inorganic coatings represents a record of man's endeavors in a very few years to cope with the problems suddenly thrust upon him by the demands of a space age.

The book is more than a record because the authors have set down, essentially in layman's language, the rudiments of coatings technology that can be used by anyone working on designs calling for high temperature operation.

The first authors in a brand new technical field are always faced with the formidable task of bringing together the known references and expressing the state of the art. In this situation the authors have done a highly commendable job of summarizing a mass of detail gleaned from summary reports of a great number of investigators (including themselves) and reducing it to a manageable body of knowledge. Making this information on high temperature coating technology available should do much to further our defense and space efforts.

The Editor is to be congratulated on his diligence, initiative and timeliness in bringing this material together.

Dr. Earl T. Hayes
Special Assistant for Materials
Department of Defense

PREFACE

The purpose of this book is to provide current information on the technology of protective coatings for materials operating above 1500°F.

It is hoped that adequate coverage of the subject will give the reader an understanding of the present state of the art through the eyes of those who are actively working in the field. An attempt is made to narrow down the great volumes of work until only the most obvious and most interesting aspects stand out for the reader. It is written primarily for those who are starting research in this field or who are engaged in the design and construction of equipment for operation in hot environments. It should also be useful as a general reference book for those already engaged in this fascinating technology.

So the reader will not be misled, it should be noted that not all of the coatings discussed herein are "off-the-shelf" production items. Many coatings are still undergoing research and cannot be expected for general use for a year or more, if at all.

It is recognized that the pages of this book do not present a complete review and evaluation of all present research; no attempt was made to do this or to present an exhaustive review of existing data on high-temperature coatings. However, it is believed that this book comprises one of the first comprehensive and authoritative presentations on this complex but timely subject.

After an introductory chapter lightly acquaints the reader with the general subject, subsequent chapters describe coating materials, processes for applying coatings, mechanisms occurring during operation and methods of testing. A chapter on designing with coatings has also been prepared in an effort to enlighten the reader as to how these essentially research items can be reliably used on production hardware. The final portion of the book speculates on the future and makes recommendations for specific areas of research.

The references in each chapter were intended to aid the reader desiring a more comprehensive study of the subject.

The editor is indebted to the U.S. Army Ordnance Corps and the U.S. Naval Bureau of Weapons for their support of his own recent researches in this field.

The editor is deeply indebted to Dr. Joseph L. Pentecost of Melpar, Inc., for his time and consideration in reviewing the manuscript and offering constructive criticism and helpful suggestions which have added considerably to the value of this book.

The assistance of Jo Ann Kilbourne was invaluable in the preparation of the index.

In addition, the editor wishes to acknowledge the invaluable assistance of Charlotte Marchal, who typed the entire manuscript.

Washington, D. C.   John Huminik, Jr.
May, 1963

ACKNOWLEDGMENT

The editor wishes to express his appreciation for the assistance given by the many companies, individuals and technical societies who helped in an unselfish manner in the preparation of this book.

Special thanks are also given to the following individuals and their respective corporations for their contribution of technical data and advice:

Dr. Joseph Lane, National Academy of Sciences
John Holden, U.S. Naval Ordnance Test Section
E. L. Robinson, Monsanto Chemical Company
Paul L. Raymond, National Research Corporation
John W. Winzeler, Plasmadyne Corporation
Ronald L. Johnson, Plasmadyne Corporation
Thomas F. Kearns, U.S. Bureau of Naval Weapons
William R. Benn, Carborundum Company
Richard A. Platt, Carborundum Company
Robert Van Houten, General Electric Company
Dwight G. Moore, National Bureau of Standards
John V. Long, Solar Aircraft Corp.
Jesse D. Walton, Georgia Institute of Technology
Zarr A. Post, Melpar, Inc.
Lt. Norman L. Hecht, Picatinny Arsenal
Commander Earl C. Vicars, Advanced Research Projects Agency
Sol J. Mateskey, U.S. Naval Bureau of Weapons
Neil N. Ault, Norton Company
Roger Kimball, Magna Corporation
Samuel Sklarew, Marquardt Corporation
Roy H. Lorenz, Fansteel Metallurgical Corporation
Martin L. Headman, Western Gear Corporation
William L. Aves, Chance Vought Corporation
H. R. Ogden, Battelle Memorial Institute
Burton S. Payne, The Pfaudler Company
L. L. Seigle, General Telephone and Electronics Laboratories
Martin H. Ortner, Vitro Laboratories
Joseph R. Palermo, Thermal Dynamics Corporation
G. D. Smith, E. I. du Pont de Nemours Company
Ronald Francis, A. D. Little, Inc.
Eugene Olcott, Atlantic Research Corporation

James Batchelor, Atlantic Research Corporation
Charles H. Martens, Army Ordnance Missile Command
Robert L. Strickman, Calorobic Materials
Daniel E. Lehane, Chromalloy Corporation
Jim Gangler, NASA
D. R. Rummler, NASA
Daniel J. Maykuth, Battelle Memorial Institute
M. G. Nicholas, General Telephone and Electronics Laboratories
J. Maltz, Bureau of Naval Weapons
E. P. Flint, Ipsen Industries
F. P. Huddle, Hughes Research
I. Machlin, Bureau of Naval Weapons
R. D. Guyton, Universal Technology Corp.
J. C. Barrett, Dept. of Defense
L. S. Croan, Army Material Command

CONTENTS

1

INTRODUCTION

The development of jet engines and rapid advancements in rocket motor technology created demands for high temperature structural materials. The service temperature of existing materials was limited by oxidation, chemical phenomena, erosion and melting. These limitations pointed to high temperature coatings as a method of providing improved reliability and higher operating temperature capability.

In the past, coatings were used primarily for corrosion protection, wear resistance and decoration. The exceptions were found in the isolated applications within industry that required protective coatings to operate in a hot chemical, electrical or metallurgical environment. Shortly after the turn of the century, the manufacturers of furnaces and the electrical industry began systematic coating research programs on a limited scale. The results of these early investigations were usually incorporated in commercial equipment on a proprietary basis and did little to advance the state of the art. In the years between the two World Wars, only a minimal research effort was directed toward high-temperature coatings except for programs aimed at improving the beauty or the corrosion and wear-resistant properties of the electroplated metals and ceramic coatings or enamels.

There was some concern, however, from the chemical industry as they began to experience catastrophic material failures in the newer processes that required high temperatures to properly react the chemicals. The chemical engineers of those early days felt that the problems could be resolved by selecting from the ever increasing variety of metals and alloys. The extensive metallurgical industry worked mainly toward the development of new alloys such as "Inconel" or processes for economical production of such metals as molybdenum or columbium. Relatively little attention was given to the possibility of a "high temperature coating" until the early years of World War II.

Even with the breaking of the sound barrier by an airplane in the 1940's, scientists were not aware of the aerodynamic heating problem;

but as planes began to exceed Mach No. 1, the problem immediately became acute. The first solutions were found with the high strength steels and aluminum alloys, rapidly followed by the stainless steels, titanium and cobalt alloys. As aircraft became more complex and capable of even higher speeds, it was apparent that new "skin" materials would be needed.

The jet engines used to propel the new planes had also reached a point where they needed new high-temperature construction materials and coatings for the existing ones if efficiency was going to be increased by operating at higher temperatures (over 1600°F).

In the period from 1945 to 1950 much interest in protective coatings for alloy steels, stainless steels and the new high nickel and cobalt alloys was apparent. From this interest in coatings and high temperature structural materials, today's more refined super-alloys and coatings for these alloys were developed. As even higher operating temperatures were required, a greater interest in the refractory metals developed and attention was given to their catastrophic oxidation and embrittlement problems. Industrial firms and government laboratories began to explore these new concerns with considerable zeal. Most of this concentrated work began around 1950, and was largely supported by the Department of Defense.

The introduction at that time of commercial grade molybdenum, in sufficient quantity to make it a candidate as a high temperature material of construction, opened the door to our modern high temperature technology, since molybdenum had the bulk properties needed to operate above 3000°F. Tantalum, tungsten, columbium, and more recently, vanadium followed in tonnages sufficient to warrant their consideration also as high temperature materials. All these metals had the major shortcoming of an intolerance for air while operating at high temperature. Even though they all had melting points above 4000°F, they vigorously oxidized at temperatures above 1500°F. The oxides formed usually sublimed at these temperatures, causing the metal literally to go up in smoke. In addition, these metals are embrittled by the presence of small traces of oxygen, nitrogen, and other elements absorbed while being heated, and hence become structurally unsound. The only answer seemed to be a barrier or coating to prevent these elements from reaching the metal. High-temperature failures of materials in general can also be attributed to overload, chemical attack, erosion, thermal shock, as well as the oxidation and embrittlement previously mentioned.

Two research approaches were taken in an attempt to alleviate these newly encountered problems: one of these was the development of oxidation-resistant alloys, and the other was the development of suitable protective coatings. Both approaches are still under research, but it is believed that the coating approach is the most feasible and has the best chance for success. This is based on the fact that when the composition of the base metal is changed so that its oxidation resistance improves, it loses the physical and mechanical properties which made it a desirable structural material in the first place. However, this may prove to be untrue if alloying concepts, as we know them now, are altered by some unique research.

Plastics have been receiving increased attention for use in structural applications in the past few years mainly because of the inherent advantages of these materials, namely, high strength, low density, low thermal conductivity, excellent resistance to chemical attack, and good electrical resistance. One of the important recent advances has been the development of new plastic materials both for short-time and for long-time resistance to temperatures below 500°F.

Polytrifluorochloroethylene and polytetrafluoroethylene plastics have been operated between 400 and 500°F for extended periods of time and have been used as ablative coatings for much higher temperatures. Phenyl silane and a trichelated aluminum have been used to 800°F. More recently, a dicycloherylphosphinoborine trimer produced by American Potash has performed well up to 900°F. Aluminum-oxygen polymers produced by U.S. Borax have been known to operate at 950°F. The latest melamine-ammeline condensation products which are ceramic-like in nature appear to be usable up to 1500°F. Perhaps coatings can prolong the operating time and increase the operating temperatures for all these materials.

The reinforced plastics are finding new uses as high-strength structural materials. The most common of these utilize a fibrous material which provides good tensile properties and an organic resin binding material which supports the fibers and helps transfer the load to the fibers. The reinforcing fiber may be any one of a variety of glasses, inorganic fibers, organic fibers, or metals. The binding materials can be polyester, silicon phenolic epoxy or melamine resins. The combination of reinforcement and binding materials determines the over-all characteristics of the composite material.

Various high-temperature electroplated coatings have been applied to these structural plastics in an effort to hold their temperatures below the deterioration point. Plastics are also coated by vacuum metallizing, cathode sputtering, vapor plating and metal spraying. These and other methods are covered in "Metallizing of Plastics," by Harold Narcus. Although specifically this book does not deal with high-temperature requirements, it would be easy to apply many of the principles explained therein to this subject.

The thickness of coating required to protect a structural plastic is determined by the time of exposure and the tolerance of the material combination to thermal shock. Frequently, an insulator such as zirconia or the foamed silicates is used over the structural plastic, followed by a suitable erosion-resistant top coat. More recently, honeycombed metals have been partially embedded in the plastic and sprayed with a cermet until the protruding honeycomb is completely covered. The composites have application as structural heat shields.

Ceramics have been coated by vapor deposition, spraying, and slurry casting to impart high-temperature resistance in certain environments. Ceramics are generally considered as being tolerant of high temperatures; however, when certain chemical or erosive environments are encountered, it is sometimes necessary to apply a protective coating. When a high-temperature ceramic requires certain thermal or electrical properties, coatings can often be of help.

From the preceding paragraphs it is evident that all materials have occasions when a high-temperature coating can improve an otherwise difficult situation. Throughout this book, numerous examples will more specifically inform the reader on the selection of coatings and base materials for high-temperature systems.

Aerospace Coating Problems

The high velocities of aerospace vehicles cause them to attain high skin temperatures within the earth's atmosphere, both on launch and on re-entry. Critical material failures and deterioration problems result from chemical attack, thermal shock, erosion, and differences in thermal expansion coefficients. Furthermore, the heat generated by propulsion systems or the heat transfer from hot skin can place strenuous temperature conditions upon instruments or life within the vehicle.

Rigid insulators are another class of materials which can be used in high-temperature designs. The better-known refractory type insulators are too heavy or bulky for many applications; they are usually limited to furnace insulation. Insulators are improving rapidly and can be expected to play a major role in the design of thermal protective systems in the future. Highly efficient insulators are presently being developed for use in high-temperature coating systems. Project Mercury and other manned space capsules use high-efficiency, light-weight insulation in conjunction with other materials to control the cabin temperature.

Such terms as reflectivity, emissivity, absorptivity, diffusion, and conductivity are becoming common in discussions between designers and the materials engineers. These terms indicate that the technology of high temperature-resistant coatings is becoming increasingly important and extremely complex. It is hoped that this book will clearly explain the relationship of these properties to coating performance.

Other, more severe material problems exist which require that coatings be developed before an advancement in the reliability of certain military items can be made. One of the better-known problem areas is found in solid propellant rocket motor nozzles, which are subjected to the most severe short-time environment of heat, erosive gases, and solid particles known to man. Erosion can cause decreased performance or even complete destruction of the nozzle in only a few seconds. Temperatures of the flame range from 4500 to 6800°F, and gas flow rates of several Mach numbers are encountered in many instances. Under these conditions the life of a material is extremely short. Several coatings which were conceived only a few years ago in research are being used presently in an effort to reduce the problem. Other coatings still in the laboratory are destined to bring new lightness, low cost, and high performance to the propulsion engineer within the next few years.

Another thermal problem which can be improved by a coating system is the temperature control and power generation systems for earth satellites and space ships. It is known that the heat generated by the sun becomes a problem outside the earth's atmosphere, and requires heat balancing in a vehicle if equipment and people are to survive. Also, since electrical power is needed within the vehicle, solar cells are used to convert solar energy to electricity. If proper coating systems are used, both the temperature within the vehicle and the solar power system will be kept in perfect balance. A complication occurring in these systems is the damage caused by the micrometeorites and the corpuscular radiation encountered in space. This radiation can destroy solar cells and coatings, thereby reducing their efficiency and throwing the system out of balance.

Research Highlights

High Temperature Paints. A promising coating system, which could be classified as a high-temperature paint, employs phosphate bonding (1). In this system, ceramic fillers are mixed with an aqueous solution of monoaluminum phosphate and then applied by spraying, brushing or dipping. The coating requires only a low-temperature cure (400°F) but is useful at temperatures to 2800°F.

Other work with the organic phosphorus compounds for high-temperature use is being conducted by Southern Research Institute (2). In this work, the zinc oxide-dimethyl hydrogen phosphate-ethyl acid phosphate combination yielded the best coatings of all those tested to date. Further studies with other bonding agents will probably yield coatings with higher temperature capability than the 1000°F, 136-hour test results of the present coating. The greater advantage of these coatings over others of this kind is that the curing temperatures are 75 to 136°F, which is essentially room-temperature curing. These systems do have their problems, however, such as the sensitivity to relative humidity during the cure.

Another paint type system is the "ceramic gold" which was evaluated at the Norair, Division of Northrop Corporation (*3*). When the performance of this paint is compared with an aluminum paint, the difference in the emittance characteristics is obvious. The gold-painted metal reached 825°F, while the aluminum-painted ones reached 1060°F when under exposure as shrouds for a jet engine. Again, the paints still have a temperature limit somewhere in the 1000°F region.

These paint systems do not actually qualify as high-temperature coatings as defined in this book. They are merely mentioned as an indication of some research that is moving toward the development of more advanced systems.

Sprayed Coatings. Coatings applied by spraying in oxygen-fuel torches, such as the well-known Norton Company "Rokide" coatings, have been used quite extensively. For example, "Rokide Z" (zirconium oxide) has found many uses as a protector of steel in the defense industry. In these cases, it served as a heat barrier or insulator to prevent heat from reaching the steel. The coatings are hard and can be considered chemically inert. They also have some deficiencies, such as slight porosity which prevents complete oxidation protection if this is a requirement. In general, sprayed coatings have been used for many of the high-temperature "emergencies" that have occurred during our rapid defense build-ups. The sprayed ceramics offer an excellent erosion barrier for short-term severe environments where oxidation protection of the base metal is not required.

For use against molten metals in the metallurgical industry, coatings such as aluminum nitride or mixtures of aluminum nitride and silicon carbide have been under development by the Carborundum Company, which also is perfecting its "Boride Z" for use over 3000°F where some electrical conductivity in the material is required.

In the writer's opinion, the metal borides will find application on a wide scale in the next few years. The oxides and borides will no doubt be among the first material considerations for sprayed coatings, due to their low cost, availability and excellent high temperature properties compared to many other compounds.

Coatings of Refractory Metals. An unusual approach to the high-temperature protection problem is the use of a refractory metal with or without an oxidation-resistant coating. The refractory metal is applied to lower-melting materials; it protects because of its high melting point and because the operational time period is short. Tungsten has been used for this purpose by applying it with a vapor plating technique.

Protection for Graphite. One area where research has been rather limited is in coatings for the protection of graphite at high temperatures. This is highlighted by a Russian report which stated (*4*) "the literature contains little information on methods for protecting these materials from high temperature gas corrosion." It goes on to state that a carbon and graphite coating of titanium disilicide has been patented in West Germany (1009093, December 1957), and that an American patent, 2449254, June 5, 1956, offers protective coatings for 1920°F. A Japanese patent, 3485, taken June 15, 1954, using a number of oxides and silicon carbide, offers some protection.

The Russians themselves have tested glassy siliceous carbide and carbide-silicide coatings. They produced one coating, for example, by mixing 80 per cent silicon oxide with 2.5 per cent aluminum oxide and 17.5 per cent beryllium oxide. Bentonite was added at 2 per cent to maintain the suspension, which was painted onto the graphite. The coatings were then fired at approximately 3000°F for a few minutes. The experimental conclusions indicated that these scientists obtained a coating good for operation at 2500°F for more than 100 hours.

Another concept of graphite protection is being developed by Value Engineering Company under government sponsorship. This work utilizes an electroplated cerment, such as chromium-zirconium boride. The system as deposited, has a melting point approaching 3400°F. More recently, experiments have been performed converting the chromium metal portion of the system to a chromium oxide, thereby raising the melting point of the system to between 4,000 and 5,000°F.

Columbium Coatings. The unique coating of zinc for columbium alloys is another example of a temperature-resistant coating from an unsuspected source (5). In this system, a zinc-columbium compound and zinc oxide are the final protective media. The process is accomplished by depositing zinc onto columbium by vapor plating, hot dipping, or electroplating. The coatings appear to be self-healing, but are limited to approximately 2000°F for operational service.

Other relatively low-melting materials could also be used to protect metals at temperatures exceeding 1500°F; a brief study of the elements easily indicates that many of the metals might form protective compounds if converted to an oxide, boride or carbide.

Diffusion Coatings. Coatings formed by diffusing a compound into the surface layer of a metal to serve as the sole source of high temperature protection are widely used. Application is usually carried out by surrounding the base material with the coating material and heating the entire assemblage at a sufficiently high temperature for a predetermined time. One problem in the diffusion of coatings into the various base materials is an undesirable chemical reaction which could damage the system. The undesirable reactions destroy the structural integrity of the base material by forming brittle compounds or low-melting eutectics.

Another problem with the diffusion type coatings is that they continue to diffuse into the base material while operating at high temperatures, resulting in a depletion of the surface coating. The reverse is also true i.e., the base material diffuses into the coating. Even if the service temperature is lower than the temperature used for applying the coating, ultimate failure can be expected because diffusion occurs even at low temperatures, if sufficient time is allowed.

Establishment of Coating Temperature Classification System

Because of the ever-increasing number of coating systems and the wide variety of high-temperature equipment that utilize coatings, it becomes necessary to develop a system to identify each coating from an engineering and design viewpoint.

Based on the author's experience and observations, it becomes apparent that two distinctly separate areas of operation can be identified, based on temperature. This is shown in Table 1.1. It is felt that the

TABLE 1.1. TEMPERATURE CLASSIFICATION SYSTEM
FOR COATING

Class I 1500 to 2000°F		Class II 3000 to 7000°F	
Ramjet		Rocket nozzles	
Turbojet		Rocket motor components	
Chemical processing equipment		Re-entry structure	
Furnace components		Re-entry nose cones	
Heating equipment		Furnace component	
Aerospace vehicles		Thermocouple housings	
Re-entry probes		Melting equipment	
		Plasma equipment	
Type IA	Type IIA	Type IB	Type IIB
Short time operation (less than one hour).	Long time operation (over one hour).	Short time operation (less than one hour).	Long time operation (over one hour).

temperature of operation can be the criterion for classification of all coatings. The temperature ranges of 1500 to 3000°F and 3000 to 7000°F were chosen because they fit the design requirements and the available coatings rather well. It should be noted that the melting point of a coating is not considered, since the latest research indicates that a molten layer can still be protective. Also, since complex compounds are formed, it is difficult to fix the melting point of the available coatings properly.

Since the time a coating operates is also an important factor in its performance, a subclassification in each of the two temperature ranges has been made which provides one designation for coatings with reliable operating ability for less than one hour, and another for coatings capable of longer operational periods.

The system outlined above can be further broken down into some finite details if it is adapted. Chemical resistance, wear resistance and emittance characteristics can be made a part of this classification.

REFERENCES

1. Eubanks, A. G., and Moore, D. G., "Investigation of Aluminum Phosphate Coatings for Thermal Insulation of Airframes," NASA Technical Note D-106, November, 1959.
2. Mileski, S. E., *et al.*, "Development of Heat-Resistant Paints for Metals," Report 5170-1264-VI, Southern Research Institute, Birmingham, Alabama, February, 1962.
3. Leonard, B. G., and Childer, H. D., "Evaluation of Ceramic Gold Coatings on Titanium," Report No. NAI-59-140, Northrop Corp., February 1959.
4. Sazonavo, M. V., *et al.*, "The Protection of Graphite Against Oxidation at Temperatures of 1200°C, "Zhur. Priklad. Khim., **34**, No. 3, 505 (1961).
5. Sandoz, G., and Lufton, T. C., "Mechanisms of Formation and Protection of Columbium-Zinc Coatings on Columbium," Paper Presented at Technical Conference on High Temperature Materials, Cleveland, April, 1962.

2

COATING MATERIALS AND COATING SYSTEMS

JOSEPH L. PENTECOST

Head, Materials Section
Melpar, Inc.
Falls Church, Virginia

INTRODUCTION

The techniques for applying high-temperature coatings are covered amply in Chapter 4 and the characteristics of the substrates are reviewed in Chapter 3. In this chapter, the materials and mixtures of materials (or entire coating systems) will be reviewed. Any discussion of materials must have some limitation; it is impractical to review the basic chemistry and physics of materials in a book of this type, and basic familiarity with the material sciences has been assumed in the preparation of this chapter.

Coating materials for high-temperature wire, superalloys, steels, ceramics and plastics, as well as refractory metals will be discussed. Many of these materials are in widespread usage for a number of applications, while others show only faint promise or have had only preliminary development work. While many of the "developmental" materials will later be proved unsatisfactory, if this summary stimulates fruitful work with any unusual or new materials, it will have served its purpose.

Two goals are set forth in this chapter; first to review briefly the characteristics of a number of compounds which used singly or in simple mixtures yield coatings, and second to describe and illustrate the principal types of coating systems in current use.

The information in this chapter has been difficult to organize logically since a single material is rarely used alone as a coating (it is always in contact with the substrate). While much general information is available about pure compounds, this information is often not as important as the specific reactions which occur between materials, and unfortunately, facts on the interactions, phase relations and stability of material combinations are much more difficult to collect or present logically. Specific discussions have been included of a number of selected materials which are in general use and of others which should receive more consideration. Where specific limitations exist, such as crystalline transitions, hydration, or high cost, these have been included. Also included is a brief discussion of stability of various combinations of oxides, metals, and intermetallics.

The characteristics of various coating systems or application techniques are described in the second part of this chapter. An effort has been made to describe briefly the various approaches to forming high-temperature coatings, the general characteristics of coatings produced by each technique, and a tabulation of commercial coating processes which exemplify each coating technique.

GENERAL COATING REQUIREMENTS

There are five basic reasons for using coatings at high temperatures:

(1) for oxidation or corrosion or diffusion control (chemical).
(2) for erosion or abrasion resistance (mechanical).
(3) for electrical applications as a conductor or insulator (electrical).
(4) for emittance control (radiation).
(5) for conductive heat transfer control (thermal).

Most coatings serve more than one of the above functions, and over-all performance is always a compromise. Since the objective of this book is a broad coverage of coatings and coating applications, some of the specific requirements for each basic coating function should be stressed. For high-temperature oxidation resistance, for example, a coating should: (1) resist oxygen and metal ion diffusion, (2) have a low vapor pressure at the operating temperature, (3) have a melting point above the operating temperature, (4) have low reactivity with the substrate, and (5) have low reactivity with the high-temperature environment. In considering materials for such coating applications, data covering all these points should be reviewed, rather than simply noting the melting point, as has been done frequently. As higher temperatures are reached (2500°F and above), the melting point of compounds rapidly ceases to be the important consideration, and reaction rates, diffusion rates and vapor pressure must receive prime attention. For coating applications where the basic coating function is control of a chemical process such as oxidation or corrosion, it is vital to understand the physical chemistry and thermodynamics of the coating-substrate system.

Coatings for mechanical protection, thermal conductivity and emittance control represent an important segment of current coating efforts. Generally the internal chemistry and reaction mechanisms within the coating-base system are less important than the external characteristics. With the wide range of coating techniques available for applying extremely hard materials to surfaces, improved wear and erosion resistance can be achieved for soft base materials. Here the primary concern is generally the adhesion, hardness and toughness of the coating. For emittance control, however only the external surface characteristics are important. Only reaction mechanisms in or on the surface of the coating, and vaporization of the coating which destroys the desired surface condition need to be considered. (Since emittance characteristics vary with surface roughness, the application technique is also an important variable.) Other coating characteristics must frequently be compromised in the selection of coating material, however, because of the limited materials with satisfactory emittance properties.

In coatings for electrical applications, the materials with satisfactory properties are also generally limited. Specific conduction or insulation characteristics are required of the coating and other factors must sometimes be compromised.

Materials have been classified into five groups for this discussion: the oxides, the "hard metals" (carbides, borides, nitrides, silicides), the intermetallics, the metals, and the pyrolytic deposits. These materials largely represent the basic materials for coatings or the major constituents. Where specific combinations of materials are in general usage in a coating formulation, an effort has been made to include the available information. Some general characteristics of materials are shown in Figs. 2.1 and 2.2.

THE OXIDES

As a group, the refractory oxide materials are generally the most interesting of the high-temperature materials. They are characterized by stability in an oxidizing atmosphere, high melting point, high compressive strength, a brittle cyrstal at low temperatures, and low or moderate cost. The oxide systems provide the basis for the ceramic, glass and refractory industries, and are the most familiar high-temperature materials. While pure oxide single crystals are being intensively investigated, it must be noted that there is still a large gap in the basic understanding of flow and deformation processes in oxide crystals and in the basic chemistry and physics of many oxide systems. While the structures of most oxide crystals are simple, they are much more complex than the metal and semiconductor structures which are better understood. This structural complexity, i.e., the presence of both metal and oxygen atoms, coupled with the difficulty of growing satisfactory high-purity single

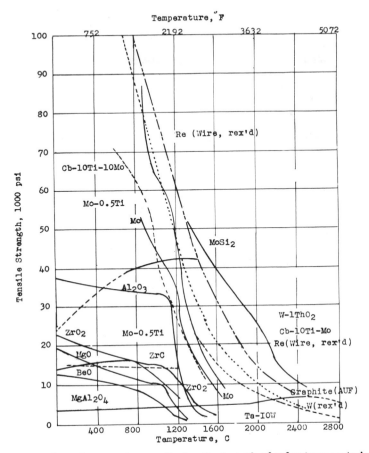

Fig. 2.1. Effect of temperature on the tensile strength of refractory materials.

crystals of the oxides with closely controlled stoichiometry, has severely hampered much basic research which would provide more accurate property information. Similarly, the influence of minute impurities on structural and electrical properties has only recently been systematically studied.

While this single crystal research will provide additional interesting and important information, coatings use almost exclusively amorphous or polycrystalline structures for which much of the available information on oxides is appropriate. In the discussions which follow, single crystal information has been included and noted where available, but most of

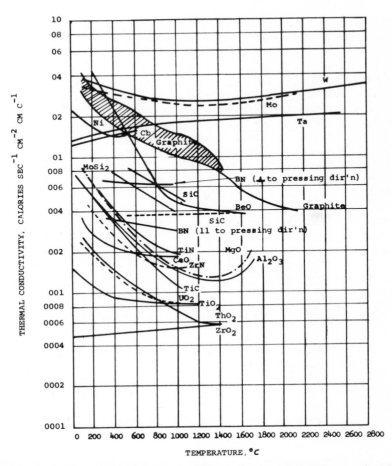

Fig. 2.2. Thermal conductivities of various refractory materials as a function of temperature.

the properties represent those of high-purity, high-density polycrystalline materials.

Aluminum Oxide (Alumina)

Alpha aluminum oxide (Al_2O_3 or corundum) is one of the most widely used refractory compounds. It receives this emphasis because of its low cost, high mechanical strength, availability in a number of forms, and a vast background of information regarding its uses. Its melting point is 3720°F and its vapor pressure is less than 1 Torr at the melting point. Its stability, even in a strongly reducing atmosphere, is excellent to above 3090°F and, in oxidizing conditions, can be used above 3450°F. While alumina is only a moderately refractory material when extreme temperatures are considered, the vast amount of experience fabricators have had with alumina also partially explains its popularity. For many refractory applications, alumina is unquestionably an excellent choice, and deserves this popularity.

Aluminum oxide occurs naturally as corundum, sapphire and ruby, the small amounts of impurities accounting for differences in color. Commercial alumina is produced, however, from hydrated alumina minerals such as bauxite and diaspore. The aluminum industry has, fortunately, provided improved alumina materials as progress has been made in treating aluminum ores. Today, most high-purity alumina is a product of the same Bayer process which supplies the feed materials for electrolytic reduction cells in the aluminum metal industry. Notable exceptions do exist. For the production of synthetic sapphire and for certain polishing applications, very fine grain alumina is required, and this is frequently produced by calcining ammonium aluminum sulfate. The resultant product can be maintained extremely pure (less than 150 ppm impurities) in rather large quantities. This form of high purity alumina is often not completely alpha alumina, but contains a portion of gamma alumina, another crystallographic form of Al_2O_3. Also, when alpha alumina is rapidly quenched from the molten condition as in flame spraying, the gamma form is predominant, though metastable, at room temperature. More complete information on the relationship between alpha alumina, gamma alumina, and its hydrated forms is available (*1*).

Alpha alumina is a hexagonal crystal, and as such is anisotropic. Its properties vary according to crystallographic direction, and for practical polycrystalline forms, the properties are an average of the properties in each of the two major crystallographic directions. The high mechanical strength of alumina can be attributed, at least partially, to the absence of cleavage or distinct parting directions in the crystal. One might speculate that even higher mechanical strength would occur in polycrystalline materials if the internal stresses due to the difference in thermal expansion did not exist in the a-axis and c-axis of each crystallite (*2*). The oxide film formed on aluminum is protective against continued oxidation; however, the low melting point of the metal precludes its use alone as a high-temperature coating material. Impure aluminum oxide and aluminates are also the protective oxidation products of the aluminide intermetallics. Since the melting point of many aluminides is above 2500°F, the formation of aluminum oxide coatings *in situ* through the oxidation of aluminide coatings has provided a practical method of "applying" aluminum oxide in coating form. A tabulation of properties of alumina are found in Table 2.1.

TABLE 2.1. PROPERTIES OF SELECTED REFRACTORY OXIDES

	Al_2O_3	BeO	CeO	Cr_2O_3	HfO_2	MgO	NiO	SiO_2	ThO_2	TiO_2	Y_2O_3	ZrO_2
Melting point, °F	3720	4660	4800±	4250±	5090	5070	3450	3140	5800	3340	4370	4870
Density, gm/cc	3.98	3.01	7.13	5.21	9.68	3.58	6.8	2.32	10.0	4.17	4.84	5.56
Crystal system	Hexagonal	Hexagonal	Cubic	Hexagonal	Monoclinic*	Cubic	Cubic	Hexagonal*	Cubic	Tetragonal*	Cubic	Monoclinic*
Specific heat, cal/gm°C												
100°F	0.21	0.20	...	(0.20)	0.17	0.22	...	0.18†	0.56	0.17	0.13	0.12
1300°F	0.29	0.85	...	...	0.18	0.31	...	...	...	0.22	...	0.16
2200°F	0.31	...	...	...	...	...	...	...	...	...	...	...
Thermal conductivity, cal/cm/sec°C												
100°F	0.10	0.50	...	(0.15)	0.0040	0.090	0.032	0.005†	0.036	0.023	(0.08)	0.0040
1300°F	0.018	0.09	...	(0.03)	0.0038	0.020	0.012	0.006	0.008	0.009	...	0.0043
2200°F	0.013	0.041	...	(0.03)	...	0.013	...	...	0.005	0.008	...	0.0049
Normal total emittance												
100°F	0.75	...	...	...	...	...	...	...	0.86	...	...	...
2200°F	0.35	0.42	...	(0.80)	...	0.28	(0.80)	0.65	1300°F	...	...	0.45
Electrical resistivity, ohm-cm												
1300°F	$8 \times 10^{+9}$	$2 \times 10^{+8}$	2×10^3	75	10^7	1×10^{10}	6×10^3	5×10^5	3×10^4	8×10^3	...	2×10^4
2200°F	$4 \times 10^{+5}$	$8 \times 10^{+5}$	20	25	10^4	$1 \times 10^{+6}$	30	3×10^4	2×10^2	40	...	4×10^2
Typical flexural strength, Psi												
RT	35,000	25,000	...	...	20,000	15,000	...	15,500†	12,000	8,000	...	20,000
1300°F	34,000	...	...	...	...	16,000	...	...	...	...	...	17,000
2200°F	18,500	...	...	...	...	8,000	...	...	...	...	...	12,000

*undergoes transition
†glass

Beryllium Oxide (Beryllia)

Beryllium oxide (BeO) is a stable oxide of low volatility with a melting point of 4660°F. The major deterrent to its usage is its reported toxicity; however, this property has been somewhat overemphasized. BeO is not normally toxic to humans in powder or dense form, even if ingested orally in sizable dosages. Neither is it toxic when in contact with the skin, but it occasionally causes a mild skin rash in sensitive individuals. Beryllium oxide is only dangerous when inhaled into the lungs, and this generally requires airborne particles $(1-5\mu)$ which can be easily eliminated even in dusty batching and machining (grinding) operations by reasonable hooding. The medical evidence for the extent of the danger from inhalation has often been disputed.

The merits of BeO as a refractory material have gone largely untried for many applications due to its reported toxic character; however, the property information available indicates that its usefulness could exceed that of alumina in many electrical and thermal applications. Its melting point is higher than that of alumina, and its thermal conductivity near room temperature approaches that of aluminum metal (however, this conductivity decreases somewhat with temperature). Its high electrical resistivity, low electrical loss and low density make it often more attractive than alumina as an electrical insulator, particularly for use at very high temperatures (3100 to 3600°F). Its mechanical strength, while somewhat lower than that of alumina, is comparable on an equal weight basis.

BeO shows no tendency toward reduction in a hydrogen atmosphere even at 4260°F, and its low vapor pressure allows use in a vacuum to 3600°F (2000°C) or higher. Above 3000°F, BeO reacts with water vapor to form volatile $Be(OH)_2$. This reaction may occur in the normal air furnace atmosphere, resulting in a gradual loss in weight in BeO parts. For gas-fired furnace atmospheres, the loss is more rapid due to the combustion products. Normal flues or hoods provide adequate personnel safety from the volatile products, however, and contamination of furnace linings is insignificant even after repeated firings of BeO (3).

Since adequate safeguards are available for handling even extremely toxic materials, BeO deserves further consideration in flame and plasma spraying, and other coating processes. Beryllium oxide is available in several grades and forms; its behavior on heating and sintering varies widely with initial crystallite size.

Cerium Oxide (Ceria)

Two oxides of cerium exist, Ce_2O_3 and CeO_2. The latter is the more stable with a melting point of 4700 to 4980°F. (This discrepancy, found in the reported melting point by various investigators, is probably due to partial reduction of CeO_2.) While cerium is considered a "rare-earth" element it is actually more abundant in the earth's crust than zinc or tin. There is a tendency to reduce CeO_2 to Ce_2O_3 (mp 3070°F) if the atmosphere is strongly reducing, but ceria, CeO_2, is generally a stable oxide of cubic structure with a fluorite type lattice, undergoing no transitions between room temperature and its melting point.

When slightly reduced, it tends to lose oxygen and discoloration of the normally white oxide occurs. Various shades of ivory, tan or brown occur with increasing loss of oxygen from the structure. The reduction of ceria from CeO_2 to Ce_2O_3 takes place in several orderly steps and includes Ce_4O_7, a blue compound.

In spite of its variable oxygen content, CeO_2 is generally an inert and valuable refractory oxide for general use. Its compatibility with a number of oxides make it an ideal choice to separate two otherwise incompatible materials. Ceria has shown particular usefulness as a coating for zirconia in contact with magnesia. As an addition to ZrO_2, it stabilizes the cubic structure similarly to additions of CaO, but CeO_2 is rarely used for this purpose due to its high cost.

Ceria is readily flame-sprayed, forming a dense coating. Since partial reduction may occur during application, the resulting oxygen deficiency in the coating structure may improve the short-term oxidation protection provided by ceria coatings.

Chromium Oxide (Chromia)

Chromium Oxide (Cr_2O_3) is frequently omitted from refractory oxide tabulations, which is unfortunate since some of the properties of chromia deserve closer consideration. Cr_2O_3 has a melting point of 4130 to 4410°F and has frequently been reported volatile above 2912°F. Recent measurements indicate a vapor pressure of 9×10^{-3} Torr at 3130°F. This is about twice as great as the vapor pressure of alumina at that temperature. If chromia and alumina are heated together to temperatures above 2900°F in the same closed atmosphere, some absorption of Cr_2O_3 with a resultant pink coloring in the alumina occurs. This evidence is sufficient to indicate its volatility. There is no indication that upon volatilization there is a loss of oxygen in Cr_2O_3, since the vaporization rate is not altered appreciably by atmospheres of CO or O_2. Under high oxygen pressures, chromium forms several other higher oxides (4), but these are not stable at elevated temperatures under normal atmospheric conditions or *in vacuo*. In a strongly reducing atmosphere, Cr_2O_3 is reduced to chromium metal (mp 3430°F) and the metal forms a eutectic with Cr_2O_3 at $\sim$ 2900°F. Chromium oxide is stable in a moist atmosphere and resists many corrosive halides at elevated temperatures. In contact with graphite, the carbide is readily formed.

Chromium oxide has rarely been used alone, but has found wide usage in combination with MgO for chrome-magnesite refractories for the steel industry. It is interesting to note that a number of high-temperature coatings for ferrous alloys contain Cr_2O_3 in high percentages, and that the oxide from many Ni-Cr alloys (containing Cr_2O_3) offers appreciable oxidation protection to the base alloy. Of the refractory metals, excluding the platinum group, chromium has the lowest oxidation rate, signifying the partial protection offered by Cr_2O_3. Further information is found in Table 2.1.

Hafnium Oxide HfO_2 (Hafnia)

Hafnium oxide normally occurs (2 to 7 per cent) with zirconium-bearing minerals and is not separated from zirconium oxide in general practice. Since its melting point is 5090°F (2810°C) and it forms a solid solution with zirconium oxide (ZrO_2), it does not impair the ZrO_2 performance. Pure hafnia is scarce and expensive due to the difficulty in separating it from ZrO_2. It would be generally preferable to ZrO_2 in most applications if cost were not a factor.

Hafnia undergoes the same transitions as zirconia; however, the inversion from the monoclinic structure occurs at a higher temperature (2200 to 3270°F), and is not accompanied by as large a volume change.

While hafnium oxide is reported to absorb an appreciable quantity of hafium metal, the existance of lower oxides has not been confirmed. Hafnia can be stabilized into the cubic form similar to zirconia by suitable additions of calcia, or other oxides such as CeO_2 or MgO.

Hafnium oxide is easily flame- or plasma-sprayed and the resulting coating is similar to those formed from zirconia. Hafnium metal is not protected by HfO_2 and oxidizes rapidly at high temperature. Efforts to form dense, adherent coatings of HfO_2 by oxidation of hafnium compounds at the surface of a coating have been generally unsuccessful.

Nickel Oxide

Nickel oxide (NiO) is an easily reducible oxide. Its melting point is 3540°F; however, its vapor pressure at the melting point is appreciable. In strongly oxidizing atmospheres at low temperatures (750 to 1100°F) it may oxidize to Ni_2O_3, but it reduces to NiO above 1100°F. The volume change accompanying this reaction is destructive to NiO bodies. NiO is the only refractory reducible to the metal by a hydrogen atmosphere.

Nickel oxide sinters readily and the raw NiO oxide is commercially available. It has a crystal structure nearly cubic like that of NaCl. NiO is produced mainly from natural sulfides, arsenides and hydrated silicates of nickel.

Magnesium Oxide (Magnesia)

Magnesium oxide (MgO) has a melting point of 5070°F (2800°C) and its cubic structure shows no inversions up to the melting point.

Magnesia shows little tendency to hydrate in the dense, well-sintered condition or as a single crystal; this hydration tendency is frequency overemphasized.

Magnesia occurs naturally as periclase, but most commercial MgO is produced from seawater by an extraction process. Coarse arc-fused magnesia grain is used extensively for electrical insulation of sheathed electrical heating elements and as a basic raw material for other magnesia specialties.

The mechanical strength of magnesia is low due to its distinct cubic cleavage. Freshly cleaved plates of high-purity MgO single crystal have exhibited appreciable plastic deformation near ambient temperatures, but equivalent deformation in polycrystalline structures has not been achieved. Magnesia exhibits a high thermal conductivity and excellent resistance to alkali or the noble metals.

The vapor pressure of magnesia is high at temperatures far below its melting point and it is not useful in a vacuum at temperatures around 3100°F. Vaporization occurs by dissociation into the elements, rather than as MgO molecules. Magnesia is flame or plasma sprayed only with difficulty due to its vaporization. Nickel and NiO additions are often used to improve deposit quality.

Magnesium Aluminate (Spinel)

Spinel ($MgAl_2O_4$) occurs in nature as a mineral and represents a large family of ($M^{+2} M_2^{+3} O_4$) compounds. Chromite ($FeCr_2O_4$), magnetite ($FeFe_2O_4$), and a large variety of other spinel structures are possible, but in this chapter the term spinel will be used to designate only the magnesium aluminate variety unless otherwise noted.

Spinel melts congruently at 3875°F and its cubic lattice shows no inversions over the entire temperature range. Spinel shows chemical properties quite different from those of alumina, and its low reactivity with oxides of vanadium, molybdenum, tantalum, columbium and tungsten should be noted. Its resistance to many strongly basic salts, oxides and slags is better than that of alumina. The thermal shock resistance and mechanical strength of spinel is reportedly inferior to that of alumina; however, spinel test specimens are not as easily prepared to a perfection comparable to that of alumina and published strength data may be misleading. The mechanical strength of spinel is superior to alumina above 2700°F, but the modulus of elasticity of spinel is probably lower than that for alumina in this temperature range.

Silicon Oxide (Silica)

Silicon dioxide (SiO_2) is the oxide most common in the earth's crust. The stable, low-temperature form is low-quartz, which undergoes several disruptive transitions between room temperature and its melting point at 3110°F. The stability conditions for each modification of cristobalite, tridymite and high-quartz are described in reference (5), and will not be reviewed. The most useful form of silica for general application is the glassy (amorphous or vitreous) form produced by cooling molten SiO_2. Liquid SiO_2 is extremely viscous (it will not pour from a crucible at several hundred degrees above its melting point); when cooled, it does not crystallize, but forms an amorphous solid of extremely low thermal expansion and low thermal conductivity. This form of silica is familiar as crucibles, tubes and laboratory ware, but vitreous silica grain and powder are also available for casting, or ramming and sintering. Parts made from such silica is often referred to as reconstituted silica, (Glasrock, Masrock*) to distinguish them from the dense glass products. Silica, as a protective reaction product from the oxidation of the silicides, accounts for the oxidation resistance of these materials.

Silica glass is the oxidation product of the silicides and other silicon hard metals such as silicon carbide, and silicon nitride. The formation of the amorphous or glassy oxide layer on these materials explains their oxidation resistance. A silica glass oxidation product containing other oxide impurities is generally responsible for the oxidation protection offered by the silicide coatings in use on molybdenum.

Thorium Oxide (Thoria)

Thorium oxide (ThO_2) is the most refractory oxide, with a melting point of 5800°F. The major deterrents to its use are its high density (9.69 gm/cc), high cost, slight radioactivity and poor thermal shock resistance. Its low vapor pressure (one of the lowest of the oxides above 3600°F), and its very low reactivity with many molten materials, are its advantages.

Thorium is not rare, but its separation from the rare earth in monazite, the chief raw material, is difficult and expensive. The slight radioactivity from thorium, though not a serious hazard, requires that the dust be removed by adequate ventilation.

A major use of thorium oxide has been in gas mantles. A soluble thorium salt with 1 per cent cerium salt is used to impregnate the cloth mantle. Upon burning away the organic fabric, the oxide skeleton remains, and glows brightly from the burning gases (surface combustion). The ThO_2–1%CeO_2 composition is reported to have maximum emittance in the visible spectrum (~ 0.86 at 0.45μ decreasing to ~ 0.24 at 0.6μ).

ThO_2, with slight impurity oxides in solid solution, is a poor electrical insulator, forming a defect semiconductor. Light sensitivity is common, the normal white color darkening to brown or purple upon exposure to visible light, the color disappearing or decreasing when

*Glasrock Products, Inc.

the exposed sample is kept in darkness. This sensitivity could be due to traces of rare earth contaminants such as Pr_2O_3.

Titanium Oxide (Titania)

Titanium dioxide (TiO_2) is a chemically stable crystal melting at 3340°F, and has received considerable interest as a dielectric material. Titania is easily reduced to Ti_2O_3 or $2Ti_2O_3 \cdot 3TiO_2$, an intermediate oxide. Titania exists in several allotropic forms— brookite, rutile and two forms of anatase. The stability relationships between these forms is not well established and several of the transitions are reported to be sluggish. There is also evidence that minor impurities may be necessary to improve the stability of several structures. Rutile is the most stable and most common form of titania.

The tetragonal structure of rutile has appreciable anisotropy of properties, which probably accounts for its poor mechanical strength and thermal shock resistance. While titania is not highly refractory, its ability to form defect structures dependent on atmosphere and minor impurities, its unique electrical properties (dielectric constant 95-100), and its very high index of refraction make it an interesting material. TiO_2 shows some volatility and both TiO and TiO_2 molecules appear in the vapor at 3600°F.

Yttrium Oxide (Yttria)

Yttrium oxide (Y_2O_3) is classed as a "rare earth" though it is more abundant than beryllium, cobalt or silver. Its melting point of 4370°F, and its cubic structure which shows no inversions make it an attractive refractory. Its high cost and slight tendency to hydrate and form the carbonate at room temperature limit its application.

The chief sources of yttria are the monazite sands and gadolinite ($FeO \cdot BeO \cdot Y_2O_3 \cdot 2SiO_2$). It has recently received emphasis as a component of magnetic yttrium iron garnet ($Y_3Fe_5O_{12}$).

Yttria has a thermal expansion similar to that of Al_2O_3, and similar thermal shock resistance. Its thermodynamic stability at elevated temperatures is frequently noted in the literature; however, its vapor pressure at 3600°F is reported to be higher than thermodynamic calculations would indicate (6).

Zirconium Oxide (Zirconia)

Zirconium oxide (ZrO_2) is a chemically stable refractory with a melting point of 4870°F. It is normally monoclinic between room temperature and 2160°F with a density ot 5.56 gm/cc. Above 2160°F, the monoclinic form inverts to the tetragonal form with a density of 6.10 gm/cc, the transition temperature shifting downward with added impurities. This large change in density signifies the large volume change ($\sim$10 per cent) which is generally destructive to any sintered shape or single crystal upon cooling from a high temperature. This disruptive transition can be eliminated or modified by additions of 3 to 15 per cent CaO, CeO$_2$, Y$_2$O$_3$ or MnO to form a solid solution of cubic structure which is stable at high temperatures and metastable below 1470 to 2000°F. This stabilized cubic form of zirconia is normally used for all refractory brick, shapes, rods and tubes. Stabilized ZrO$_2$ has a high (but linear) thermal expansion and is fairly resistant to thermal shock. Completely stabilized zirconia exhibiting no evidence of the transformation at 1800 to 2200°F can be achieved, but it is often more desirable to retain about 15 per cent monoclinic zirconia to lower the total thermal expansion.

Zirconia may be stabilized with either 5 per cent CaO or 15 per cent Y$_2$O$_3$, but CaO is most common due to its low cost. Calcia-stabilized zirconia has a higher electrical resistivity than yttria-stabilized zirconia, but the oxygen transfer from the former to a molten metal or metal contact is greater than from the latter. This would indicate that Y$_2$O$_3$-zirconia compositions are preferable in protective coating applications. Effective stabilization can be achieved with mixtures of CaO, Y$_2$O$_3$ and CeO$_2$ often in total percentages of the mixture less than that required of an individual oxide.

The thermal conductivity of ZrO$_2$ is the lowest of all common oxides, with the possible exception of amorphous silica at low temperatures, and there is less change in conductivity with temperature than with all other oxides. The electrical resistance of stabilized ZrO$_2$ is somewhat low, and its use as an electrical insulator has been questioned. This high electrical conductivity, however, is 10^3 to 10^4 lower than the conductivity of most metals at 3600°F, and in practice ZrO$_2$ can be used as a *low* voltage insulator at high temperature.

Zirconium oxide is normally associated with 2 to 7 per cent hafnium oxide in the native minerals zircon and baddeleyite. This HfO$_2$ is not normally removed in processing and forms a solid solution with ZrO$_2$, not deteriorating the refractoriness or other properties.

Zirconia is reported to be stable in vacuum, hydrogen or in contact with carbon to 4170°F and no reaction is reported between ZrO$_2$ and molybdenum to 3600°F (8).

ZrO$_2$ does not form a protective film over zirconium metal and efforts to form oxygen impervious coatings of ZrO$_2$ on refractory metals have been unsuccessful.

Zirconium Silicate (Zircon)

Zircon (ZrSiO$_4$), has a "melting point" of the reported 4400°F only when heated very rapidly to that temperature, not allowing equilibrium to occur. The actual phase relationship between ZrO$_2$ and SiO$_2$ shows a peritectic at 3230°F for ZrSiO$_4$ and a eutectic in the system at 3050°F. If ZrSiO$_4$ is heated slowly, it is unstable above 3000°F.

The low thermal expansion of zircon and resistance to molten metals such as aluminum, platinum and high nickel alloys make it particularly useful in coating applications. Its electrical insulating characteristics are generally inferior to Al_2O_3 or BeO, but useful at low temperatures.

Stability and Compatibility of the Oxides

Selected refractory oxides have been discussed briefly and their pertinent properties given in Table 2.1. The compatibility of binary combinations of these oxides may be summarized from Table 2.2, which shows the approximate liquidus temperature, or in most cases, the eutectic temperature for each combination. These temperatures generally represent the maximum temperature possible without a melting reaction occuring at equilibrium. In most cases the useful temperature limit will be somewhat lower than the indicated temperature.

Since primary emphasis is being placed on coating materials, the reaction of the oxides with metallic materials is important. A tabulation of the maximum use temperature for various metal-oxide combinations appears in Table 2.3. The data in this table are a compilation of data from several sources and estimates where only qualitative information is available. These reaction temperatures are generally realistic for 10 to 100 hours surface contact. Obviously, a material may be suitable for a melting crucible at 4170°F (2300°C) where the contact is maintained only for a short time, while the same combination of elements react substantially at 3630°F (2000°C) over a 100-hour period. An example of zirconia melted on tungsten foil at 5410°F without indication of reaction is reported by Resnick (9), while Kieffer (10) reports ZrO_2-W combinations useful only to 2900°F for resistance-heated furnace construction. This indicates the difficulty in establishing realistic values for the reaction temperatures in Table 2.3.

In considering the stability of materials and combinations at high temperatures, some consideration must be given to the atmosphere surrounding these materials. In addition to diffusion, several processes may occur at temperatures above 2700°F which are not apparent to the casual observer. Beryllia has been noted to react with water appreciably at 3000°F and above:

$$BeO + H_2O \rightleftharpoons Be(OH)_2$$

This cycle occurs transporting the BeO to a cooler point. Magnesium oxide under the same conditions would show no reaction (6).

Generally, oxides which have high melting points become less stable above the boiling point of the metal. Magnesium oxide and hafnium oxide can be compared on the basis of melting point; however, MgO is much more volatile than HfO_2 and this can be attributed to the thermodynamic stability of MgO decreasing rapidly above the boiling point of Mg metal.

TABLE 2.2. LIQUIDUS TEMPERATURES (°F) FOR SELECTED OXIDE COMBINATIONS

	Al_2O_3	BeO	CaO	CeO_2	Cr_2O_3	MgO	SiO_2	ThO_2	TiO_2	ZrO_2	Spinel	Zircon
Al_2O_3	3720											
BeO	3450	4580										
CaO	2550	2640	4660									
CeO_2	3180	3580	3630	4980								
Cr_2O_3	3720	4030	1870	4080	4110							
MgO	3470	3270	4160	3990	3850	5070						
SiO_2	2810	3040	2620	3090	3090	2800	3110					
ThO_2	3180	3900	4160	4710	3230	3810	3090	5520				
TiO_2	3130	3090	2590	2730	3180	2910	2800	2960	3320			
ZrO_2	3090	3630	3990	4350	4220	2730	3050	4850	3180	4890		
$MgO \cdot Al_2O_3$	3470	~3130	~3360	~3090	~3450	3680	2450	~3180	~2910	3880	~3880	
$ZrO_2 \cdot SiO_2$	2800	~3000	~2550	~3090	~3090	~2730	3050	~3060	2730	3050	2370	4390

TABLE 2.3. ESTIMATED MAXIMUM USE TEMPERATURES (°F)
FOR OXIDES IN CONTACT WITH VARIOUS METALS
AND CARBON (10–100 HR)

	Al_2O_3	BeO	Cr_2O_3	HfO_2	MgO	SiO_2	ThO_2	TiO_2	Y_2O_3	ZrO_2	Spinel
W	3600	3800	3300	3800	3600	2900	4150	3300	3600	3450	3600
Mo	3600	3450	3300	3900	3300	2700	4000	3300	3600	3800	3600
Ta	2900	2900	2900	3450	3300	2700	4000	3200	3450	3450	3550
Nb	3300	2900	3100	2900	3200	...	3200	2700	3100	2900	3100
Cr	3450	3450	2800	3450	3450	2700	3450	...	3450	3450	3450
V	3100	3100	2900	3100	3100	2700	3100	...	3100	3100	3100
Ti	2900	2900	...	3100	...	...	3100	2900	...	3100	2900
C	3000	3600	...	3600	3000	2700	2900	2700	3600	3600	2900

For hydrogen atmospheres, the only refractory oxides which show pronounced reduction are CeO_2 and NiO. CeO is only reduced to Ce_2O_3, but NiO can be reduced to the metal. However, the slight partial pressure of water vapor formed from the equilibrium reaction of H_2 with many oxides is sufficient to cause the same water-cycle transport that may occur with BeO in air. For CeO_2, MgO, NiO, SiO_2, Ta_2O_5, TiO_2 and V_2O_5, appreciable reaction may occur if the hydrogen flow is continuous (6).

With carbon and carbon monoxide atmospheres, the situation is quite different, for the reaction:

$$\tfrac{1}{2} TiO_2 + 2\ CO \rightleftharpoons \tfrac{1}{2}\ TiC + \tfrac{3}{2}\ CO_2$$

The stability of TiO_2 in a CO atmosphere decreases with temperature; the stability of CO increases with temperature while the stability of TiC decrease with temperature. The decrease in stability of TiO_2 is more than balanced by the increase in stability of the CO and the free energy of reaction becomes more positive with increased temperature. Hence TiO_2 is as stable in CO as in H_2.

In vacuo, most of the oxides have an appreciable vapor pressure, although few measured vapor pressures are available. In many cases the species in the vapor is not known, since vaporization may occur by dissociation to the elements, or to stable gaseous molecules of a composition different from the solid, or by sublimation to gaseous molecules with composition identical to that of the solid.

Table 2.4 gives the pressure in atmospheres of various oxides at 3150°F. From Table 2.4, it can be seen that the vapor pressure of MgO and NiO would be appreciable *in vacuo.* The actual vapor pressure of ThO_2, however, has been estimated about 10^5 times higher than the calculated value, suggesting that ThO_2 sublimes or vaporizes as stable gaseous molecules. For MgO the vapor pressure is in general agreement, signifying vaporization largely as the elements. ZrO_2, however, probably vaporizes as a stable gaseous molecule since its vapor

TABLE 2.4. CALCULATED DISSOCIATION
PRESSURES AND MEASURED VAPOR
PRESSURES (ATM) OF VARIOUS
OXIDES AT 3150°F

	Calculated	Experimental
Al_2O_3	2.6×10^{-8}	5.7×10^{-6}
BeO	6.6×10^{-9}	$\sim 1.2 \times 10^{-7}$
CeO_2	2.3×10^{-9}	
Cr_2O_3	4×10^{-7} (est)	1.2×10^{-5}
HfO_2	10×10^{-16}	$\gg 10^{-16}$
MgO	5.0×10^{-6}	$\sim 5 \times 10^{-6}$
NiO	9.0×10^{-4}	$\sim 9 \times 10^{-4}$
SiO_2	3.0×10^{-9}	$\gg 10^{-9}$
Ta_2O_5	3.2×10^{-13}	
ThO_2	1.8×10^{-15}	1.3×10^{-10}
TiO_2	1.5×10^{-10}	$\gg 10^{-10}$
V_2O_3	3.0×10^{-9}	$\gg 10^{-9}$
Y_2O_3	1.6×10^{-11}	$> 10^{-11}$
ZrO_2	3.34×10^{-14}	$\sim 10^{-6}$

pressure is reported as 10^{-6} atm at 3150°F. Similarly, Al_2O has been reported and a measured vapor pressure of 5.7×10^{-6} is consistent with this observation. SiO_2 vaporizes as SiO and its vapor pressure is considerable when near the melting point SiO_2. V_2O_3, TiO and TiO_2 are stable gaseous species; consequently, V_2O_3 and TiO_2 would be expected to have a higher vapor pressure than calculated. NiO vaporizes largely by decomposition and its actual vapor pressure is consistent with that calculated. Cr_2O_3 probably vaporizes largely as its elements, but complex molecules are also indicated by the calculated versus actual vapor pressures.

This discussion of vapor pressures has been based on 3150°F, a relatively low temperature; yet all the common oxides exhibited a measurable vapor pressure, often substantially greater than that calculated thermodynamically. This vapor pressure must be considered constantly in calculating possible reactions, since the materials need not even be in contact at these temperatures to react appreciably.

Most oxides are not stable in contact with carbon at temperatures above 2750°F, since they readily react to form the stable carbide, particularly under reduced pressures. Even Al_2O_3 and ThO_2 react readily with carbon at 3100°F and only BeO can be heated as high as 3600°F in contact with carbon without carbide formation.

Unsaturated valence forces on the surface of oxide crystals appear as the surface energy of the oxide and determine the calalytic activity, sintering characteristics and wettability. The surface energy is related to the lattic energy and since oxides exhibit large lattice energies, high surface energy would be expected also. Surface energy is reduced by surface ion polarization and surface absorption of gases. Of these mechanisms, the first is probably more important at high temperatures. In studying these oxide compounds at high temperatures, the surface condition must be considered, particularly when H_2 or CO reactions are encountered, or where gas adsorption on the surface is a first step in the reaction.

Summary of Oxide Materials

Of the oxide materials considered, most have received experimental application as coating materials. Possibly Cr_2O_3 and CeO_2 have been neglected because of the reported reduction tendencies, but this very tendency could be employed to advantage in oxidation protection by prereduction before application. Prereduction of a number of oxides would disproportion them slightly and make them more compatible with metal substrates, minimizing the oxides as a source of oxygen for the base metal. Vaporization and reactivity, unfortunately, are increased when oxides are stoichiometrically deficient in oxygen, so some compromise is required.

Spinel ($MgAl_2O_4$) possibly offers a coating system for the refractory metals (assuming suitable deposits could be formed) if the compatibility of spinel with the oxides of W, Ta, Mo, and Nb is as good as reported.

Workers in the field of emittance control coatings should particularly consider the color oxides NiO, CoO, MnO, FeO, Cr_2O_3, Ce_2O_3, Fe_2O_3 and combinations of these oxides in stable spinel structures. The early work of Nernst and Auer in glow lamps and gas mantles also point to certain ZrO_2-Y_2O_3-ThO_2-CeO_2 systems, which merit more study.

Y_2O_3 and HfO_2, though expensive, deserve further consideration. CaO and La_2O_3 were not discussed, since they are susceptible to rapid hydration, but they could be used in many applications by simply maintaining the refractory at a hundred degrees above room temperature to prevent moisture absorption.

Further progress in selection of suitable oxide coating materials is dependent on better information on diffusion rates of the various metals in oxides, the dissociation pressure of the oxide-metal system, and other pertinent chemical and thermodynamic data. Application techniques to form impervious adherent oxide coatings from many of these oxides also require careful study. The success of SiO_2 as an oxide coating formed *in situ* over the silicide coatings points toward further work to develop intermetallics or compounds as coatings which through oxidation in service provide a protective oxide coating.

THE HARD METALS— CARBIDES, NITRIDES, BORIDES AND SILICIDES

The grouping of carbides, nitrides, borides and silicides will be referred to as the "hard metals" for simplicity. As a group, the carbides and nitrides have similar structures in that the carbon and nitrogen atoms are found in the interstitial spaces in the metal lattice. The carbides and nitrides can properly be called interstitial compounds. In the carbides and nitrides, the metal-metal bonds and the metal-carbon bonds are the important ones, and the structures may be viewed as metal lattices stabilized by electron transfer from the non-metal atom. The borides and silicides, however, have more complex and varied structures since the increased size of the boron or silicon atom forces a separation of the metal atoms so that metal-silicon (or metal-boron) and silicon-silicon (or boron-boron) bonds become more important.

As a group, the carbides, borides, nitrides and silicides exhibit low electrical resistance and a positive temperature coefficient of resistance, evidencing their metallic nature. Notable exceptions to this do exist in BN, Si_3N_4, and AlN. Most of the carbides, borides and nitrides also exhibit high thermal conductivity and a high degree of hardness.

The most refractory solids known are found among this group of hard metals. As a generalization, all refractory carbides, borides, nitrides and silicides exhibit excellent thermodynamic stability, with generally low vapor pressure and high mechanical strength at elevated temperatures. Unfortunately, however, the oxidation resistance of most hard metals is poor. Many hard metals oxidize much more slowly than the refractory metals, but not sufficiently so to provide the desired protection. Exceptions to the poor oxidation resistance are found in some silicides and silicon hard metals which form a protective coating of SiO_2 upon oxidation.

Many applications of the hard metals have involved a composite structure where a metal was used to bond the hard metal phase and impart additional impact strength. The use of cobalt bonded tungsten carbide for cutting tool tips is an example. The lack of suitable bonding metals for many of the borides and nitrides has hampered their use in similar applications, but a few coating formulations have been developed using metal-hard metal combinations.

Excellent summaries of the properties and uses of hard metals have been published in several reviews (*10, 11, 12*). It is hoped that this selection will be used as representative of only typical compounds and typical properties, and that interest in these materials will stimulate reference to the more complete summaries. The evaluation of many of these materials has been rather haphazard and the data upon which judgments have been made are often rather incomplete; however, the strong trends noted throughout in oxidation behavior, strength, hardness and thermal properties are probably reliable.

Carbides

The most refractory solids are 4TaC·ZrC, mp 7110°F and 4TaC·HfC, mp 7128°F. The carbides as a group represent the most common hard metals. Silicon carbide (SiC), and boron carbide (B_4C) are common abrasives and titanium carbide (TiC) and tungsten carbide (WC) are common as cemented (metal-bonded) carbide compositions. Table 2.5 summarizes the properties of several selected carbides.

Boron Carbide. Boron carbide (B_4C) is widely used as an abrasive, having a hardness superior to silicon carbide. Its melting point is 4400°F. It has high compressive strength (over 400,000 psi) at room temperature and can be readily self-bonded (sintered) by hot pressing. The oxidation resistance of B_4C in air is good up to 1800°F but degrades rapidly above this temperature.

Hafnium Carbide. Hafnium carbide (HfC) has the highest reported melting point of a simple compound, 7030°F. Very pure crystals of HfC can be grown from the vapors of $HfCl_4$ and toluene on a hot filament at 3810 to 4530°F. Large quantities of hafnium carbide are usually made by reducing HfO_2 with carbon. The major difficulty is in obtaining zirconium-free hafnium oxide. Though extremely refractory, HfC has found little usage because of its cost, but some use in experimental nozzles, induction furnace susceptors and induction-heated light sources has been reported. It forms a complete solid solution with a number of other carbides, including NbC and TaC, and the composition $4TaC \cdot HfC$ has a higher melting point 7130°F (3940°C) than HfC alone. HfC is reported only slightly volatile *in vacuo* at 4050°F. Little data have been published on oxidation behavior or reaction with metals or oxides, but the high density (12.2 gm/cc) and high cost of HfC discourage large-scale use.

Titanium Carbide. Titanium carbide (TiC) has been studied extensively for high-temperature applications. It has a low density and good thermal shock resistance. It is wet by nickel, cobalt, iron and chromium and can be bonded into a cermet using combinations of these metals. Most of the experimental work performed on TiC has been directed toward structurally strong, refractory materials for use in the oxidizing atmosphere of a jet turbine. For this purpose no satisfactory compositions have been found, indicating the difficulty of achieving outstanding oxidation resistance. However, some of the metal-bonded TiC compositions are very strong at high temperatures in reducing atmospheres. TiC has been found to have oxidation resistance similar to that of ZrC, and a vapor pressure of 10^{-7} atm at 4050°F.

Zirconium Carbide. Zirconium carbide (ZrC) has a higher density than TiC and generally poorer oxidation resistance. However, its strength is reported to be greater than that of TiC at 2300°F. The vapor pressure is sufficiently low for use to 4000°F *in vacuo*. Little usage of ZrC is reported.

Tantalum Carbides. Both TaC and Ta_2C can be easily formed by several techniques including vapor pyrolysis and direct combination of the elements. Because of the high density of this carbide, its use has

TABLE 2.5. PROPERTIES OF SELECTED CARBIDES

Formula	Melting Point, °F	Density, gm/cc	Resistance, micro-ohm-cm	Thermal Conductivity, Cal/cm sec °C	Thermal Expansion, °C × 10⁻⁶	Hardness, Kg/mm²	Color	General Stability	Crystal Structure	Lattice Constants A	Lattice Constants C	Tensile Strength, psi	Compressive Strength, psi
HFC	7030	12.20	109	...	...	2910	Gray Metallic	...	FCC	4.64°	...	...	...
TaC	7000	14.48	20	0.053	6.61	1800	Dk to lt brown met	Fair	FCC	4.45	...	...	...
ZrC	6380	6.70	63.4	0.049	6.93	2600	Gray Metallic	Excellent	FCC	4.68	...	16K @ 1800°F / 190K @ 2190°F	238,000
NbC	6430	7.82	74	0.034	6.84	2400	Gray brown Metallic	Fair	FCC	4.46	...	...	...
Ta₂C	6150	15.10	...	...	...	1000	Gray	...	Hex	3.09	4.39	...	109,000
TiC	5880	4.25	105	0.041	7.61	1500	Lt gray Metallic	Excellent	FCC	4.32	...	113K @ 1800°F / 14K @ 2190°F	109,000
VC	5130	5.36	156	...	...	2800	Gray Metallic	Excellent	FCC	4.16	...	...	89,000
W₂C	4950	17.20	81	...	5.9	3000	...	Fair	Hex	2.98	4.71	...	...
MoC	4880	8.4	49	...	...	...	Gray Metallic	Fair	FCC	4.28	...	...	...
MO₂C	4870	8.9	97.5	...	...	1800	Dk gray Metallic	Fair	Hex	3.00	4.72	...	...
ThC₂	4810	9.6	...	...	...	...	Yellow	Hydrolyzes	Mono	...	...	...	...
WC	4770[A]	15.50	12	...	6.1	2400	Gray	Excellent	Hex	2.90	2.83	50,000	...
ThC	4760	10.65	...	...	...	...	...	...	FCC	5.34	...	...	...
UC₂	4260	11.28	...	0.079	12.5	...	Metallic	...	Tetragonal	3.52	5.99	...	...
UC	4080	13.63	...	0.20	...	...	Metallic	...	FCC	4.95	...	...	82,000
Cr₃C₂	3440	6.68	...	...	8.8–11.0	1300	Gray Metallic	Excellent	Ortho	...	...	...	...
SiC	5130[A]	3.21	107–200	0.10	4.7	2480	...	...	Rh	...	...	...	414,000
B₄C	4440	2.51	3×10^5	0.07–0.20	4.5	2750	Black	...	Cubic	...	...	...	105,000
Be₂C	3900[A]	2.26	63×10^3	0.05	10.5	2410	...	...	...	4.34	...	...	...
Cr₄C	3510	...	...	...	...	...	...	...	...	...	...	...	...

[A] Decomposes

been limited. Its use as an additive to carbide cutting tools is common, and its high melting point (7020°F) and low vapor pressure makes it suitable for high temperature suceptors.

Chromium Carbides. The carbides Cr_4C, Cr_7C_3 and Cr_3C_2 all melt incongruently and represent the stable phases. CrC can be formed at high temperatures and stabilized at room temperature by addition of other isostructural carbides. The excellent erosion and corrosion resistance of chromium carbide has led to uses in chemical process equipment, bearings and valve parts. Nickel is usually used to bond chromium carbide, since CrC has a high solubility in chromium metal.

Vanadium Carbide. Vanadium carbide (VC) has a wide range of composition and the nominal VC composition can exist with vanadium in solid solution to the composition equivalent to V_4C_3. Vanadium carbide is easily prepared and occurs in many vanadium steels, but because of its low hardness has found little usage.

Columbium Carbide. Columbium carbide (NbC) forms hard solid solutions with a number of carbides. Its vapor pressure at 3600°F is reported less than 10^{-7} atm *in vacuo.*

Rare Earth Carbides. Lanthanum, holmium, dysprosium, erbium, and other rare earths usually form the tetragonal dicarbide. In general, they are similar in both structure and physical properties to calcium carbide. They are hard and refractory, but are unstable in moist air. Rare earth carbides appear to be useful only for specialized applications where they can be protected from moisture.

Silicon Carbide. Silicon carbide (SiC) is the most common carbide, and its usefulness extends from abrasives and refractories to semiconductors. Several crystal structures of SiC exist and the properties of the crystal are highly dependent on the minor impurities. For refractory applications, SiC has been self-bonded (recrystallized), Si_3N_4-bonded, silicate-bonded, and graphite-bonded. The oxidation resistance and thermal shock resistance of SiC accounts for its use as a high-temperature refractory. The coating of SiO_2 formed on the surface in an oxidizing atmosphere accounts for this oxidation resistance.

Tungsten Carbides. The tungsten carbides (WC and W_2C) are both stable at low temperature, WC decomposing to W_2C and graphite upon heating to 4770°F. They can be prepared by the direct combination of the elements, reduction of WO_3, vapor phase reaction of WF_6 and a hydrocarbon vapor, or several other techniques. The commercial value of these materials lies in their hardness and toughness when bonded with a suitable metal binder (such as a cobalt alloy) to form a cemented carbide.

The oxidation resistance of tungsten carbide is poor at temperatures above 1000°F, and its high density makes it unattractive for many applications.

Molybdenum Carbides. The molybdenum carbides include MoC and Mo_2C, the latter being isomorphous with W_2C. MoC, however, has two reported structures, one being similar to WC. While molybdenum carbides are easily produced, unfortunately they are softer than tungsten carbides and are not as useful. In solid solution with titanium carbide, molybdenum carbide has formed useful materials for cemented carbides and cermets.

Summary. For more detailed information on the carbides, excellent summaries are available (*11, 12*). Carbides are widely used as cemented carbides for cutting and wear resistance, and this commercial interest has produced a larger amount of data on properties of carbides than on other groups of hard metals such as the nitrides and borides.

One difficulty in using these materials as coatings lies in their application. It is necessary either to use the metal bonded carbides, attempt to sinter or react the carbide powder on the surface, or deposit the carbide on the surface from vapor phase reactions which generally require high temperatures.

Perhaps interest should be directed toward some highly anisotropic carbide, if such exists, and improvement sought such as has been obtained in pyrolytic deposits of graphites. This eliminates most of the common carbides, but SiC is hexagonal in structure and should be somewhat anisotropic. It exhibits good oxidation behavior in unoriented dense form. Otherwise, the carbides appear unattractive except for abrasion, wear, or corrosion resistant coatings and for emittance control. In the latter usage, the metallic nature of these materials should offer quite different emittance characteristics than those of the oxides.

Nitrides

Generally the nitrides are characterized by properties similar to those of the carbides, but their susceptibility to oxidation is even more pronounced. Some, such as the rare earth nitrides, hydrolyze in moist air to form ammonia. The most stable nitrides are HfN and ZrN. These materials would be useful in vacuum applications to 3270°F (1800°C), but offer little advantage over the carbides. Generally the usefulness of the nitrides is limited by their dissociation pressures rather than by their melting points. When in contact with carbon, nitrides react to form carbides, and a nitrogen atmosphere is usually ineffective to suppress this reaction.

As in the case of carbides, nitrides exhibit considerable solid solubility with metals and form eutectic systems, limiting their use in contact with metals. In contact with oxides, the nitrides react to form the corresponding oxide:

$$ZrN + 2SiO_2 \longrightarrow ZrO_2 + 2SiO + \tfrac{1}{2}N_2$$

Table 2.6 summarizes the properties of several selected nitrides.

Rare Earth Nitrides. The nitrides of lanthanum, holmium, dysprosium, erbium, and other rare earths usually exist as the cubic mono-

TABLE 2.6.　PROPERTIES OF SELECTED NITRIDES

Formula	Melting Point, °F	Density, gm/cc	Resistivity, micro-ohm-cm	Thermal Conductivity, Cal/cm sec°C	Thermal Expansion, $°C^{-1} \times 10^{-6}$	Hardness, Mohs or Kg/mm²	Color	Vapor Pressure and General Stability	Crystal Structure	Lattice Constants A	C
HfN	5990	14.0	Conductor	...	...	...	Yellow-brown	10^{-5} atm @ 4040°F	...	...	...
Ta_2N	5610	14.1	135	...	...	8 −	Dark gray		Hex	3.05	4.95
ZrN	5400	7.32	13.6	0.040	6-7	8 + 1510	Yellow-brown	Fair, 10^{-5} atm @ 4040°F	FCC	4.56	...
TiN	5310	5.43	21.7	0.070	...	8 + 1770	Lt brown / Blue gray ?	Fair, 10^{-3} atm @ 4040°F	FCC	4.23	...
ScN	4800	4.21	...	...	...	...	...	...	FCC	4.88	...
UN	4800	14.30	...	0.011	...	...	...	...	FCC	5.2	...
ThN	4670	11.50	...	...	...	...	...	...	FCC	4.375	...
NbN	3720A	7.30	200	...	...	8 +	Lt gray	Fair, 10^{-3} atm @ 4040°F	FCC	4.129	...
VN	3720	6.04	85.9	0.04-0.12	0.05	1.2 (100)	Gray-brown	Fair	FCC	4.129	...
BN	5430B	2.27	10^{19}	...	10.0	...	...	...	...	...	...
AlN	4050	3.05	10^{17}	0.048-0.072	4.03 / 6.09	7 + (1200)	...	...	...	...	...
Be_3N_2	3990	...	...	...	...	...	...	...	...	...	...
Si_3N_4	3450B	3.44	143×10^9	0.045	2.47	...	...	Fair	Hex	...	...
Nb_2N	...	...	...	...	...	...	...	Fair	FCC	4.14	...
CrN	2732A	6.10	...	...	...	...	...	Fair	Hex	4.80	4.47
Cr_2N	...	...	...	...	...	...	...	...	FCC	4.16	...
Mo_2N	...	...	...	...	...	...	Yellow	...	Hex	2.860	2.80
MoN	...	...	...	...	...	...	Yellow	...	FCC	4.16	...
$W_2N\ \beta$	...	...	...	...	...	...	...	...	FCC	4.118	...
$W_2N\ \alpha$	...	...	...	...	...	...	...	...	Cubic	4.13	...

A Decomposes
B Sublimation

nitride. Like the rare earth carbides, the nitrides are also unstable in moist air. They hydrolyze to form a hydroxide and ammonia gas.

Exceptions to these generalizations about the nitrides are the nitrides of aluminum, boron and silicon which are not metallic in character and have quite different properties. These three nitrides are gray or white dielectric materials and in the dense form are more stable in air atmospheres than the other nitrides, but slowly oxidize at high temperatures.

Boron Nitride (BN) is isomorphous with graphite but does not provide the lubrication under high loads that might be expected. As with graphite, BN can be produced in a cubic form isomorphic with diamond by using high pressures. Because of the normal hexagonal graphite structure, BN is very anisotropic and when hot-pressed it exhibits preferred orientation and anisotropy in properties similar to graphite.

Boron nitride is most interesting because of its excellent dielectric properties and its high thermal conductivity (in one direction). Considering dielectric materials, the thermal conductivity of boron nitride is only exceeded by BeO at low temperatures, and at intermediate temperatures the conductivity of BN is higher (in one direction) that any other dielectric. (This anisotropy will be discussed further in the discussion of pyrolytic deposits.)

Confusion about the thermal conductivity of BN has arisen because in powder form the material is an excellent thermal insulator (comparable to carbon black).

Boron nitride oxidizes slowly to B_2O_3, but *in vacuo* or reducing atmospheres is a good electrical insulator material ($\sim 10^6 \; \Omega \, cm$) at temperatures up to 4000°F.

Aluminum Nitrides (AlN) has shown promise as a refractory for molten aluminum at temperatures up to 3600°F. Its low thermal expansion and its high thermal conductivity results in reasonably good thermal shock resistance. It is strong at 2550°F with 18,400 psi modulus of rupture and a modulus of elasticity of 40×10^6 psi. In many respects, its properties are similar to those of Al_2O_3, its oxidation product.

Other Nitrides. Silicon Nitride (Si_3N_4) is similar to BN and AlN except that it is not as refractory or as good an insulator at high temperatures. In high purity, its electrical properties at low temperatures are excellent. Its thermal shock resistance is also good, and since its oxidation product is SiO_2, it shows good oxidation resistance.

Little information is available on Be_3N_2, but its oxidation product, BeO, would be stable and should provide oxidation resistance for the dense Be_3N_2. Its electrical properties should be similar to those of AlN.

As oxidation-resistant coating materials, the most promising nitrides are discussed above. The metallic nitrides might provide unique emittance properties or wear resistance in coatings, and their solid solubility with metals would make them easily wet by or reacted with a substrate.

(Of course this could be a disadvantage for long usage where diffusion would continue.)

Borides

The borides are most interesting because of their stability from 3600 to 5400°F. Low volatility, low electrical resistance, high hardness and high thermal conductivity are common properties of almost all borides. The oxidation rate of borides is appreciable above 2700°F and the full extent of their refractoriness can only be achieved *in vacuo* or in an inert atmosphere. At temperatures around 4500°F, the borides are among the few materials which are sufficiently stable and have a sufficient low volatility to be useful as refractories.

Table 2.7 summarizes the properties of selected borides. It will be noted that each metal element generally forms several borides, but that the diboride is usually the most stable. From the carbon-boride stability data, it can be seen that a number of borides are more stable at high temperatures than their respective carbides. The oxidation behavior is quite varied depending on what type of coating the oxidation products form. Where B_2O_3 glass reacts with a refractory oxide such as TiO_2 or ZrO_2 upon oxidation of the borides, a semiprotective coating is formed at temperatures up to 2700°F, and this coating may be quite thick. Other reaction products are fluid glasses, such as V_2O_3-B_2O_3, which offer little protection to the boride.

Generally, the low density of the borides is attractive, with some exceptions, but the difficulty of finding suitable metallic phases which can bond the borides has limited their commercial development (*12*). Some of the borides are among the hardest materials, but a problem exists in developing satisfactory cemented compositions, consequently only a few cemented borides are commercially available.

Zirconium Borides (ZrB_2) is one of the most stable borides and has been used in hot-pressed compositions showing strengths of 29,000 psi in bending. It has excellent corrosion resistance and hardness and has found use in cermets and hot-pressed rocket nozzles. Solid solutions of ZrB_2 and TiB_2 are reported to have a higher hardness (4200 kg/mm^2) than that of any other hard metal; for example, the hardness of tungsten carbide is 2,400 to 3000 kg/mm^2, and of boron carbide 2750 kg/mm^2. The brittleness of the borides, however, has limited their application as cutting and abrasive compounds. The high hardness of TiB_2 and ZrB_2 at temperatures above 1000°C makes them attractive for high-temperature wear resistance.

Titanium boride (TiB_2) is similar in properties to ZrB_2 and is one of the more stable borides. Its oxidation resistance is similar to ZrB_2. Both TiB_2 and ZrB_2 have been used in bonded compositions and TiB_2 bonded with cobalt silicide has one of the highest stress rupture strengths at high temperatures ever measured; however, its extreme brittleness

TABLE 2.7. PROPERTIES OF SELECTED BORIDES

Formula	Melting Point, °F	Density, gm/cc	Resistivity, micro-ohm-cm	Thermal Conductivity, cgs	Hardness, Mohs or Kg/mm²	Color	General Stability	Oxidation Temperature, °F	Stability to Carbon	Crystal Structure	Lattice Constants A	C
TiB_2	5400	4.52	15.2	0.058	3400	Gray metallic	Good	2000–2300	Stable	Hex	3.03	3.23
TiB			40					2000	Unstable	FCC	4.24	
Ti_2B_5									Unstable	Hex	2.98	13.98
Ti_2B	5400		28.4	0.0624	(9 + Mohs)				Unstable	Tetr	6.11	4.56
ZrB	5500	5.7	30.0					1500–2000	Unstable	FCC	4.65	
ZrB_2	5500	6.09	9.2	0.055	2200	Gray metallic	Good	1800–2000		Hex	3.17	3.53
ZrB_{12}	4860	3.63	60–80	0.029					Unstable	FCC	7.408	
HfB	5610	12.8				Metallic					4.62	
HfB_2	3810 A	11.2	10		(8 + Mohs)			1500–1800		Hex	3.14	3.47
VB_2		5.10	16							Hex	3.00	3.06
VB	5250 A	5.28	35							Ortho		
NbB_2		7.21	32	0.040	(8 + Mohs)	Gray metallic	Fair		Stable	Hex	3.09	3.31
Nb_3B_4	3630									Ortho		
NbB	5430 A		64.5						Stable	Ortho		
TaB_2	3630	12.60	68	0.026		Gray metallic	Fair	1800–2000	Stable	Hex	3.09	3.24
TaB		14.29	100						Unstable	Ortho		
Ta_2B	2820									Tetr	5.78	4.86
CrB	3560	6.2	64		(8.5 Mohs)		Good		Stable	Ortho		
Cr_3B_2		6.7	21		(9 + Mohs)	Gray metallic						
Cr_2B	3362					Gray metallic			Stable	Ortho		
Cr_7B	3630 A											
CrB_2	3760	5.6	21		1800			2200–2300	Stable	Hex	2.97	3.07
Mo_2B	3956	9.31	40		1660				Stable	Tetr	5.54	4.74
Mo_3B_2	3810						Poor-fair					
MoB	5180	8.77	45		1570				Stable	Tetr	3.11	16.95
MoB_2	5020	7.78	40		1280				Stable	Hex	3.05	3.11
WB		16.0			(9 + Mohs)	Gray metallic			Unstable	Tetr	3.11	16.92
W_2B	4530	16.72	21					1800–2000	Stable	Tetr	5.56	4.74
W_2B_5		13.1							Unstable	Hex	2.98	13.87
ThB_4		8.54								Tetr	7.26	4.11
UB_2		12.71								Hex	3.14	3.99
UB_4		9.38										
UB_{12}		5.82								FCC	7.47	

A Decomposes

and poor thermal shock resistance limit its usefulness. The strength of hot-pressed TiB_2 is reported to be lower than for corresponding ZrB_2 samples. In combination with B_4C, high tensile strengths (90,000 psi) have been found.

Rare Earth Borides. Little is known about the borides, carbides, nitrides and silicides of the rare earths; but of these compounds, more is known about the borides than any of the others. The borides also appear to be the most stable. Generally, the borides of the rare earths crystallize into the tetragonal tetraboride and the cubic hexaboride. Both are refractory and stable compounds. The high-temperature stability of the tetraboride is usually greater than that of the hexaboride except in some cases where the hexaboride disproportionates. In this case, the tetraboride is also rather unstable. Little is known about the physical properties of the rare earth borides, but melting temperatures of many are above 3600°F and they are metallic in nature. Preliminary tests on holmium, yttrium and dysprosium tetraborides show fairly good high-temperature oxidation resistance (*13*).

A molybdenum boride base composition has been used to braze molybdenum metal. The braze was reported to be ductile near the joint and of low volatility *in vacuo*. A unique property of LaB_6 is its high thermionic emission and low evaporation rate. Its use in high power electron tube filaments would be advantageous. For silicon borides, see the discussion on boron silicides.

Summary. As a group, the metallic borides represent compounds with greater thermodynamic stability than that of the corresponding carbides. The oxidation resistance is also better than for the carbides. The chief difficulty seems to lie in the fact that they are not wet or bonded by most metals and oxides. One possible solution to this problem lies in the use of other hard metals such as the silicides or the nitrides to bond the borides. Since the nitrides and silicides show better reaction with metals, these combinations could improve the usefulness of the borides as coating materials. Investigations could consider the similarity in structures of the borides and other hard metals, and the possible oxidation products in seeking possible solid solutions. Since ZrB_2, TiB_2, CrB and MoB are stable in contact with silicon at high temperatures, the use of the borides in combination with silicides, which do not form boride solid solutions, or with silicon is possible.

Silicides

The silicides may be considered intermetallics or hard metals, since they have some properties common to both. The silicides have been the source for a large amount of protective coating work for the refractory metals, since $CbSi_2$, WSi_2 and $MoSi_2$ are all more oxidation-resistant than the respective metals, and coating techniques for diffusing silicon into the refractory alloys have developed rapidly.

The silicides have a variety of crystal structures, largely a result of the atomic packing consideration; this causes compounds of the same formula type to have quite different structures and properties. For example, $ThSi_2$ is a body-centered tetragonal structure and not isomorphous with any of the disilicides of the transition metals. This variety of crystal structure makes broad generalizations about the silicides less accurate than in the case of other hard metals. A summary of the properties of several silicides is found in Table 2.8.

TABLE 2.8. PROPERTIES OF SELECTED SILICIDES

Formula	Melting Point, °F	Density, gm/cc	Resistivity, micro-ohm-cm	Color	General Stability	Crystal Structure
$TiSi_2$	2800	4.39	123	Iron gray	Fair	Ortho
Ti_5Si_3	3850	4.32	. . .	Gray	Good	Ortho
$ZrSi_2$	. . .	4.88	161	. . .	. . .	Ortho
VSi_2	3180	4.71	9.5	. . .	Fair	Hex
$NbSi_2$	3630	5.29	6.3	. . .	. . .	Hex
$TaSi_2$	4350	8.83	8.5	Blue-gray met.	Good	Hex
$CrSi_2$	2860	4.40	. . .	. . .	. . .	Hex
$MoSi_2$	3400	6.24	21.5	Gray metallic	Good	Tetr
WSi_2	3900	9.3	33.4	Blue-gray	Good	Tetr
$ThSi_2$	. . .	7.79	. . .	. . .	. . .	Tetr
U_3Si_2	3030	12.20	. . .	. . .	. . .	Tetr

The silicide of molybdenum, $MoSi_2$, has received widespread investigation as an oxidation-resistant structural material and coating material for oxidation protection of molybdenum metal. $MoSi_2$ has poor mechanical and thermal shock properties, but in low stress conditions it is amazingly oxidation-resistant due to the protective SiO_2 coating formed on the surface. It may be prepared by direct reaction of the elements; this is frequently done in coating where elemental silicon is applied in vapor or powder form to molybdenum, and $MoSi_2$ is formed by diffusion at high temperatures. Continuous coatings of $MoSi_2$ give excellent resistance to oxidation, but any pinholes allow catastrophic oxidation at high temperatures. As a coating, $MoSi_2$ has another shortcoming. While oxidation-resistant at temperatures above 1800 to 2200°F, in the range from 1650 to 2900°F, a decomposition (14, 15) may occur. This "pest" is possibly explained by the contamination of the SiO_2 coating by MoO_3, which is volatile at these temperatures, but not sufficiently so to be removed rapidly from the SiO_2. Compared with SiC and Si_3N_4, $MoSi_2$ forms the same SiO_2 glass for oxidation protection, and it can be reasoned that the vapor pressure of MoO_3 contributes to this "pest" reaction. Other explanations are based on the impurities present in $MoSi_2$ since high-purity $MoSi_2$ is reported not subject to the "pest." Figure 2.3 illustrates the microstructure of typical silicide coating on molybdenum wire. Figure 2.4 shows a typical "pest" oxidation occurrence as it penetrates the silicide layer.

The oxidation of molybdenum silicide, and other silicides, at reduced pressures is rather surprising. A slower oxidation might be expected; however, the oxidation of the silicide at oxygen pressures below 5 Torr results in the formation of silicon monoxide, SiO, which vaporizes rapidly at high temperatures and reduced pressures. The protective coating of SiO_2 fails to form immediately, and rapid oxidation occurs.

Rare Earth Silicides. Lanthanum, holmium, dysprosium and erbium silicides usually appear as the tetragonal disilicide. These materials are usually characterized by fairly low melting points, about 2700°F, but are more stable in normal moist atmospheres than the rare earth carbides and nitrides. They conduct electricity, are hard and brittle, fairly strong, and stable and resistant to oxidation.

The boron silicides B_6Si and B_4Si (or silicon borides) are useful at high temperatures, and are stable for long periods at 2500°F. The thermal shock resistance is very good and the coating formed upon oxidation is a borosilicate glass. The B_4Si disproportionates to B_6Si and Si upon heating.

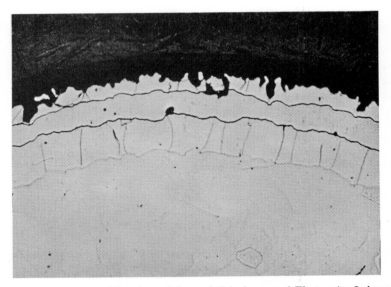

(Courtesy of General Telephone and Electronics Laboratory)
Fig. 2.3. Molybdenum disilicide coating oxidized 70 hr. at 2280°F. Outer-coating (dark) is SiO_2, next layer is Mo_5Si_3, next $MoSi_2$ lower layer is Mo_5Si_3 and substrate is Molybdenum. This represents typical appearance after high temperature oxidation.

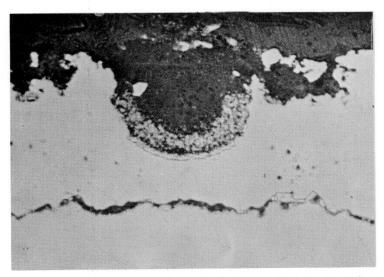

(Courtesy of General Telephone and Electronics Laboratory)
Fig. 2.4. A specimen similar to that of Fig. 2.3, except oxidized at low temperature (around 1600°F). Dark outer layer is an unidentified oxide, light layer is largely $MoSi_2$ over a substrate of molybdenum. Note extensive oxidation of $MoSi_2$ layer by "pest" attack. (Some Mo_5Si_3 is possibly present at the dark interface between $MoSi_2$ layer and the molybdenum substrate).

Other information on the silicides of tungsten, chromium, rhenium and columbium indicates properties similar to those of $MoSi_2$ and oxidation protection from the coating of SiO_2 formed on the surface. However, the oxidation resistance of these materials is generally not as good as that of $MoSi_2$.

Of the tungsten silicides, W_3Si_2 has a higher melting point than WSi_2, but the latter is more oxidation-resistant and is isomorphous with $MoSi_2$. The chromium silicides Cr_3Si, Cr_2Si and $CrSi_2$ have been reported; the Cr_3Si structure is isomorphous with the V_3Si and Mo_3Si, but has poorer oxidation resistance than the disilicide.

Since the silicides of most metals are easily formed, and the oxidation behavior is similar in that a semiprotective coating usually forms on the silicide, this is a fertile field for further experimentation. Silicon can be readily applied and reacted at moderate temperatures, and forms several different silicides with many other metals. This use of silicides and the solid solution of borides, silicides and aluminides has been the basis for many commercial coating processes for the refractory metals, though most are not completely reliable at this time.

The solid solution of ZrB_2 and $MoSi_2$ has been reported to show excellent oxidation resistance and good mechanical properties. This solid solution would not be immediately predicted from structural considerations. The oxidation products ZrO_2 and SiO_2 should form a stable $ZrSiO_4$ coating at high temperatures and this probably accounts for the good oxidation resistance of this material. This approach to oxidation-resistant coatings would be realistic.

$MoSi_2$ coatings on molybdenum metal have been treated with melted gold-silicon alloys to provide improved thermal shock resistance and to aid in sealing the coating against oxygen diffusion. Unfortunately, upon diffusion to the molybdenum, the gold forms a brittle intermetallic compound with the molybdenum.

In analyzing the performance of $MoSi_2$ as an oxidation-resistant coating for Mo, one may wonder why a coating of pure SiO_2 would not perform as well as the SiO_2 formed by oxidation of the $MoSi_2$. The protection must be closely tied to the oxygen transport mechanism through the coating which allows the molybdenum to oxidize slowly, the MoO_3 to diffuse into the SiO_2 glass and the MoO_3 to evaporate at the surface. The presence of silicon in the molybdenum undoubtedly influences the rate at which this reaction can occur. The solubility of MoO_3 in the SiO_2 and the vapor pressure of the MoO_3 probably accounts for the difference in the oxidation of WSi_2 and $MoSi_2$. The oxidation resistance of the silicides is thus also a function of the metal ion and the properties of the complex silicate formed upon oxidation. The low surface tension and wetting action of MoO_3-SiO_2 glasses is probably also involved.

THE INTERMETALLICS

Several recent surveys of the intermetallics (*12, 16, 17, 18*) have indicated the extensive number of compounds in this group which exhibit high-temperature stability. In this discussion, the beryllides, silicides, aluminides, phosphides and stannides will be covered briefly. The oxidation behavior óf many of these compounds has been studied and the oxidation resistance of several have been reported to be excellent in the range from 2000 to 2800°F.

Extensive investigations into the beryllides of Zr, Hf, Mo, Cb, Ta, Ti, and W and a variety of other intermetallics have been made by Paine *et al.* (*16, 18*). A tabulation of the oxidation resistance of several more promising compounds is shown in Table 2.9 for 2500 and 2300°F exposures in air.

Other observations on the intermetallics from this same investigation included a tabulation of intermetallic compounds showing good oxidation resistance. Of these compounds, two are aluminides, two are silicides and the remainder beryllides:

Composition	100 hr Use Temperature, °F, for .002 in. oxide layer		
$CbAl_3$	2500	$TaBe_{12}$	2800-2900
$TaAl_3$	2600	Ta_2Be_{17}	2800
$CrBe_2$	2600	$TiBe_{12}$	2600-2700
$MoBe_{12}$	2600-2700	$ZrBe_{13}$	2800-2900
Cb_2Be_{17}	2600-2700	Cr_3Si	2500-2700
$CbBe_{12}$	2600-2700	Ti_5Si_3	2500-2700

Molybdenum silicide should be included in this tabulation, however, Paine *et al.* (*16*) eliminated it from their study because of other work in progress on $MoSi_2$ at that time.

Of the aluminides, NiAl and Ni_3Al show good oxidation resistance and strength only up to 2010°F. TiAl was reported to have a 100,000 psi strength in bending at 1830°F and fair oxidation resistance. $TaAl_3$ oxidized at 2300°F and formed a tough protective scale. $CbAl_3$ was

TABLE 2.9. OXIDATION RESISTANCE OF
SELECTED INTERMETALLICS

Compound	Melting Point, °F	Density,[a] g/cm³	Sample Density, % of absolute	100 hrs @ 2300°F		100 hrs @ 2500°F	
				Wt Gain mg/cm²	Penetration,* Mil	Wt Gain mg/cm²	Penetration,* Mil
$CbAl_3$	2550	4.57 (X)	90	2.8	0.4		
$TaAl_3$	2730	6.92 (X)	92	7.1	0.9		
$CrBe_2$	3340	4.34 (X)	96	2.4	0.3	24.9	2.8
$MoBe_{12}$	3100	3.03 (X)	94	2.6	0.2	4.5	0.4
Cb_2Be_{17}	3000	3.28 (P)	94	2.6	0.3		
$CbBe_{12}$	2800	3.04 (SP)	95	1.7	0.2	17.1	2.1
$TaBe_2$	3350	9.79 (P)	90	4.1	0.4		
$TaBe_{12}$	3000	4.18 (X)	90	18.0	2.1	12.7	1.5
$TiBe_2$	2600	3.21 (SP)	98	5.2	0.6		
$TiBe_{12}$	2600	2.26 (X)	94	3.0	0.4	8.3	1.0
"WBe₅"	3250	6.91 (SP)	93	5.1	0.6		
Zr_2Be_{17}	2790	3.15 (SP)	96	9.1	1.0		
$ZrBe_{15}$	2910	2.72 (X)	93	7.8	1.0		
Cr_3Si	3190	6.46 (X)	91	7.3	0.8		
Ti_5Si_3	3670	4.32 (X)	91	2.3	0.2	10.1	1.0
"TiSi"	3200	4.25 (SP)	94	3.4	0.3		
$TiSi_2$	2700	4.12 (X)	96	2.2	0.2		
$TaCr_2$	3540	11.23 (X)	82	46.3	5.1		

[a]Density reported is that considered most reliable for the material tested.
(X)—X-ray density of compound
(P)—Pycnometric density of compound preparation
(SP)—Pycnometric density of fabricated material after powdering
*Calculated penetration of oxidation based on weight change

observed to be very hard and to form a thin, tough oxide scale at 2300°F. Low temperature (1000 to 1500°F) aluminide coatings for columbium and tantalum have exhibited "pest" failure similar to that in molybdenum disilicide. The aluminides generally show poorer oxidation resistance* above 2500°F than the beryllides or silicides (17).

The beryllides have a surprising resistance to oxidation, a low density and high mechanical strength. Several beryllides are compared in Table 2.10. These materials have been invesitgated for coating tantalum and

TABLE 2.10. SUMMARY OF THE PROPERTIES OF SELECTED BERYLLIDES

Compound	$ZrBe_{13}$	Zr_2Be_{17}	$CbBe_{12}$	Cb_2Be_{17}	$TaBe_{12}$	Ta_2Be_{17}	$MoBe_{12}$
Melting point, °F	3500	...	3070	...	3360	3610	3000
Crystal structure	Cubic	HCP	Tetragonal	HCP	Tetragonal	HCP	...
X-ray density, g/cm³	2.72	...	2.91	...	4.18	...	3.03
Max 100 hr service temp in dry air, °F	2900	...	2700	2700	2800	2800	2700
Modulus of rupture, 1000 psi							
2300°F	36	40	39	70	56	78	42
2500°F	36	40	39	63	43	56	30
2750°F	25	35	18	36	26	35	13
Young's modulus, 10^6 psi							
2300°F	25	...	25	...	24	...	15
2500°F	20	20	15	25	14	20	12
2750°F	10	...	10	...	10	...	1
Thermal conductivity, btu hr^{-1} ft^{-2} ft, °F							
1400°F	...	...	...	18.8	...	17.7	...
1600°F	21.0	...	17.9	...	11.0	...	18.2
2600°F	20.8	...	19.0	...	10.5	...	17.5
2700°F	...	...	...	19.8	...	21.7	...
Specific heat, btu/lb, °F							
1600°F	0.41	...	0.40	...	0.28	...	0.41
2600°F	0.46	...	0.43	...	0.30	...	0.45
Thermal expansion, ×10^{-6} 68−2600°F, in./in./°F	9.8	8.4	9.2	8.8	8.3	8.7	...

columbium, but their high expansion coefficients and the rapid diffusion into the base metal are inherent problems. Booker (18) felt that the maximum service temperature for 10-hr oxidation resistance would be 3000°F or less for the beryllides; however, he was primarily concerned with dense, hot-pressed compositions. No work on these materials as coatings was reported by Booker, and little effort to combine beryllides with other hard metals has been cited. From the limited use of beryllides

---

*Using finely divided Al in preparing hot pressed specimens of the aluminides always incorporates a small percentage of Al_2O_3 (from the surface oxide of the aluminum particles) in the specimen. If this Al_2O_3 of the samples used in these investigations influenced the microstructure, the oxidation characteristics could have been affected appreciably. Also, the Al_2O_3 or complex aluminate oxidation product simply may not offer the barrier to further oxidation due to its physical or chemical characteristics.

as coating materials, diffusion of the beryllium into the substrate also appears to be an important factor. The beryllides oxidize according to an exponential law, which is cubic or a higher power in the temperature range above 2300°F. Typical activation energy for the cubic rate process was calculated to be 35 Kcal for $TaBe_{12}$ and 50 Kcal for Hf_2Be_{21}.

The beryllides find their oxidation protection in the BeO complex oxide coating which forms on the surface of the compound during oxidation. This stability of the BeO containing coating is not unexpected; the oxidation resistance imparted by the BeO-rich coating suggests further protective coating work in the beryllium metal or the BeO systems.

The beryllides, because of their low density, could be used in thicknesses of up to twice that for $MoSi_2$ and WSi_2 for the same equivalent weight coating. On this basis, even though the oxidation rate of the beryllides may appear slightly higher than that for the silicides at 2900°F, the two materials compare more favorably on an equal weight basis.

METALS FOR HIGH TEMPERATURE COATINGS

The properties of metals which have melting points above 3200°F are shown in Table 2.11. Since metals have poor mechanical properties considerably below their melting points, only metals with melting points above 3200°F have been listed. The elements aluminum, zinc, silicon and boron should possibly be considered in a tabulation of this type, but since they form intermetallic compounds with the base metal and these intermetallics provide the actual high-temperature coating, they will not be discussed among the metals.

From Table 2.11, it can be seen that only platinum, rhodium, chromium, hafnium and iridium can be considered for use in an oxidizing atmosphere without a coating for oxidation protection; even at 2600°F, the rate of loss by vaporization or oxidation is not insignificant for any metals except platinum and rhodium. The oxides of these metals can be considered the most protective.

Of the common refractory metals, tungsten, tantalum, columbium and molybdenum all have high melting points and low vapor pressures, but oxidize too rapidly to be considered for use in oxidizing atmospheres. In considering metals for high-temperature coatings, the selection must be based on the greatest need— high temperature resistance or oxidation resistance, since both are not usually found in the same metal.

The Platinum-Group Metals

The platinum-group metals, platinum, rhodium and iridium, can offer oxidation protection in thin coatings since their oxides are the most protective of the high-temperature metals. These metals are expensive and it is doubtful if they could be obtained in large quantities, even if their price was not restrictive. Their high densities also increase their

TABLE 2.11.   PROPERTIES OF HIGH TEMPERATURE METALS

Metal	Density, gm/cc	Melting Point, °F	Temperature, °F, for Vapor Pressure of 10^{-6} atm	Weight Loss in Air at 2600°F, mg/cm²/hr	Thermal Conductivity, cal/cm/sec°C	Electrical Resistivity, micro-ohm-cm	Thermal Expansion, $\times 10^{-6}$ °C -1
Tungsten	19.3	6170	4300	1000	.48	5.5	4.5
Rhenium	21.0	5760	4000	3000	.17	19.3	6.7
Tantalum	16.6	5430	4250	500	.13	13.5	6.6
Osmium	22.5	4900	3330	1500	...	9.5	6.6
Molybdenum	10.2	4730	3340	8–10,000	.35	5.2	5.4
Iridium	22.4	4450	3050	3	.35	5.3	6.5
Columbium	8.56	4470	3630	3000	.125	14.8	7.1
Ruthenium	12.2	4530	2910	100	...	9.5	9.6
Hafnium	13.36	4030	3630	1.2	.053	30.0	6.0
Rhodium	12.4	3570	2700	7×10^{-3}	.36	4.7	8.5
Vanadium	6.1	3450	2430	...	.074	24.8	9.7
Chromium	7.2	3410	1830	11	.16	12.8	6.2
Zirconium	6.49	3370	3150	1000	.21	40	7.4
Thorium	11.72	3180	2600	...	.09	13	13.7
Platinum	21.45	3217	2700	4×10^{-4} to 4×10^{-2}	.165	10.6	10.2

price further on a volume basis. The low emittance of these silvery metals can be useful in forming high temperature reflecting surfaces, but where high emittances are desirable, this is a disadvantage.

Excellent reviews of the platinum group metals have been presented by Douglas *et al.* (*19*) and by Vines and Wise (*20*). The reader is encouraged to examine these references.

The vapor pressures of platinum, iridium and rhodium have been measured in recent studies (*25*) and the results appear reliable. A summary of vapor pressure data for these metals appears as Table 2.12.

TABLE 2.12. PROPERTIES OF PLATINUM, RHODIUM AND IRIDIUM

Metal	Boiling Point, $^\circ$F	Vapor Pressure, atm, at 3150°F	Log P atm near 2000°K	Heat of Sublimation, K Cal/mole
Platinum	6900° ± 180°	1×10^{-7}	$6.761 - 27,575/T$	134.9 ± 1
Iridium	8190° ± 180°	3×10^{-10}	$6.894 - 27,276/T$	159.9 ± 2
Rhodium	6740° ± 180°	2×10^{-7}	$7.139 - 33,337/T$	132.5 ± 2

The major deterrent to the use of the platinum metals for oxidation is simply the cost; however, there are other considerations as well. Platinum has a wide range of solid solution with molybdenum and tungsten, and would be expected to diffuse into refractory-base metals rather rapidly. Brittle intermetallics form between platinum and Mo or W and the diffusion should result in the formation of these intermetallics. These solid solution alloys and intermetallics oxidize preferentially, losing W or Mo. The later observation would indicate that the oxide of platinum offers less protection for the tungsten in the alloy, and that oxygen may be rather mobile in platinum metal, diffusing through any platinum coating to the base metal. While these comments have mentioned platinum specifically, rhodium would be a better choice judging on oxidation resistance. However, the same characteristic intermetallic formation, diffusion and preferential oxidation might be expected.

Coatings of the platinum-group metals are normally formed by electrodeposition or possibly flame spraying in the case of iridium. Since many of the silicides and beryllides have adequate conductivity to be electroplated, these intermetallics could possibly be used as diffusion barriers under a thin coating of some platinum group metal. This assumes that suitable surface preparation techniques can be developed to achieve proper adhesion of the electroplate to the intermetallic.

Another difficulty arises in the thermal expansion mismatch between the platinum-group metals and the refractory metals, and in cycle heating some difficulty might be anticipated in maintaining coating integrity.

Other Metals and Alloys

Several investigations have reported protection of molybdenum and tungsten to temperatures up to 2200°F by electroplated nickel and chromium. Generally, the best results were obtained by alternating layers of nickel and chromium (approximately 22 per cent Cr and 78 per cent Ni total). Work with high-temperature diffusion barriers of Ir, Os, Re and Rh on tungsten, that would aid in maintaining a surface coating of base metals, was generally inclusive (*21*).

Electrophoretically deposited "Nichrome" and an alloy of 50 per cent Ni (by volume) and Cr_3C_2 is reported to have withstood temperatures up to 3450°F. Coatings of an aluminum-silicon alloy applied by dipping and subsequently oxidized to an aluminum silicate coating was reported to withstand 2500°F in air.

Coatings of electroplated chromium with occluded hard metal or oxide particles have provided surprising protection to molybdenum, tungsten and graphite for short times (5 to 20 min) at temperatures above 3500°F in oxidizing atmospheres. The protection of this coating apparently depends on the slow oxidation of the chromium metal into a dense coating of Cr_2O_3, or Cr_2O_3-Cr eutectic plus solid solution, which retards the diffusion of oxygen sufficiently to provide short-term protection. The physical state of the chromium coating is important because pure chromium deposits do not provide similar protection.

Coatings of nickel with nickel oxide have been flame-sprayed on superalloy metal surfaces such as HS-25 and "Inconel" to improve the oxidation resistance of thin foils. The NiO-Ni coating offers some protection for short term (less than 10 min) exposures to temperatures of 2200 to 2600°F (*22*).

Chromium diffusion coatings for low alloy steels offer some protection from oxidation and corrosion below 2200°F. These coatings are prepared simply by a pack diffusion process, or by brushing, dipping, spraying or possibly electroplating and diffusing at high temperatures. These coatings could offer particular advantages in chemical process industries where extremely high temperatures are not encountered.

Flame sprayed "Inconel," alone and with oxide additions, has been used as a high-temperature coating on ceramics, composite and metallic surfaces for emittance control. The resultant oxide formed on the rough "Inconel" coating is highly emissive (.8 to .9) and can be used at temperatures above 2500°F for short periods.

PYROLYTIC COATINGS

The use of high-temperature pyrolysis of organic or inorganic vapors to form coatings on a surface could be considered simply a coating technique. Since the deposits formed by this process are often unique in properties, due to physical form or orientation of crystallites in the coatings, this method deserves special attention, even where the basic materials of the deposit have been previously discussed.

Vapor pyrolysis is not a new technique for forming coatings; high-purity crystals of the hard metals, metals and inorganic compounds have frequently been prepared by decomposing vapor-phase raw materials on a hot wire. Only recently has this been applied to large shapes, and tungsten, graphite and boron nitride coatings are prepared routinely by heating the substrate and decomposing a suitable gaseous material on the surface. The properties of pyrolytic graphite have drawn widespread attention due to the extreme anisotropy in the properties of the coating parallel and perpendicular to the surface. Thermal conductivity and strength properties with differences of an order of magnitude according to direction are not uncommon (*23, 24*). Here the properties of the pyrolytic graphite deposit are quite unlike those of the common graphites, and pyrolytic graphite can be considered almost a new material.

Since pyrolytic graphite as a coating material is normally applied at temperatures above 3600°F and only to a graphite surface, only a brief discussion is warranted. At 3600°F pyrolytic graphite could only be applied to BeO, some of the more stable carbides and borides such as those of hafnium, zirconium, titanium, molybdenum and tantalum, and perhaps to certain rare earth sulfides. Therefore, its use as a coating material is limited to the extremely refractory materials unless application techniques can be developed for using lower temperatures. The unusual thermal properties of pyrolytic graphite coating deposits are evident from the thermal conductivity data in Figures 2.5 and 2.6. The "a" direction is parallel to the substrate surface and the "c" direction is

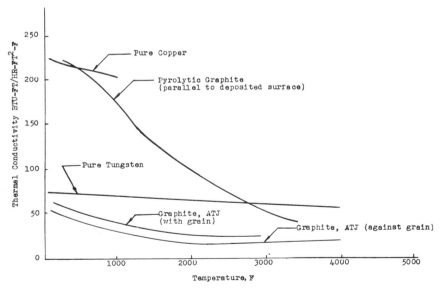

Fig. 2.5. A comparison of the thermal conductivity of pyrolytic graphite (parallel to surface).

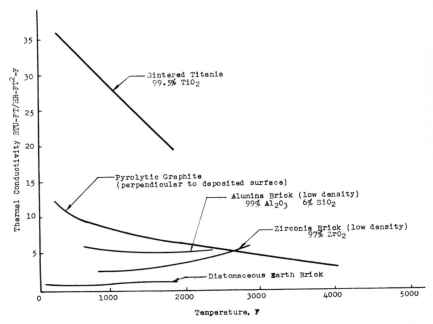

Fig. 2.6. A comparison of the thermal conductivity of pyrolytic graphite (perpendicular to surface).

perpendicular to it. It can be seen that the difference in thermal conductivity in the two directions is over two orders of magnitude. While ordinary graphite, such as ATJ, exhibits some anisotropy, the thermal conductivity is nearer an average of the values for the two directions. Other properties of pyrolytic graphite show similar anisotropy. Pyrolytic graphite has greatly improved strength and oxidation resistance compared to conventional graphites, and has found use as both a coating material and substrate for ultrahigh temperature applications. Further data on pyrolytic graphite is available in reference *24*.

Pyrolytic boron nitride is deposited like pyrolytic graphite, except by decomposing boron trichloride and ammonia gases. The resulting deposit is highly anisotropic and possesses greater oxidation resistance than ordinary hot-pressed BN and pyrolytic graphite (Figure 2.7). While BN can be readily produced as pyrolytic coatings, free-standing pyrolytic BN shapes can also be produced by forming thicker deposits. Figure 2.8 shows typical BN shapes made from thick pyrolytic BN "coatings." Its electrical insulating characteristics make it attractive for radome applications. The sublimation temperature for BN is 5400°F compared to 6700°F for graphite.

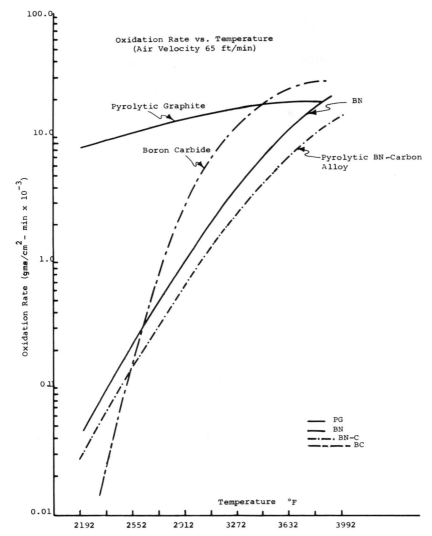

Fig. 2.7. Oxidation rate of pyrolytic materials as a function of temperature.

Pyrolytic tungsten can be prepared from tungsten hexafluoride pyrolysis and is similar to pure tungsten produced by other processes, exhibiting no anisotropy, since the tungsten crystal is cubic and thus isotropic. Both coatings and free-standing shapes are produced from pyrolytic tungsten deposits. Figure 2.9 shows a section of a thick pyrolytic tungsten coating on graphite.

Fig. 2.8. Examples of pyrolytic boron nitride shapes formed as thick pyrolytic coatings.

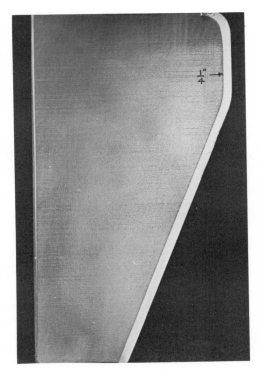

Fig. 2.9. A pyrolytic coating of tungsten on graphite; coating is 0.250 inch thick.

Pyrolytic deposits of the refractory carbides of hafnium, tantalum and columbium have been produced from reaction of the metal halide and graphite or the metal halide and a hydrocarbon gas. Deposits formed by the pyrolytic process are generally tightly adherent to the substrate, near theoretical density, impermeable, and cover the entire surface.

Some limitations of pyrolytic coatings appear with their other unique characteristics. The anisotropic coatings of BN and graphite formed pyrolytically are often highly stressed and must be carefully annealed to remove sufficient internal stresses and allow the material to remain intact upon cooling to ambient temperature. The reactivity of the pyrolytic coating with the substrate and the extreme temperatures required provide certain other process limitations.

The Germanides, Stannides, Phosphides and Sulfides

There is little known about the stannides and germanides, but on a structural and thermodynamic basis, refractory compounds of tin and germanium should exist. Their oxidation resistance would probably be poor, but SnO_2 in combination with some other oxide from the stannide might form as stable an oxidation resistance coating as some of the silicides.

Phosphides are known only from the semiconductor work done on InP and BP, but other more refractory phosphides are possible. Like the nitrides, they are probably more volatile than the carbides. The structure of several phosphides is the same as that of some of the borides, and some solid solution of these compounds might be expected.

The sulfides of the rare earths are generally more stable than the carbides, and thus many of the sulfides are stable even in contact with carbon at high temperatures. The high melting point and low contamination introduced by CeS and Ce_2S_3 crucibles have made them useful for many applications. CeS has been used also as a dissolvable refractory mandrel for casting, brazing, and jigging. Many of the sulfides hydrolyze in moist atmosphere to yield H_2S at ordinary temperatures.

Ablative Coating Materials

No high-temperature coating materials discussion would be complete without a mention of short-term protection systems using organic coatings. A tabulation of several commercial coating compositions and their performance is given in Table 2.13.

Several approaches to providing low-temperature ablation from 300 to 1000°F are obvious from Table 2.13. Silicone rubber or silicone resins are useful; polyamid (nylon) and polyetetrafluorethylene ("Teflon") polymers are also common. For some applications, polyethylene is useful if the heat flux is sufficiently high to cause decomposition before appreciable melting. An approach common to several proprietary compositions is to use an organic compound which decomposes, or

TABLE 2.13. ABLATING COATINGS

	Density, lb/cu ft	Spec Heat, btu/lb-°F	Thermal Conductivity btu-in/hr-sq ft-°F	Ablation Temp, °F	Heat of Ablation, btu/lb
Dyna-Therm Chemical Dyna-Therm D 65	68.6	0.25	0.63		
Avco Avcoat	70 80	0.48	1.2	330 450	1700
General Electric RTV 77	81.0	0.29 (0°F) 0.33 (190)	1.9	800	2580
RTV 88	92.0	0.35 (500)	1.9	800	17,500
GE 123 C	77.0	0.30 (150) 0.55 (320)	1.25	700	
GE 523 C	51.0	0.30 (150) 0.55 (320)	0.86	700	
DuPont Teflon	140	0.25	1.68	900	2550
Armstrong Cork Cork 2755	33.5	0.34 (0°F) 0.56 (200)	0.48	350	1400
Dyna-Therm Chemical Dyna-Therm D-100 M	17	0.27	0.36 (350) 0.84 (500)		
Nylon	69.9	0.4	1.44	600	1945
Stoner Rubber SMR 7–12	94.2	0.44	2.9	850	675

sublimes near the desired temperature and to bond this, if required, with a silicone-base carrier.

Two protection mechanisms are evidenced in this type of coating: (1) the coating is used up in providing heat absorption through melting, sublimation decomposition, and vaporization; (2) the coating may also be formulated to expand upon heating, forming a foam-like insulation which progressively carbonizes, decomposes and is replenished from below until the coating is consumed. The foam thus provides further thermal insulation.

In use, these coatings protect components during a brief high-temperature exposure, and may perform this function very reliably with low coating application weights. This approach to protection must always be compared with the cost, weight, and complexity of high-temperature-resistant coatings which remain unaffected after exposure. The ablation approach is particularly useful when the thermal shock environment is so severe that other coating systems are impractical.

REQUIREMENTS OF BASIC COATING SYSTEMS

A high-temperature coating must generally resist oxidation by thermal cycling, thermal shock, mechanical loading, erosion, vibration, abrasion, radiation, and hypersonic flow. While all these environmental conditions seldom exist simultaneously, the important ones must be defined and considered in selecting materials for coatings. Often the properties exhibited by materials in coating form are quite different from the bulk properties, because of the surface area or physical state of the coating. Extrapolation of the bulk properties is not always accurate, but lacking other information, it is required.

A prime consideration in coating technology is adherence. Without sufficient bond to the substrate, the coating is subject to failure by practically every source of stress such as mechanical loading, thermal stressing and differential expansion. Much experimental work has been performed on adherence, and numerous theories or explanations for interface bonding have been presented. In generalizing, the explanations rely on factors such as: mechanical interlocking, epitaxial overgrowth, mutual wetting or mutual solution of constituents at the interface, chemical reaction and diffusion. For each coating system, the importance of each factor varies. For example, Ault and Wheildon (26) felt that flame spray coatings depended largely on mechanical interlocking for attachment to the substrate and interlocking of individual particles. In applying siliconized coatings, diffusion and reaction to form new compounds at the surface or interface are largely responsible for "coating" adherence; the coating in this case has no abrupt end, but exhibits a smooth transition into the base metal. For sintered or vitreous coatings, adherence depends on coating reaction with the surface oxide, or the metal and solubility of the metal or oxide in the coating. A more complete discussion of adherence would require consideration of many specific interfaces and is prohibitive. An excellent summary of adherence is found in the reference by King et al. (27)

The actual adhesion or bond strength of the coating metal interface is often quite misunderstood. Most studies of "adherence" have not evaluated the actual interfacial adherence, but rather whether the interfacial adhesion is as great as the cohesive strength of the coating. Impact tests, for example, frequently measure largely the strength of the coating material under a rapid, complex loading. A weak coating material might fail, with many particles adhering to the base metal, and be evaluated as having "excellent" adherence; on the other hand a very strong coating material with actually better interface adherence could fail at the interface, parting clearly from the metal, and be evaluated as having "poor" adherence because there was little evidence that coating particles remained on the surface. King's work indicates that attempts to measure actual interface strength usually result in cohesive failure of vitreous coatings.

Thermal expansion matching is a part of the adherence problem. For brittle materials and most refractory materials having little or no ductility at low temperatures, severe shear stress can be induced at the coating-base interface, or severe compressive or tensile stresses induced in the coating by differences in thermal expansion between the coating material and the base. Analysis and measurement of these stresses has been made and reasonable agreement has been found between values predicted from thermal expansion, mechanical, and deformations properties, and those measured experimentally (*29, 30, 31*). Whether the internal stresses caused by thermal expansion differences are destructive to the coating integrity depends on the magnitude of these stresses, the additional stresses from the thermal gradients across the coating, and the ability of the base, interface of coating to deform plastically to relieve these stresses.

Thermal shock resistance is less of a problem at temperatures above 2200°F than at or near room temperature, because even the brittle oxides, hard metals and intermetallics exhibit some plastic deformation at high temperatures and this deformation, though small, can provide some stress relief. In addition, the modulus of elasticity of most materials decreases with increased temperature and the lower modulus of elasticity of the coating materials reduces the induced stress level. Typical modulus of elasticity values for several metals and oxides is shown in Figure 2.10. To calculate the stress in a coating-base system, it is also necessary to know the modulus of the composite as a function of temperature. Measurements and calculation techniques are available (*32*) for approximating this property for a complete stress analysis of the composite system. The conclusions from several investigations (*29*) indicate that for brittle coatings, the thermal shock resistance can be increased by introducing moderate residual compression stresses into the coating at low temperatures. Decreasing the thickness of the coating also improves the thermal shock resistance.

The thermal expansion of many materials has been completely bypassed as a consideration thus far. Table 2.14 provides a detailed listing of thermal expansion data compiled by Lawrence Radiation Laboratory (*33*). It is apparent that the matching of the low expansion coefficients of the refractory metals will not be an easy task, and further, that materials which provide a good match in one temperature range are unsatisfactory in other temperature ranges. The difference in thermal expansions determines the residual compressive stress in a coating at low temperatures, and is an important consideration in thermal shock resistance.

Thermal shock resistance is closely allied with the absolute values of thermal expansion, the mechanical properties of the coating and base, and the thermal conductivity of the coating and substrate. Excellent reviews of this entire problem are available (*34*). In general, the thermal stress resistance of a body is proportional to two factors which relate

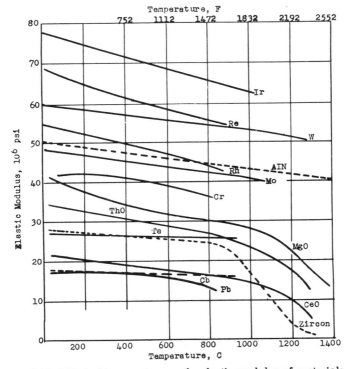

Fig. 2.10. Effect of temperature on the elastic modulus of materials.

the maximum temperature gradient to which a brittle body can be subjected without fracturing, to the mechanical and thermal properties of the body:

$$R \approx \frac{s(1-\mu)}{E\alpha} \quad \text{and/or} \quad R' \approx \frac{s(1-\mu)k}{E\alpha}$$

where

s = Strength
μ = Poisson's ratio
R = First thermal stress resistance factor
R' = Second stress resistance factor
E = Modulus of elasticity of the material
α = Thermal expansion of the material
k = Thermal conductivity of the material

TABLE 2.14. THERMAL EXPANSION OF HIGH-TEMPERATURE MATERIALS

Material	Per Cent Expansion From 25 C (77 F) to Indicated Temperature				
	500 C (930 F)	1000 C (1830 F)	1500 C (2730 F)	2000 C (3630 F)	2500 C (4530) F
Elements:					
Be	0.75	1.80			
B	0.39	0.81			
Nd	0.36	0.70 (800 C)			
Gd	0.32	0.97			
Tb	0.45	1.14			
Dy	0.49	1.20			
Er	0.50	1.25			
U (α)	0.85	1.27 (662 C)			
U (β)	1.57 (662 C)	1.77 (770 C)			
U (γ)	1.70 (770 C)	2.25			
Ti (α)	0.50	0.91 (882 C)			
Zr (α)	0.33	0.62 (870 C)			
Zr (β)	0.40 (870 C)	0.52	0.82 (1300 C)		
Hf	0.28	0.58			
Th (α)	0.60	1.22	1.72 (1400 C)		
Th (β)		1.69 (1400 C)			
V	0.46	1.04			
Cb	0.38	0.81	1.28	1.78	
Ta	0.31	0.69	1.10	1.53	2.05
Cr	0.42	1.07	2.02	2.18 (1800 C)	
Mo	0.28	0.56	0.96	1.47	1.98
W	0.215	0.465	0.75	1.07	1.45
Mn (α)	1.70	2.53 (727 C)			
Mn (β)	3.83 (727 C)	4.94	5.34 (1101 C)		
Mn (γ)		5.66 (1101 C)	5.81 (1137 C)		
Mn (δ)		6.17 (1137 C)	6.61 (1244 C)		
Re	0.32	0.67	1.04	1.44	
Fe (α)	0.68	1.32 (900 C)			
Fe (γ)	0.96 (900 C)	1.17	2.09 (1390 C)		
Fe (δ)		2.27 (1390 C)	2.54		
Ru	0.37	0.46 (600 C)			
Os	0.26	0.32 (600 C)			
Co (β)	0.63	1.80			
Rh	0.45	1.05	1.79		
Ir	0.34	0.77	1.27	1.80	
Ni	0.75	1.67			
Pd	0.61	1.36			
Pt	0.46	1.02	1.67	2.04 (1770 C)	
Cu	0.88	2.10	2.35 (1083 C)		
Au	0.73	1.65	1.80 (1063 C)		
C (diamond)	0.122	0.344	0.647		
Si	0.168	0.383			
Borides:					
SiB$_6$	0.25	0.58			
CaB$_6$	0.24	0.57			
BaB$_6$	0.28	0.63			
LaB$_6$	0.23	0.56			
CeB$_6$	0.30	0.65			
SmB$_6$	0.28	0.63			
ZrB$_2$	0.27	0.64	1.03		
HfB$_2$	0.25	0.54			

TABLE 2.14. (*Continued*)

Material	Per Cent Expansion From 25 C (77 F) to Indicated Temperature				
	500 C (930 F)	1000C (1830 F)	1500 C (2730 F)	2000 C (3630 F)	2500 C (4530 F)
Carbides:					
Be_2C	0.48				
B_4C	0.23	0.54	0.89	1.29	1.75
SiC	0.22	0.50	0.81	1.14	1.47
TiC	0.34	0.75	1.20	1.74	2.40
ZrC	0.29	0.64	1.04	1.51	
HfC	0.30	0.61			
CbC	0.31	0.69	1.10		
TaC	0.30	0.65	1.05	1.51	2.08
Cr_3C_2	0.38	0.97			
Mo_2C (β)	0.26	0.60			
W_2C	0.17	0.37	0.59	0.84	1.17
WC	0.21	0.48	0.79	1.15	
UC	0.44	1.04	1.74	2.58	
U_2C_3	0.36	0.89	1.58	2.02 (1800 C)	
UC_2	0.30	0.92	1.86	2.60 (1800 C)	
Silicides:					
Cr_3Si	0.47	1.08			
$CrSi_2$	0.57	0.87 (700 C)			
Mo_3Si	0.27	0.68			
$MoSi_2$	0.37	0.83			
WSi_2	0.37	0.81			
Nitrides:					
BN	0.58	1.30			
AlN	0.23	0.54			
Si_3N_4 (α)	0.10	0.28	0.54		
Si_3N_4 (β)	0.07	0.22	0.46		
UN	0.38	0.84			
Oxides:					
BeO	0.36	0.88	1.52	2.19	
MgO	0.61	1.33	2.23	2.82 (1800 C)	
CaO	0.56	1.28	2.25		
SrO	0.59	1.32	1.64 (1200 C)		
TiO	0.43	1.20			
FeO_{1-x}	0.56	1.42			
ZnO	0.28	0.66	0.82 (1200 C)		
SiO_2 (α-quartz)	0.92	1.22 (575 C)			
SiO_2 (β-quartz)	1.53 (575 C)	1.42			
SiO_2 (α-trid.)	0.17 (117 C)				
SiO_2 (β_1-trid.)	0.23 (117 C)	0.38 (163 C)			
SiO_2 (β_2-trid.)	0.44 (163 C)	0.92 (500 C)	1.02 (1000 C)		
SiO_2 (vitreous)	0.025	0.055			
TiO_2	0.39	0.86	1.40		
ZrO_2 (monocl.)	0.31	0.74	0.79 (1050 C)		
ZrO_2 (tetr.)		-2.23 (1050 C)	-1.64	-1.50 (1600 C)	
HfO_2 (monocl.)	0.26	0.57	0.93	1.08 (1700 C)	
HfO_2 (tetr.)			0.22 (1700 C)	0.60	
CeO_2	0.39	0.87			
ThO_2	0.41	0.92	1.50	1.75 (1700 C)	
UO_2	0.45	1.09	1.43 (1200 C)		

(*Continued*)

TABLE 2.14. (*Continued*)

Material	Per Cent Expansion From 25 C (77 F) to Indicated Temperature				
	500 C (930 F)	1000 C (1830 F)	1500 C (2730 F)	2000 C (3630 F)	2500 C (4530 F)
Oxides: (*Continued*)					
SnO_2	0.16	0.41			
Al_2O_3	0.36	0.83	1.37		
Sm_2O_3 (B form)	0.43	1.02			
Eu_2O_3 (B form)	0.45	1.08			
Gd_2O_3 (C form)	0.43	1.02			
Dy_2O_3 (C form)	0.36	0.95			
Cr_2O_3	0.40	0.84	1.30		
Fe_2O_3 (α)	0.54	1.20			
Co_2O_3	0.55	0.72 (635 C)			
Cd_2O_3	0.44	1.02			
WO_3 (monocl.)	0.42 (330 C)				
WO_3 (orthorh.)	0.42 (330 C)	0.58 (500 C)	0.86 (730 C)		
WO_3 (tetr.)	0.81 (730 C)	1.32			
$MgAl_2O_4$	0.37	0.82	1.35		
$MnAl_2O_4$	0.31	0.70			
$FeAl_2O_4$	0.38	0.84			
$CoAl_2O_4$	0.38	0.83			
$NiAl_2O_4$	0.37	0.82			
$ZnAl_2O_4$	0.38	0.85	1.05 (1200 C)		
$MgCr_2O_4$	0.34	0.77			
$MnCr_2O_4$	0.41	0.91			
$FeCr_2O_4$	0.39	0.87	1.10 (1200 C)		
$ZnCr_2O_4$	0.39	0.85	0.96 (1200 C)		
$MgFe_2O_4$	0.49	1.18			
$ZnFe_2O_4$	0.43	0.96			
$Li_2O \cdot 5Al_2O_3$	0.34	0.81			
$Li_2O \cdot Al_2O_3$	0.55	1.21			
$BeO \cdot Al_2O_3$	0.35	0.78			
$3CaO \cdot 5Al_2O_3$	(0.09)	(0.22)	0.49 (1200 C)		
$BaO \cdot Al_2O_3$	0.32	0.73			
$2B_2O_3 \cdot 9Al_2O_3$	0.18	0.41			
$2CeO_2 \cdot 3Al_2O_3$	0.42	0.93			
$2ThO_2 \cdot 3Al_2O_3$	0.37	0.83			
$Co_2O_3 \cdot Al_2O_3$	0.37	0.83			
$2SnO_2 \cdot 3Al_2O_3$	0.34	0.75			
$BeO \cdot Cr_2O_3$	0.32	0.73			
$2BeO \cdot SiO_2$	0.27	0.62			
$2MgO \cdot SiO_2$	0.49	1.14			
$2CaO \cdot SiO_2$ (β)	0.63	1.40			
$MgO \cdot SiO_2$	0.50	1.05	1.60		
$CaO \cdot SiO_2$ (α)	0.47	1.09			
$CaO \cdot SiO_2$ (β)	0.27	0.40 (700 C)			
$2FeO \cdot SiO_2$	0.45	0.97			
$2ZnO \cdot SiO_2$	0.14	0.31			
$3Al_2O_3 \cdot 2SiO_2$	0.22	0.50	0.83		
$ZrO_2 \cdot SiO_2$	0.18	0.45	0.78		
$HfO_2 \cdot SiO_2$	0.14	0.32	0.44 (1300 C)		
$2MgO \cdot TiO_2$	0.48	1.07			
$MgO \cdot TiO_2$	0.34	0.77			
$MgO \cdot 2TiO_2$	0.39	0.88			
$CaO \cdot TiO_2$	0.62	1.37			
$SrO \cdot TiO_2$	0.41	0.92			
$Al_2O_3 \cdot TiO_2$	0.41	0.93			

TABLE 2.14. (*Continued*)

Per Cent Expansion From 25 C (77 F) to Indicated Temperature

Material	500 C (930 F)	1000 C (1830 F)	1500 C (2730 F)	2000 C (3630 F)	2500 C (4530 F)
Oxides: (*Continued*)					
$ZrO_2 \cdot TiO_2$	0.35	0.77	1.03 (1200 C)		
$MgO \cdot ZrO_2$	0.49	1.17	1.98		
$CaO \cdot ZrO_2$	0.43	1.02	1.31 (1200 C)		
$SrO \cdot ZrO_2$	0.42	0.94			
$BaO \cdot ZrO_2$	0.37	0.83			
$Cr_2O_3 \cdot ZrO_2$	0.23	0.55			
$CaO \cdot HfO_2$	0.29	0.71			

The first factor, R, is the most important when large heat transfer rates are encountered such as a water quench. The second factor, R', represents the more important factor when low heat transfer rates are considered such as an air quench. For intermediate rates, both factors must be considered. A tabulation of R and R' for various materials appears in reference *34*. While the factors R and R' relate to only the stress development in the coating (or substrate) due to the thermal gradients across or along the coating, they represent the additional stresses which are superimposed on the mechanical and differential thermal expansion stresses.

The emittance of a high-temperature coating is often important, not simply because a particular emittance is desired, but because in a high heat flux environment, the equilibrium surface temperature is dependent on the emittance of the surface. This means that the temperature under which the coating must operate is determined by the surface emittance. Obviously, lowering the operating temperature is always desirable and if this can be effected by a change in surface emittance, then surface emittance control becomes more important. Unfortunately, the surface finish, evaporation from the surface, diffusion of the coating into the substrate, and the transparency of the coating, in addition to the basic coating material emissivity, all influence the final emittance. To choose a material of desired emissivity alone is insufficient and the translation of bulk properties to coating performance in this area is particularly difficult. This partly explains the discrepancies in emittance values observed throughout the literature.

Stability to high-energy radiation has generally not been a necessary consideration in choosing high-temperature coating materials. While it is conceivable that high dosages could change the thermal, optical and mechanical properties of refractory materials sufficiently to warrant consideration, many of the induced defects are "annealed" out at high temperatures, and also the inherent stability of the refractory materials makes them less susceptible to radiation damage. A more important consideration of sources for coating damage would be the sputtering losses caused in a space environment by high energy ions and neutral atoms.

CHARACTERISTICS OF HIGH TEMPERATURE COATING SYSTEMS

The previous discussion has centered on the materials for high temperature coatings and Chapter 4 discusses the methods of application. The characteristics of the final coating-metal composite deserves critical attention. For convenience, coatings have been divided into: (1) vitreous and sintered coatings, (2) flame or plasma sprayed coatings, (3) diffusion coatings, (4) metallic coating, and (5) cermet coatings.

A summary of the currently available coatings for refractory metals has been compiled by Defense Metals Information Center at Battelle Memorial Institute (*34*). This summary is presented in Table 2.15, and shows the diversified effort currently in progress. In addition, the coatings for a variety of other uses, electrical insulation, corrosion protection, emittance control and wear resistance are covered briefly in the following sections.

Vitreous, Recrystallized and Sintered Coatings

The porcelain enamel industry has applied high-temperature coatings for many years. From this diverse technology, further advances primarily in oxide coatings have evolved. Included in the following discussions are the coatings which are applied essentially as a slurry or in particulate form and later fused or sintered at high temperatures. Excluded (on the basis of the extensive coating-metal interaction) are the metallic or intermetallic coatings applied as slurries which depend upon extensive diffusion for the production of the final coating. These can more properly be classed as diffusion coatings and covered in that section.

As operating temperatures in heat exchangers and aircraft engine exhaust systems increased, the rapid oxidation and corrosion of many conventional iron base and stainless steels grew excessive and attention was turned to protective coatings similar to conventional porcelain enamels. Early developments utilized conventional porcelain-enamel-glass compositions with the addition of refractory oxides to increase the high-temperature viscosity and stability. Some of the more familiar vitreous high-temperature coatings for low alloy and stainless steels have been the "Solaramic" coatings by Solar aircraft and the coating developed by Harrison, Moore *et al.* (*35*) at the National Bureau of Standards, designated A-417. Similar coatings were also studied extensively at the University of Illinois. Several of these early ceramic coatings have substantial additions of Cr_2O_3 to the slip which results in a typical chrome green color. Because of the coating thickness (less

TABLE 2.15. PROTECTIVE COATINGS FOR REFRACTORY METALS

METALLIC COATINGS	Status	Substrate Base	Coating Composition as Applied	Maximum Reported Protection Temp, °F	Time, Hrs	Remarks
Fe, Ni, Co Base:						
Allison GMR (for Mo)	Semicomm	Mo	...	2100	1000	Physical properties of coating essentially equivalent to Nichrome. See Note 1.
NBS Electrodeposited Cr-Ni	Res	Mo	Cr-Ni; Cr-Ni-Al.	2000	800	Separations within coating when thermocycled.
Nuclear Metals Stainless Steel	Dev, semicomm	Mo, Cb	Stainless steel, austenic and ferritic.	...	...	Coextrusion process; thermal expansion mismatch of coated system.
Reaction Motors	R and D	Mo, W	Ni-Si-B-Cr.	2000–2500	1–200	Unsuitable for long periods above 2000 °F.
Wall Colmonoy	Semicomm, comm	Mo, Cb, W	Ni-Si-Cr-B, Ni-Si-Cr-B-W, Ni-Cr-P, Ni-Si-B alloys.	2200	...	Good in air—1800–2200 °F; melting or oxidation gives max temp limit.
Noble-Metal-Base Coatings:						
Am. Machine and Foundry	R and D	Mo, W	Pt or Pt-base alloy (e.g., 30 Rh Pt.)	3000	5–10	Failure due to pinholes rather than oxidation consumption or diffusion.
Mond Nickel	Comm	Mo	Pt over Al$_2$O$_3$ diffusion barrier	2160	900	Thermal expansion mismatch, no bond between coating and substrate, and difficult to apply to complex shapes. Used for stirrers in melting of glass.
Quantum	Res	W	Pt	2000	10–20	Poor protection for sharp corners, recesses, etc.
Reaction Motors	R and D	Mo, W	Au + Ni-Cr	2000–2500	500	Unsuitable for long periods above 2500 °F.
Misc Metal-Base Coatings:						
Climax Molybdenum Al-Cr-Si	Dev	Mo	21Al-45 Cr-33 Si-1 Fe	2800	4	Mo diffuses into coating at elevated temp. See Note 2.
General Electric GE300	Dev	Mo	Flame-sprayed Al$_2$O$_3$ over Cr plate.	3000	2	Cannot be applied to complex internal surfaces. See Note 3.
Picatinny Al-Cr-Si	Comm	Mo	20 Al-80Cr, Si alloy.	4000	1 min	Among best 5 out of 23 materials. See Note 4.
Thompson-Ramo-Wooldridge	Dev	Cb	Cr-Ti-Si	2500	90	Diffusion concurrent w/vacuum-metallizing. See Note 5.
INTERMETALLIC COATINGS						
Aluminide Base:						
General Electric LB-2	R and D	Cb	Slurry of Al-10 Cr-2Si; powder followed by slurry of Al powder.	2500	2	Will be used on WADD/MAC contract AF33(616)–6578. See Note 6.
McDonnell Aircraft	Dev	Cb	Base coat: 88Al-10Cr-2Si, LS-866-Reynolds. Overcoat: 30 LN-Reynolds.	2500	2	Base coat slurry. See Note 7.
Pratt and Whitney Aircraft	R and D	Cb	Pack-cementation coatings produced	...	...	Room temp hardness in range 1200–1800 DPH. See Note 8.

(*Continued*)

TABLE 2.15. (*Continued*)

INTERMETALLIC COATINGS (*Continued*)	Status	Substrate Base	Coating Composition as Applied	Maximum Reported Protection Temp, °F	Time, Hrs	Remarks
			on most Cb-base compositions using mixtures of metals of group (Al), Mo, Ti, Si, Cr, B, Ta, Be, Cd, Sn.			
Sylvania-Corning Nuclear G-14	Res	Cb	Al-5Cr-5T; $CbAl_3$ + X phases.	2600	10	Withstands high temp deformation and thermal shock. See Note 9.
1595	Res	Ta	Al-15Cr-9Si-5Sn } $TaAl_3$	2500	10	Withstands high temp deformation and thermal shock.
34S	R and D	Ta	50Al-50Sn $TaAl_3$ + Sn } + X phases	2500-3000	10	Withstands deformation and thermal shock. See AF33(616)-7462.
Al-Si-Y	Res	Ta	Al-11Si-5Y	2500	10	Withstands high temp deformation and thermal shock.
Silicide-Base Coatings:						
Battelle	Res	Ta	Si + Mn, B, Al	2700	24	Research currently in progress under AF33(616)-7184.
Bell Aerosystems	Comm	Mo, Cb, W	Proprietary	...	...	Best of 30 coatings evaluated from standpoint of reproducibility. See Note 10.
Boeing Airplane Disil-1	Dev	Mo	$MoSi_2$	3000	1	Coating not as ductile as desired. See Note 11.
Brush-Beryllium	R and D	Ta, W	MSi_2	...	...	Research on coating techniques and degree of protection afforded its infancy.
Chromalloy						
N-2	R and D	Cb	Proprietary	...	...	Environmental temp: 2000-4000°F. Up to 7200 hr protection reported at 2000°F. Continuous oxidation life varies w/temp. Self-healing
T-2	Dev	W	Proprietary	...	...	properties good at approx 2600°F. Coating is
W-2	Comm	Mo	Proprietary	...	...	intermetallic and brittle at room temp. See Note 12
Chromizing Durak-B	Comm	Mo	...	2700	180	Preliminary tests and initial experience indicate superiority over earlier coatings, see Note 13.
Fansteel Metallurgical	Res	Cb, Ta	Outer surface: $MoSi_2$ Inner surface: $Cb, (M_1,)_x Si_2$ or $Ta, (M_1,)_x Si_2$	2300	60	Potential of coating appears to be well in excess of current status. Elimination of defects, such as pinholes, appears likely to extend life of coating considerably.
General Electric liquid-phase coating	R and D	Mo	50 Mo-31Au-19Si ($MoSi_2$ in continuous matrix of Au-Si alloy.	2500	1000	Less than 1 hr life at 1000-1500°F. Heating and cooling through range does not affect life. See Note 14.

TABLE 2.15 (*Continued*)

INTERMETALLIC COATINGS (*Continued*)	Status	Substrate Base	Coating Composition as Applied	Maximum Reported Protection Temp, °F	Time, Hrs	Remarks
General Telephone and Electronics	Res	W	...	3300	10	Coated on W wires.
Linde LM-5	Dev	Mo Cb	40Mo-40Si-10Crb-10Al	2400	500	Some loss of Si and some oxidation during application. See Note 15.
Ling-Temco-Vought II, IX Vought ICb, IICb	Comm	Mo	Two or more of Si, Cr, Al, B, Ti, Cb, C (excl. substrate) consists of intermetallics incl. borides (when introduced) and silicides.	2800	8	Multicycle pack cementation often used. Paint and diffuse method being employed to touch up accidentally damaged areas of coatings. Coatings not as ductile as desired. Self-healing at temperatures over 1500°F. Where B allowable for use in coating, self-healing characteristics improve. Coatings for Cb being optimized under AF 33(616)-7896.
	Semicomm	Cb		...	...	
	Dev	Ta		...	...	
	Dev	W		...	...	
Metallwerk Plansee Silicide	R and D	Mo, (Cb), Ta, W	Silicides	...	...	...
Namco Industries	Dev, semi-comm	Mo, Ta, W	Mo-Si-Ni + additives (Cr, Al, Mn, etc.)	2000–2100	1000	Coating self-healing via stabilized molybdate. See Note 16.
NASA-Langley Chromalloy W-2	Comm	Mo	Proprietary	2800	30	See NASA tech. Note D-447 for additional information.
National Research	Dev	Mo, Ta	Al-Si	3000	1.5	Complex silicide after thermal stabilization. Not self-healing below 2000°F.
NYU disilicide	Res	W	WSi2	3300	> 10	Coating brittle and exhibits accelerated oxidation "pest" problem at 1200–2300°F.
N. Am. Aviation Chromalloy W-2	Semicomm	Mo	Unknown	2600	> 25	At 2750°F, coating reacted w/alumina, fireclay, magnesia, and zirconia specimen holders.
Pfaulder PFR-1	Dev	Cb	...	3000	...	Typical life at 3000°F, 0.5–0.75 hr on FS-82.
PFR-5	Dev	Mo	Proprietary Mo-Cr-Si.	3000	6.5	Diffusion stability and self-healing properties good at 3000°F.
PFR-6	Dev	Mo	Silicide and other intermetallics.	...	...	Diffusion stability, good; self-healing properties, good; currently being optimized.
PFR-7	Dev	Mo	Silicide and other materials.	3000	9.5	Diffusion stability, satisfactory; self-healing properties, good.
PFR-8	Dev	Mo	Silicide and other materials.	...	...	Diffusion stability, good. self-healing properties, good.
PFR-9	Dev	Mo	Silicide and other materials.	...	...	Diffusion stability, satisfactory; self-healing properties, fair.
Picatinny Molybdenum disilicate	Comm	Mo	Proprietary	4000	1 min.	Among best 5 out of 23 materials and coatings evaluated for possible use. See Note 17. Unsuitable for long periods above 2500°F.
Reaction Motors	R and D	Mo, W	MoSi2 and Ni-Cr	2000–2500	500	Static oxidation resis. of LM-5. Undercoat improves self-healing and thermal-shock properties.
Solar Aircraft S14-720	Res	Mo	D945 base coat, 44 Cb-32Ti-15Cr-5U-4Al	2000	100	
Union Carbide Metals LM-5 and DO45	R and D	Cb		...	...	

(*Continued*)

TABLE 2.15. (*Continued*)

INTERMETALLIC COATINGS (*Continued*)

	Status	Substrate Base	Coating Composition as Applied	Maximum Reported Protection Temp, °F	Time, Hrs	Remarks
Misc. Base Coatings:						
Vitro Labs	Res	Mo	$MoSi_2$ – 6 Ni	2700	20	Self-healing above 1500 °F.
Brush-Beryllium	R and D	Mo, Cb, Ta	M_2Be_{17} or MBe_{12}	2300	> 5	Research on coating techniques and degree of protection afforded is in its infancy.
NRL Zinc-Base Coating	Res	Cb	Various Cb-Zn intermetallics + Ti + Al	2000	100	ZnO on surface after oxidation exposure. Self-healing properties excellent. See Note 18.
Picatinny Zirconium diboride	Comm	Mo	ZrB_2	4000	...	Among best 5 out of 23 materials and coatings evaluated for possible use. See Note 19.
CERAMIC COATINGS						
Oxide-Base Coatings:						
General Electric GE400	Dev, semi-comm	Cb, Ta	Al_2O_3 + proprietary glass.	2500	100	Flame spray Al_2O_3, then spray on glass frit in water and sinter at 2700 °F. See Note 20.
U. of Illinois 9–60 Zircon-glass fused coating	R and D	W	Milled slip: 50-3/4 (65 Zircon 35 Coming MX glass) 4 Clay 1/4 Bentonite 45 Water.	3000	10	Covered in WADC tech. report 59–526, parts I and II.
Norton Rokide	Comm	Mo	ZrO_2, Al_2O_3, Cr_2O_3, etc. plus impregnants according to application.	...	...	As-sprayed coatings inherently slightly porous and permeable. See Note 21.
Coatings with Other Bases:						
Am. Machine and Foundry	Dev	Mo, Cb, Ta, W	Cermet: Ceramic w/ metal binder; several combinations.	2500	> 5	Electroplate and electrophoresis in same bath. See Note 22.
Amfkote-2	R and D	Mo, Cb, Ta	...	4200	45 min	Good in thermal shock. Being tested at NASA.
Amfkote-3	R and D		...	2500	264(Mo) 396(Cb) 275(Ta)	
Amfkote-4	R and D	Cb, Ta	...	2500	34(Cb) 312(Ta)	Poorer in thermal shock than Amfkote-2.
General Electric	Res	Cb	Proprietary, classified as nonmetallic diffusion coating.	2500	200	Hot dip and slip cast. Work in early stages. Interdiffusion limits life.
Gulton Industries 165 GI	Res	Mo	Composite of metallic and nonmetallic materials.	...	...	In early stages of research; "fairly good likelihood," of protection above 2000 °F.
Metallizing Engr	Res	Mo, Cb, Ta, W		...	...	
Picatinny Gradated Zirconia	Comm	Mo	Undercoat: metal-rich cermet (ZrO_2 + metal)	4000	1 min	Among best 5 out of 23 materials and coatings evaluated for possible use on hypersonic probe for leading edge application at Mach 8.5.

TABLE 2.15. (*Continued*)

CERAMIC COATINGS (*Continued*)	Status	Substrate Base	Coating Composition as Applied	Maximum Reported Protection Temp, °F	Time, Hrs	Remarks
Linde LW-6210	Comm	Mo	Overcoat: ceramic rich cermet $(ZrO_2 + metal)$ 90W-10ZrO_2	4000	1 min	Among best 5 out of 23 materials and coatings evaluated for possible use on hypersonic probe for leading edge application at Mach 8.5. Primary emphasis is on short-time erosion resistance and secondary emphasis is on oxidation resistance. Preliminary rocket firings indicate coatings reduce nozzle-throat erosion considerably. Coating is inexpensive.
Value Engineering	Dev	Mo, Ta, W	Cr + titanium boride Cr + zirconium boride	...	...	

Note 1. Coating is relatively soft and not too erosion resistant. Difficult to apply on sharp corners. Chromium plate prior to spray coating minimizes diffusion. Some tendency toward self-healing.

Note 2. Up to 36% Mo has been observed. Life shortened in high concs. of MoO_3. Low resistance to ballistic impact. Coating raises ductile-brittle trans. temp. Cannot coat deep holes (depth diameter).

Note 3. Ultimately fails by thermal-stress cracking of Cr plate.

Note 4. And coatings evaluated for leading-edge application at Mach 8.5; relatively poor erosion resistance.

Note 5. Being further developed under AF33(616)-7215.

Note 6. Will protect complex joined structures made of heavy- and thin-gauge material. Specifications prepared.

Note 7. 49 w/o LS-886, 27 xylene, 22-8 acetone, 0.7 Bentone 34. Overcoat applied as received. Coating being developed for MAC by General Electric Co., FPLD, under subcontract.

Note 8. Considerable elevated temp deformation tolerated if strain rate is sufficiently low. A degree of self-healing has been encountered in certain coating-substrate combinations.

Note 9. Oxidation rate at 1400°F relatively high, but still has over 10 hrs of life.

Note 10. Good on blind holes; poor on chambers and radii of 10 mils or less; good on radii of 30 mils.

Note 11. Self-healing properties good above 2500°F. Process expected to be applicable to Cb, Ta, and W-base alloys.

Note 12. Fairly expensive but large-scale use could result in drastic price reduction. Currently being used in re-entry components, probes, ram-jet tail pipes. Process currently being optimized.

Note 13. From company with respect to reliability, reproducibility, service life, and tolerances for surface imperfections in substrate. Total emissivity: 0.74-0.78, 1700-2600°F; 0.95, 2960 to 3140°F.

Note 14. Liquid phase gives self-healing. Interdiffusion limits life. Application method is hot dip and slip case and/or paint and sinter.

Note 15. Also applied by Linde flame plating process. Self-healing properties good over 1800°F. Cannot coat complex shapes by present methods. Difficult to apply or impractical on thin sheet.

Note 16. Life at 2175°F is zero hrs. Little can be done to raise max temp more than 200°F. Subject of U.S. Patent 2,878,554.

Note 17. On a hypersonic probe for a leading-edge application at Mach 8.5. Carbon contamination of substrate adversely affects quality of coating.

Note 18. Max temp 2050°F. Requires oxidizing atm at elevated temperatures.

Note 19. On a hypersonic probe for a leading-edge application at Mach 8.5.

Note 20. Excellent thermal-shock resistance. Impact resistance poor below 1800°F, excellent above 2200°F. Self-healing properties fair. Cannot be applied to thin sheet due to contamination problems. Currently being used in parts for turbojets, space power components, and nuclear rockets.

Note 21. Impregnation w/resins will render coatings substantially impervious up to 950°F. Development of new sealants necessary for impervious coating at more elevated temperatures.

Note 22. Ceramic content can be varied from 0 to 80 or 90 percent. Electroplated coatings tend to have pinholes.

than .005 in.), the low mobility of the coating at the firing temperature and the addition of refractory particles which do not dissolve in the glass, many of these coatings have matte surface texture.

The application temperature for these glassy ceramic coatings ranges from 1500 to 1900°F, depending on the coating composition and alloy. The composition for NBS A-418 is typical of coatings for heat-resistant alloys such as "Inconel" and is given in Table 2.16. The firing temperature for A-418, 1875°F, is too high for the low-alloy steels without the use of protective atmospheres; otherwise a thick oxide film forms on the metal before the coating matures. More suitable coatings for the low alloy steels are represented by Solar Aircraft "Solaramic" S9918 BC and S9919D which fire at a temperature of 1600°F. An extensive tabulation of compositions and designations, and a reference list for vitreous coatings is presented in reference (*36*).

TABLE 2.16. COMPOSITION OF TWO NATIONAL BUREAU
OF STANDARDS CERAMIC COATINGS

| Mill Batch Compositions | | | Frit Composition | | |
	Coating A-417	Coating A-418		Frit 331	Frit 332
Frit 331	70	...	SiO_2	38.0	37.5
Frit 332	...	70	BaO	44.0	44.0
Cr_2O_3	30	30	B_2O_3	6.5	6.5
Enamelers clay	5	5	CaO	4.0	3.5
Water	48	48	BeO	2.5	...
			ZnO	5.0	5.0
			ZrO_2	...	2.5
			Al_2O_3	...	1.0

The oxidation protection provided by these ceramic coatings is substantial. The useful service temperature for many low alloys and stainless steels can be raised 300 to 400°F by suitable ceramic coatings. The oxidation resistance available from uncoated superalloys in the 1500 to 1800°F range can generally be matched by coating less oxidation resistant alloys.

The glass bonded ceramic coatings have been applied to the superalloys with notable improvement in oxidation resistance at temperatures from 1800 to 2200°F. Typical of these coatings are the "Solaramic" S5210-2C and S6100, the Pfaudler "Nucerite" (a recrystallized vitreous coating), and the NBS A-418.

All these glass-bonded refractory coatings for iron, nickel and cobalt base alloys consist of a glassy matrix filled with undissolved or recrystallized refractory crystals. The coating composition is designed to provide a barrier to the diffusion of oxygen, and yet to be just sufficiently fluid to cover and seal the metal surface. The coefficient of expansion of the coating system matches rather closely the expansion characteristics of the coated alloys, and good thermal shock resistance is achieved. The excellent adherence of the glass-metal bond also contributes to this thermal shock resistance. The adherence is generally attributed (at least partially) to the solution of the metal oxide in the glass at the coating-metal interface, and possibly the partial reduction of oxidic constituents in the coating at the interface.

Upon initial firing, the glassy phase softens below the firing temperature and begins to dissolve the more refractory additions, increasing glass viscosity and the coating refractoriness. The initial coverage and wetting is provided by the reactive, fluid glass, but this reactivity decreases rapidly as the coating composition becomes more homogeneous. Finally, the coating approaches an equilibrium, reaction rates are slow and the coating provides stable oxidation protection, maintaining the coverage and integrity provided by the initial wetting of the glass phase.

The disadvantages of glass-bonded coatings for high-temperature protection lie in the nature of the glasses. It is necessary to use as high a firing temperature as possible to provide sufficient fluidity in the glass for wetting and flow; yet this temperature must be within that tolerated by the alloy. Use temperatures, while sometimes above the firing temperature, are limited by the viscosity of the glass at the operating temperature. Often the excessive solution of the refractory filler in the glass at operating temperatures near or above the initial firing temperature results in sufficient change in coating expansion characteristics to degrade adherence. The slow oxidation of the metal under the coating and the reaction of this oxide with the coating result in eventual coating failure.

Vitreous or glass-bonded coatings have also been used as high-temperature wire insulations, for temporary oxidation protection during heat treating, for refractory metal protection, for sealing flame spray coatings, and for emittance control coatings, to mention only a few. Several of these coating systems deserve further description.

Vitreous coatings for titanium are available to prevent absorption of gases during heat treatment and oxidation. Titanium coatings, if improperly compounded or applied, tend to provide another source of impurities which may diffuse into the titanium and cause embrittlement. The affinity of titanium for many contaminants demands the use of protective coatings for high temperatures. The galling characteristics of titanium can also be minimized during forming operations by some expendable coatings. While these expendable coatings for temporary protection during heat-treating and formings are designed to spall completely from the metal after cooling, sometimes particular shapes or alloys retain a portion of the coating.

Vitreous coating for electrical insulation on copper- and nickel-coated wire have shown good insulation at temperatures at 1000°F and higher (*37*). The coating is applied by dragging the wire through the slurry and into a furnace continuously. The brittle nature of the coating causes cracking when the coated wires bend around a small radius, but the electrical insulating characteristics are maintained even after cracking occurs. The coatings acts as a mechanical spacer between the wire and an adjacent conductor even though there are cracks in the coating. The composition of the vitreous coating was found to be important in achieving the highest insulation resistance at high temperatures.

The protection of tungsten by vitreous coatings or glass-bonded coatings has been studied by Bergeron *et al.* (*38, 39*). A number of coating formulations were found to offer some protection to tungsten and operation at 3000 to 3300°F was achieved for periods of several hours. Most of the work on this program was restricted to small rods and wires and the application of these systems to structural shapes and sheets may offer some further problems. The coatings which offered the best protection for tungsten were 35 per cent to 65 per cent zircon coatings. The glass composition was a high silica borosilicate glass (Corning 726 MX) closely matching the expansion of the tungsten. Other coating techniques using combinations of silicide and vitreous coatings were generally unsuccessful.

Vitreous coatings of the types useful for nickel-base alloys have been used to protect chromel-alumel thermocouple wires from oxidation at temperatures up to 2100°F. The change in emf calibration of small (22 ga) wire due to the protective coating was found to be equivalent to 5 to 15°F at low temperatures; however, such changes in calibration are common for small bare wires subjected to similar heat treatments without coatings. The emf calibration at high temperatures was changed only slightly by coating and firing.

A vitreous coating system for oxidation protection of columbium has been reported by Hall and Graham (*40*) and consists of a flame spray alumina impregnated with a baria-alumina-silicate glass to seal the surface. The desired thermal expansion characteristics and compatibility of the glass with the columbium were achieved and over 500 hr protection at 2300°F and 100 hr at 2500°F were obtained.

Among the sintered coatings used at high temperature, the alumina coating on fine tungsten filament wire for electron tubes is typical. In this process the tungsten operates in a vacuum and requires only a well sintered coating of alumina for mechanical separation from adjacent filament wire. The alumina is applied by dragging the wire through a slurry of high-purity alumina and through an inert atmosphere furnace continuously. Several applications are required for the desired coating thickness. The final coating has little adherence and offers little oxidation protection, but it provides good electrical insulation and mechanical isolation of the tungsten filament wires.

Many other ceramic coatings could be mentioned as either sintered or low temperature-bonded coatings. A commercial insulating coating (*41*) of aluminum silicate fibers ("Fiberfrax", Carborundum Co.) in a silicate base is available which cures at 400°F and provides thermal insulation and some oxidation protection to graphite. Application is by brushing, spraying or troweling. Upon heating to 1600°F, a ceramic bond is developed in the coating and the use temperature extends to 2300°F and higher. Many phosphate compositions have been developed for low-temperature application and curing and use at high temperatures. The coating developed by Eubanks and Moore (*42*) is representative of this type. Monoaluminum phosphate was used as the bonding agent for a coating cured at 400°F which was useful to 1600 to 1800°F on various nickel base alloys and stainless steels. High emittances were achieved by using color oxide additions, and emittances as high as 0.9 to 0.94 were reported.

Among the thick insulating coatings which have been studied, the Marquardt Corporation work on reinforced ceramic coatings deserves special mention. Thick coatings ($\sim$ 0.5 in.) have been applied by troweling on various metal surfaces reinforced with mesh or ribbon. Figure 2.11 shows an example of a large shape with an insulative coating. The coating is a low temperature curing system which will withstand severe thermal shock and cycling. Much work with phosphates and the fluoride-containing acids such as the flurophosphates has provided suitable binders for aluminum oxide base coatings serviceable at 3500°F and zirconia base coatings serviceable at 4000°F. Characteristics of two coatings are given in table 2.17 (*43*). Some limitations of this system are the progressive deterioration of the reinforcing metal during extended exposures and the time-consuming application technique.

A cermet diffusion coating technique which borrows from vitreous coating technology is reported by Moore and Cuthill (*44*). Several commercial coatings use a similar technique for applying the material for diffusion. In this cermet technique, the metal constituents to be diffused into the metal surface are incorporated in a vitreous matrix. Upon application, the metallic particles migrate to the metal surface and the vitreous phase remains on the surface. The resulting coating produces a hard, oxidation resistant coating on low alloy and ingot iron for 1500°F service.

Electrophoretic deposition as a method of coating parts has been mentioned previously (*45*). Ceramic, metallic or vitreous compositions can be applied electrophoretically and sintered or fused similar to slurry-coated shapes. The prime advantage of electrophoretic deposition is the coating thickness uniformity which can be achieved with complicated shapes, and the high uniform density in the applied coating.

Heat-resistant paints based on zinc oxide and dimethyl hydrogen phosphite-ethyl phosphate have been used for 1000°F service (*46*). Some organic-base aluminum flake type paints have provided low-cost,

(a)

(b)

(Courtesy of Marquardt Corp.)

Fig. 2.11. A large ram-jet component (a) showing reinforcing ribbon before coating; (b) after coating with a thick insulative coating.

TABLE 2.17. PROPERTIES OF TWO TYPICAL REINFORCED
REFRACTORY COATINGS

Properties	TherMarq* P-150	TherMarq* ZPF-100
Density of ceramic plus reinforcement, lbs/cu in.	0.10 to 0.12	0.14
Percentage porosity	23–24	20–30
Thermal drop through 0.250 in. at steady state heat flux of 10,000 to 100,000 btu/ft^2/hr, °F per 0.001 in.	approx 8°	approx 11°
Maximum service temperature	3500°F	4000°F
Thermal conductivity (calculated from thermal drop data) btu/hr/ft^2/in. at		
800°F	0.98	0.72
1200	0.83	0.60
1600	0.72	0.52
2400	0.60	0.43
Coefficient of Linear Expansion 68° 2000°F-in./in./°F	6.4×10^{-6}	8.3×10^{-6}
Specific Heat—btu/lb/°F		
1000°F	0.22	0.12
1500	0.22	0.12
2000	0.23	0.13
2500	0.27	0.15
Emittance at 3000°F (considerably higher with additives)	0.2 to 0.3	0.3 to 0.4
Reinforcement metal	Mild steel, stainless steel, or molybdenum	Stainless steel, molybdenum, tantalum or tungsten
Curing temperature	850°F	450°F
Curing cycle	approx 15 hrs	approx 4 hrs
Modulus of rupture, psi at		
room temp	4500	1900
1000°F	3750	1800
1500	. . .	2200
1800	1500	. . .
2000	. . .	1760
Compressive strength, psi at room temp		
(450°F curing temperature)	. . .	2000
(850°F curing temperature)	8500	. . .
(2400°F curing temperature)	12000	. . .
Thermal shock resistance	RT to 3300°F to RT in 2 min— no change	RT to 4200°F to RT in 2 min— no change
Recycling capability	5 cycles RT to 3300°F— total time 100 min— no change	7 cycles RT to 4200°F— total time 34 min— no change

*TherMarq is a trademark of Marquardt Corp.

high-emittance coatings after carbonizing and diffusion on nickel-base alloys.

Plasma and Flame Spray Coatings

Almost any materials which melt congruently into a fluid liquid and have a reasonably low vapor pressure can be flame- or plasma-sprayed. The ability to coat a low-temperature alloy or material with a higher-melting coating has promoted the rapid growth of this technology. The methods of producing flame-spray coatings are covered in Chapter 4. The characteristics of some of the coatings formed by these processes are covered briefly in this section. Ault and Wheildon (27, 47) have provided an extensive comparison on flame- and plasma-sprayed ceramic coatings and the reader is referred to this source of further information.

Almost all sprayed coatings are somewhat porous because the application process is unable to eliminate all the fissures and joints between the particles. This porosity is frequently the most important physical characteristic of the coating because it provides the lower modulus of elasticity and the extra "flexibility" required to absorb the differential thermal expansion stresses and the thermal shock stresses. Conversely, if oxidation protection is desired, the porosity is a limitation.

Rather than describe conventional flame-spray coatings such as alumina, zirconia, spinel and ziron, a variety of coating materials which have been used will be mentioned. In discussing flame or plasma spraying, however, it is important to realize that extremely rapid heating and cooling has occurred in each cooling particle, and to understand how this rapid heating and quenching "locks in" extremely high stresses, metastable crystallographic forms and unstable or nonequilibrium phases. For example, normal alpha-alumina, after flame spraying, consists largely of gamma-alumina, and zircon after flame spraying is a mixture of zirconia and silica glass. Here is an excellent example of how the bulk characteristics of a material may not be representative of the characteristics of the coating. The modulus of elasticity of alumina in a coating is 4.5 to 6.5×10^{-6} psi compared with 53×10^6 psi for the bulk; the strength in bending is 4,000 to 6000 psi compared to 40,000 psi in the bulk. Similar differences are found in other materials.

To discuss all types of coatings that have been produced by flame-spraying is impractical. A partial listing of reported coatings is given in Table 2.18 with some brief comment. Generally, it can be seen from this table that almost any material can be plasma-sprayed, even some of the easily oxidizable or pyrophoric materials. The quality of the coatings obtained is frequently not described or carefully investigated, so the value of many of these reported coatings must be viewed with some reservation. For materials that dissociate, such as SiC, or decompose

TABLE 2.18. FLAME AND PLASMA SPRAYED COATING MATERIALS

Material	Flame or Plasma	Remarks
Aluminum	either	For corrosion, oxidation
Aluminum oxide	either	Erosion, high temperature
Barium titanate	either	Loses oxygen, dielectric
Beryllium	plasma	Toxic, requires dry box
Beryllium oxide	either	Toxic, requires hood
Boron	plasma	X-ray transparent
Boron carbide	plasma	Hard, wear resistant
Brass	either	Dense deposit
Calcium zirconate	either	Dielectric, dense
Cerium oxide	either	Refractory, emittance
Columbium	plasma	Refractory metal
Columbium carbide	plasma	Refractory, hard
Chromium	either	Oxidation protection
Chromium boride	either	Hard
Chromium carbide	plasma	Hard, refractory
Chromium oxide	either	Dense coating for oxidation
Copper	either	High conductivity
Diopsite	either	Glassy(?)
Hafnium oxide	either	Thermal insulation, refractory
Hafnium carbide	plasma	Refractory
Ilmenite	either	Dense coatings
Iron	either	Shapes
Lithium aluminate	flame	W/other oxides to aid melting
Magnetite	either	Magnetic
Molybdenum	plasma, either	W/Al_2O_3 layers, undercoat
Molybdenum borides	plasma	Refractory, hard
Molybdenum carbide	plasma	Refractory, hard
Molybdenum silicide	plasma	Oxidation protection
Mullite	either	Glassy (?) refractory
Monel	either	Corrosion resistant
Nichrome	either	Undercoat for oxides
Nickel	either	Dense with NiO, for oxidation
Nickel oxide	either	Emittance
Rare earth oxides	either	Refractory
Rhenium	plasma, flame?	For oxidation
Silicon carbide	either(?)	Dissociates
Spinel	either	Good oxide coating
Stainless steels	either	Corrosion resistance
Tantalum	plasma	Refractory
Tantalum carbide	plasma	Refractory, hard
Titanium	plasma	Spray in inert gas
Titanium boride	plasma	Refractory
Titanium carbide	plasma	Hard
Titanium nitride	plasma	Hard refractory
Titanium oxide	either	Dense, for oxidation, dielectric
Thoriated tungsten	plasma	Electron emission
Thorium oxide	plasma	Low v.p., refractory
Tungsten	plasma	Refractory
Tungsten carbide	plasma	Hard
Vanadium boride	plasma	Hard, refractory

(Continued)

TABLE 2.18. (*Continued*)

Material	Flame or Plasma	Remarks
Yttrium oxide	either	Refractory
Zircon	either	As SiO_2 and ZrO_2 in coating
Zirconium	plasma	Spray in inert gas
Zirconium boride	plasma	Hard
Zirconium carbide	plasma	Hard
Zirconium oxide	either	Thermal insulation, refractory

as does zircon, the coating is not the same as the starting material. Dissociation, decomposition, or sublimation of materials during spraying are the greatest limitations of the spraying process. The quality of the coating, adherence, structure and porosity are largely dependent on the substrate and on the spraying technique. Some art and experience on the operator's part is essential in most coating operations.

The basic flame-spray coatings produced by powder guns, rod guns and the detonation guns are similar, but they differ greatly in respect to (1) the velocity of the molten particle, and (2) the feeding process and transit time in the hot zone. For the detonation gun* the particle is hurled at supersonic speeds to the substrate by the explosive force of a pulsating jet. This provides molten particles at very high velocities and more local flow upon impact. For the rod gun spray process,† particle velocity is 400 to 800 ft/sec compared to 2400 ft/sec for the "flame plating" process. This results in less flow at the surface, but since all particle are molten, good flow and interlocking occurs. For the powder guns,‡ particle velocities are 100 to 150 ft/sec, and some particles which pass through the flame may not be completely molten. This results in a slightly higher porosity and less flow upon particle impact. Solid particles which may get to the surface without being melted usually bounce off and are not included in the coating.

The plasma spray guns generate a much higher temperature (up to 30,000°F) so complete melting almost always occurs, even for extremely refractory materials. The particle velocity is from 1000 to 2000 ft/sec slightly higher than for most flame spray guns. The coatings produced by the high velocity and very fluid plasma spray particles are then generally more dense than the corresponding flame spray coating. Table 2.19 compares the properties of coating materials applied by several techniques.

The density of the coating and the microphysical characteristics of the coating deposit also depend on the viscosity, specific heat and thermal conductivity of the molten coating material, and strongly on the

---

*"Flame Plating," Linde Corp.
†"Rokide," Norton Co.
‡"Thermospray," Metco Co.

TABLE 2.19. COMPARISON OF TYPICAL PLASMA SPRAYED
AND FLAME SPRAYED COATINGS

	Alumina	Alumina	Zirconia
Type analysis	99% Al_2O_3	96.5% Al_2O_3 2.5% TiO_2	93% ZrO_2 5% CaO_2
Melting point	$\sim$3700°F	$\sim$3700°F	$\sim$4650°F
Coating density, gm/cc			
Oxy-acetylene flame (powder)	2.6–2.9	2.6–3.1	3.6–4.3
Plasma flame (powder)	3.0–3.4	3.2–3.6	5.0–5.3
Oxy-acetylene flame (rod)	3.0–3.3	. . .	4.7–5.2
Spray rate, lb/hr			
Oxy-acetylene flame (powder)	3.5	2.0–3.3	1.0–2.0
Plasma flame (powder)	3.5–4.0	3.5–4.0	4.0–4.5
Oxy-acetylene flame (rod)	0.5–1.0	. . .	0.4–0.8
Thermal conductivity	19 btu/hr/sq ft/in. °F at 1000–2000°F	19 but/hr/sq ft/in. °F at 1000–2000°F	8 btu/hr/sq ft/in. °F at 1000–2000°F
Thermal expansion	4.1×10^{-6}/°F 70 to 2000°F	4.1×10^{-6}/°F 70 to 2000°F	5.4×10^{-6}/°F 70 to 2250°F
Total emissivity	.3 to .4	.3 to .4	.3 to .4
Coating color	White	Gray	Cream

thermal conductivity of the substrate since this determines the flow before
solidification. When the droplet viscosity is low, the individual particles
blend into one another better, forming dense coatings. When the liquid is
more viscous, flow is inhibited and micro recesses are not filled. The
mass and thermal conductivity of the substrate also affect the coating
quality. High conductivity substrates quench the molten particles rapidly,
limiting flow and the coating density. The particle size of the feed material determines whether complete melting can occur in powder guns,
and to some extent determines the transit time through the flame. The
distance of the work surface from the spray nozzle also affects coating
characteristics radically. For short distances from the nozzle, complete
melting may not have occurred in powder guns; for long distances, the
particle may have partially solidified.

Feeding material to be flame-sprayed is difficult when the materials
are fine powders. The difficulty in supplying the powder at a uniform
rate causes temporary surplus and deficiency of spray particles. Particle
size distribution is also important. Very fine powders are difficult to
feed and are undesirable; coarse particles may not be completely melted.
Thus, it is important to exercise careful control over the raw materials.
Rod guns can use only materials which are previously fabricated into

rods, and the cost and difficulty of fabricating these rods limits this process.

Flame- and plasma-spray coatings can be combinations of more than one material, either homogeneous, in layers, or gradated. This provides a technique for making heat-resistant coatings that are more thermal shock-resistant because of configuration or composition. High thermal shock resistance can often be achieved by alternating thin layers of metal with oxide coatings. The metal provides reflection and lateral heat transfer to minimize hot spots while the low conductivity oxide provides insulation.

Dense sprayed coatings can be obtained with a number of materials. Most metals, because of the low liquid viscosity, form dense coatings. Oxides such as chromia, nickel oxide, titania and ilmenite, melt to form very fluid liquids and spray as dense coatings. Much is said about the residual porosity of flame- or plasma-spray coatings, but most materials can be applied with less than 10 per cent porosity with optimum techniques. This corresponds to a density of better than 90 per cent of the theoretical and this density is often difficult to achieve in sintered ceramics or powder metallurgy parts. The difference in the porosity in the two cases is quite different. A porcelain is often impervious at 90 per cent theoretical density, while even the most dense sprayed coatings have some open pores and are open to diffusion of gases. For example, even a glassy sprayed coating can still be quite porous. Only a few composite coatings which completely seal the surface have been reported, though much development has been directed toward this problem. The detonation gun coatings seem to have the lowest porosity, less than 1 per cent, but are still permeable.

To obtain dense coatings, metal additives to oxides have been used, such as nickel-nickel oxide, nickel-magnesium oxide, and nickel-zirconia. Some combinations of oxides used alone give very low porosities. Titania and chromia alone yield dense coatings. Some oxides such as alumina have been sprayed in combination with a glass which aids in sealing the coating.

The open microstructure of sprayed oxide coatings, however, contributes to their thermal shock resistance, and as coatings are made more dense, their thermal shock resistance suffers. The unique overlapping, interlocking structure (Figure 2.12) provided by spraying, contributes to the coatings ability to be strained ("stretched") from 0.5 to 1.5 per cent without failure. The normal 10 per cent porosity and excellent adherence are desired for good thermal shock resistance. The use of base coats of molybdenum, nickel-chromium alloy or copper under oxide coatings improves adherence and thermal shock resistance.

Sprayed coatings can be applied to substrates which decompose at low temperatures. Wood and plastic can be easily coated with low

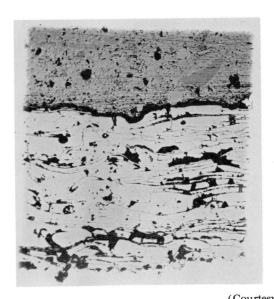

(Courtesy of Norton Co.)
Fig. 2.12. Microstructure of a flame-sprayed coating (ROKIDE-A) on stainless steel. Note extensive interlocking of particles. Since the coating has less than 10% porosity, the dark voids do not represent normal voids in the coating, but are a result of polishing technique.   100X

melting metals such as zinc or aluminum. With care and proper surface preparation, excellent aluminum oxide coatings have been applied to organic plastic surfaces. Obviously, the surface temperature during spraying must be carefully controlled. Sprayed coatings of nickel-zirconia over a zirconia intermediate layer provided substantial erosion resistance for reinforced plastic substrates subjected to an oxygen-kerosene torch (48).

Diffusion Coatings

In this grouping, all the coating processes will be considered in which a heat treatment is required to react the coating material with the substrate to form the coating. Rather than group the coating processes by application techniques, it appears more logical to discuss and compare all coatings of the same composition, though applied by quite different techniques.

A discussion of diffusion and diffusion mechanisms is given in Chapter 7, and the application techniques for preparing diffusion coatings are covered in Chapter 4. This discussion will cover only the characteristics of the coatings achieved by each process, and particularly the essential characteristics of commercial coatings of similar composition. While the coatings which are given most attention are those for the refractory metals, the diffusion process is not limited to these metals and some examples of low alloy stainless steel and superalloy diffusion coatings will be mentioned. The emphasis on refractory metals is based largely on the current interest in the higher temperature coatings and the intense efforts in progress at this time to improve refractory metal coating technology.

For convenience, the diffusion coatings will be grouped according to base metals to include the iron, stainless and superalloy coatings; molybdenum coatings; tungsten coatings; tantalum coatings; and columbium coatings. Coatings for vanadium, chromium, and rhenium will be summarized briefly due to the limited work on coatings for these materials.

Essentially all high-temperature coatings are diffusion coatings to some extent. There is always some mutual solubility and diffusion process occurring at an interface, though in many coating systems it can be neglected. At operating temperatures of 2500°F and above, the diffusion process, being temperature-dependent, is usually sufficiently important that reactions which are thermodynamically possible occur even though the reactants and products remain in the solid state. Coatings are no longer simply "sintered" or fused on the surface; the atoms of the coating material are sufficiently mobile to move into the base material, reacting to form new compounds or entering the lattice of the base metal. Most promising oxidation protection coatings depend upon this extensive reaction of the coating material with the base metal to form an oxidation-resistant intermetallic or hard metal. This reaction product, rather than the original coating material, usually provides the protection.

Diffusion Coatings for Iron, Stainless and Superalloys. Diffusion coatings are useful with many common alloys. The carburizing and nitriding for forming hardened cases on iron-base alloys may be considered diffusion coatings; however, since the hardened case is not useful much above 1100°F, these are beyond the scope of this book.

Iron-base alloys may be diffusion coated with chromium by a simple pack treatment, and commercial preparations are readily available for the pack. A case several mils thick, rich in chromium (18 to 40 per cent) is readily formed on most steel alloys containing less than 0.2 per cent carbon. Higher carbon content inhibits the diffusion process because of chromium carbide formation and limits coating thickness. The coating formed on steels by chromizing resembles high-chromium stainless steels in composition, corrosion resistance and oxidation resistance.

A number of aluminum-base coatings are available for steels, stainless steels and superalloys. Many aluminum, nickel-aluminum, iron-aluminum or aluminum-glass base coatings are available commercially. Solar Aircraft Co. and Haynes Stellite Co. produce compositions suitable for a number of iron base, nickel base and cobalt base superalloys. Many of these coatings are applied by slurry coating the part and sintering (diffusing) at 1600°F to 2100°F. Heat treatments may require up to 24 hours to complete.

The oxidation protection offered by these diffusion alloys is substantial. Table 2.20 shows typical alloys exposed to high-temperature oxidation and the difference in oxidation rates of coated and uncoated alloys. Most of the diffusion coatings have little effect on the mechanical properties of the substrate. In some cases, however, the high temperature diffusion treatment may require modification to conform to the heat treatment required for a particular alloy.

TABLE 2.20. OXIDATION RESISTANCE OF
DIFFUSION COATED ALLOYS

Temp, °F	Time at Temp, hrs	Condition	Wt Change, mg/sq cm
Nickel-Aluminum Over Nickel-Base Superalloy[a]			
2000	500	Uncoated	−3.3
		Coated	+0.37
2300	100	Uncoated	−49.2
		Coated	−3.1
2300	400	Coated	−45.7
Iron-Aluminum Over Cobalt-Base Superalloy[b]			
2000	500	Uncoated	−200
		Coated	+12.4
2300	20	Uncoated	Destroyed
		Coated	+1.1
Iron-Aluminum Over Alloy Steel			
1800	100	Uncoated	+262.5
		Coated	+7.5

[a]Haynes No. 713C.
[b]Haynes No. 152.

Diffusion Coatings for Molybdenum. Several commercial silicide coating processes are available for the protection of molybdenum and molybdenum alloys. The most important of these are: "Disil", Boeing Aircraft Co.; "Durak-B", Chromizing Corp; "PFR-6", Pfaudler Company; "Vought II and IX", Chance Vought Corp.; and "W-2", Chromalloy Corp. The general characteristics of these coatings are shown in Table 2.15.

All these coatings can be applied by the pack cementation process. For each coating, the pack composition is somewhat different, but the processes are similar in that they yield a coating largely consisting of molybdenum disilicide, but modified by B, Al, Mn, Ti, Nb, Cr, or Be, singly or in combinations.

All comparative coating evaluation programs require the establishment of a criterion to establish the relative merits of a coating. While few comparative evaluations have included all the major silicide coatings of current interest, "W-2" coating, because of its availability for earlier evaluations, has shown superior performance in a number of investigations. A recent comparative investigation which included several recent silicide coatings was performed by Rummler, *et al.* (*49*) Oxidation protection at 2500°F under static and cyclic heating was evaluated by weight change on coated specimens with several type edges (sheared, tumbled and broken). Strength characteristics were evaluated on coated specimens at room temperature. The results of this investigation are shown in Figures 2.13, 2.14, 2.15, and 2.16. Mo-0.5Ti alloy was used in this investigation and the coatings were applied by the coating supplier. A summary of the coatings is given in Table 2.21.

Most of the comparative evaluations of molybdenum coatings have shown "W-2" coating to be superior to other systems available for the evaluation. More recently, other diffusion coatings have exhibited performance comparable to "W-2." The inconsistency in sample perform-

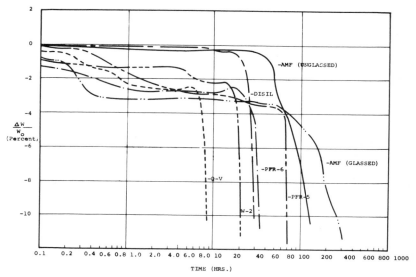

Fig. 2.13. Typical weight changes vs time for continuous exposure at 2500°F for coated Mo-0.5Ti (tumbled edges).

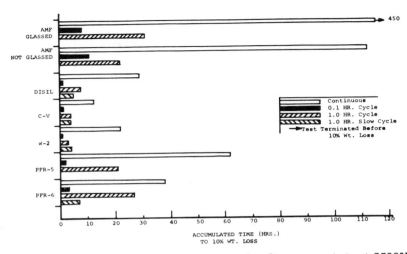

Fig. 2.14. Comparative results for continuous and cyclic exposure tests at 2500°F.

ance is always a problem in comparative evaluation and continued research should minimize these problems and make future comparative evaluation more meaninghful. Figure 2.17 shows the results obtained in another comparative investigation.

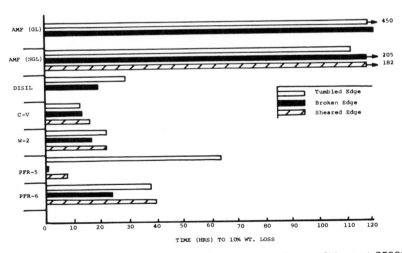

Fig. 2.15. Continuous exposure coating life for various edge conditions at 2500°F.

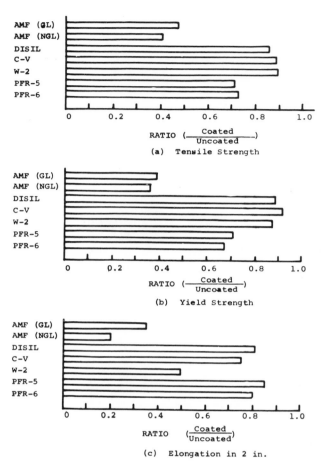

Fig. 2.16. Comparison of room temperature tensile strength of coated specimens.

Some further description of individual coatings is needed to expand the information in Table 2.15. While some of these commercial coatings are proprietary compositions and processes, general descriptions are available.

"Disil 1" is applied in a pack cementation process in a sealed retort containing silicon and iodine. A fluidized bed application technique in which volatilized iodine flows through a heated silicon bed is also under development. The ductility of the substrate after coating is excellent, but less than that of the uncoated metal. Thermal shock resistance is good and the normal total emittance is above 0.85 from 2300 to 2800°F. Coating weight is about 0.01 lb/ft^2 side. "Disil-2"

TABLE 2.21. CHARACTERISTICS OF COATINGS
EVALUATED BY NASA

Supplier	Designation	Avg. Coating[a] Thickness, in.	Substrate Thickness, in.[a]		Wt. Change (per cent)
			Before Coating	After Coating	
American Machine & Foundry	AMF (Glassed)[b]	0.0017	0.0122	0.0092	2.20
American Machine & Foundry	AMF (Not Glassed)	0.0017	0.0122	0.0099	2.20
Boeing	Disil	0.0015	0.0108	0.0081	−3.81
Chance Vought	C-V	0.0014	0.0120	0.0106	3.43
Chromalloy	W-2	0.0012	0.0121	0.0109	4.40
Pfaudler	PFR-5	0.0023	0.0118	0.0091	13.67
Pfaudler	PFR-6	0.0019	0.0116	0.0097	7.92

NOTE: [a]Based on cross-section of tumbled specimen.
[b]Preglassed 1 hr at 2800°F by AMF.

is a coating applied by a hot dip in molten Al-12Si. Diffusion occurs in the hot dip and excess aluminum is removed. Ductility of the substrate is good. "Disil-3" is similar to "Disil-1" except in application technique. Oxidation protection provided by the latter may be inferred

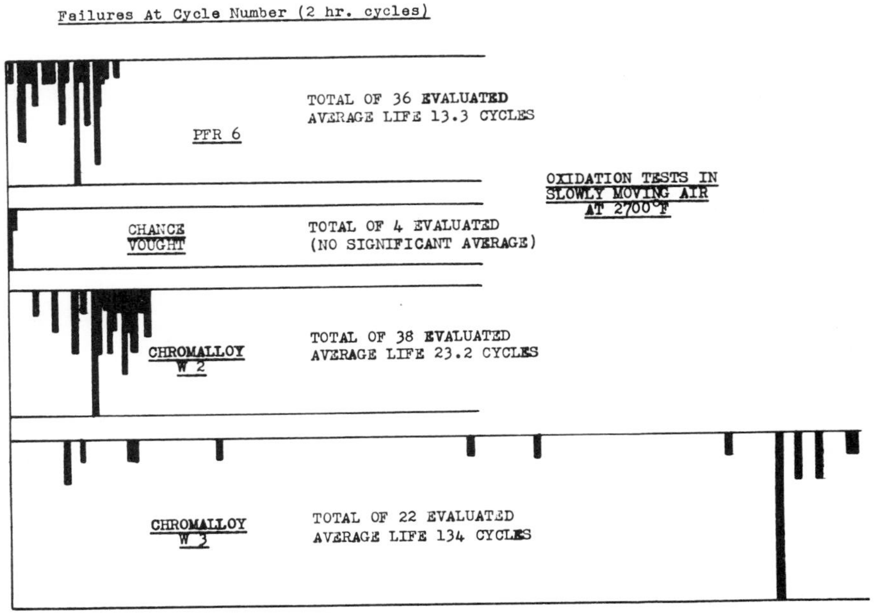

Fig. 2.17. Comparative life of several molybdenum coatings in cyclic heating. (Chromalloy Corp.) data.

from Figures 2.12 and 2.13; 10 hr at 2700°F and 1 hr at 3000°F have also been reported (*50*).

"Durak-B" is the latest in a series of coatings developed by Chromizing Corporation. It is a modified silicide coating applied by the pack process. Improved reliability, reproducibility, service life and tolerance for surface imperfections are reported. At 2700°F, 180 hr life in static heating is reported and in oxygen with cyclic heating to 2880°F in about 4 min, 8 cycles were tolerated before failure. Normal total emittance is 0.78 at 2420°F to 0.95 at 2960°F. Preferential failure at edges and corners did not occur with "Durak-B" (*51*).

"PFR-6" is a single or 2 cycle pack cementation coating of Si-Nb. Oxidation protection is provided up to 3125°F for 2.1 hr and for 0.5 hr in an oxyacetylene flame. After bending the coated substrate prior to oxidation tests at 3125°F, 1.4– 1.9 hr. of protection was obtained. The ductility of the substrate and thermal shock resistance are good. Good protection is achieved on the edges of thin materials (*52*).

"Vought II" is a silicide coating applied by pack cementation. This coating is usually applied as a base for a dual coating system using "Vought IX" as the overcoat. The latter is a chrome-aluminum coating also applied by a pack cementation process (*53*).

"W-2" was one of the first commercial silicide coatings and has received more evaluation than the others. It is basically a chromium-modified silicide pack cementation process, but has been improved under a recent development program which resulted in an improved coating designated "W-3." Substrate preparation is critical and rounded corners and edges are necessary to prevent premature failure. Typical coating life is shown as Figure 2.18 (October, 1960 data) (*54*) for static oxida-

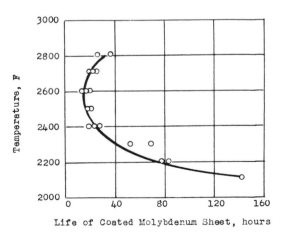

Life of Coated Molybdenum Sheet, hours

Fig. 2.18. Life of W-2 coated molybdenum. Specimens were tested in static air atmosphere in a furnace.

tion and a coating thickness approximately 2 mils. Although somewhat disputed, the normal total emittance value generally used for "W-2" is about 0.6 for the 2700°F temperature range. Typical microstructure for a "W-3" coating is shown in Figure 2.19 and is representative of most silicide coatings on molybdenum substrates.

Other Diffusion Coatings for Molybdenum. An Al-Cr-Si flame sprayed and thermally diffused coating by Climax Molybdenum Company has received several comparative evaluations (*55, 56*). Its effect on tensile strength and elongation of Mo-0.5Ti alloy is similar to that of "W-2."

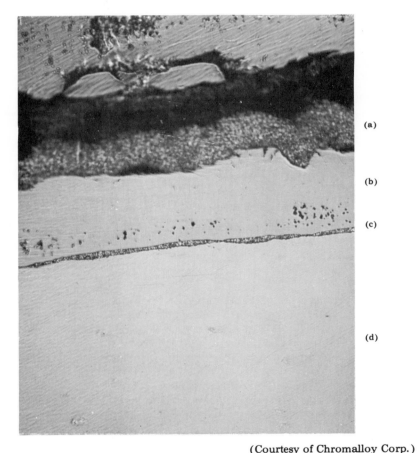

(a)

(b)

(c)

(d)

(Courtesy of Chromalloy Corp.)
Fig. 2.19a. The specimens have been copper plated to retain edges in polishing. The granular grey area (a) is copper. The white area (b) below is $MoSi_2$. The thin grey structure (c) next to the substrate (d) does not resolve clearly in microprobe analysis, but diffraction suggests $Mo_5 Si_3$.

(Courtesy of Chromalloy Corp.)
Fig. 2.19b. Microstructure of W-3 coated Mo after 4 hours at 3000°F. This specimen could not be plated because of the heavy glassy oxide surface layer, and was wrapped in Mo foil as a substitute. The thin outermost layer (of $MoSi_2$) no longer clearly resolves in the microprobe. Below it are the now thicker layers of Mo_3Si_2 and Mo_3Si. Mo_5Si_3 may also be present.

Oxidation results were rather erratic. A sprayed silicide coating (40Mo-40Si-8Cr-2B-2Al) (Linde Air Products LM-5 process) provided protection in the 2200°F range but was inferior to several other types of diffusion coatings (55). Flame-sprayed and diffused Al-Si coating by National Research Corporation provided substrate mechanical properties similar to those of "W-2," but the oxidation protection provided was inferior to other silicide diffusion coatings (56).

Silicide coatings offer great protection to oxidation; however, recent research (58) has shown that the oxidation of silicide coatings on molybdenum proceeds more rapidly at reduced pressures than at atmospheric. This result is not expected, but upon further analysis is reasonable. The vapor pressure of silicon monoxide, SiO, is appreciable above 2600°F; at oxygen pressures below 5 mm Hg, SiO is formed and vaporized rather than a protective layer of SiO$_2$ glass. By suitable modification of alloys and coatings, improvements are possible, but this effect is difficult to eliminate from silicide coatings. Figure 2.20 shows the protection afforded molybdenum by a silicide coating exposed to various temperature and pressure conditions.

Effect of Substrate Quality. Coatings for molybdenum have been explored extensively and excellent protective coating systems are available, but the reliability is inadequate for most applications. While not often attributed to the substrate, the variable performance of molybdenum coating systems may be strongly dependent on the quality and uniformity of the alloys currently produced. The difficulty of producing uniform structural rod or sheet alloy of reliable and reproducible properties is recognized; generally over 60 per cent of the rolled rod or sheet from an ingot is not of structure quality (*69*). The oxidation protection requirements place even more importance on microstructure, minute inclusions and microfissures, and surface characteristics. Diffusion-coatings have been popular because they help mask microfissures and surface effects, but the reliability may be largely dependent on substrate perfection rather than optimum coating techniques. Unfortunately, after a coating has been applied and failed, the original sheet stock surface can not be retrieved to carefully examine the "failure" area and establish the substrate role in the failure mode.

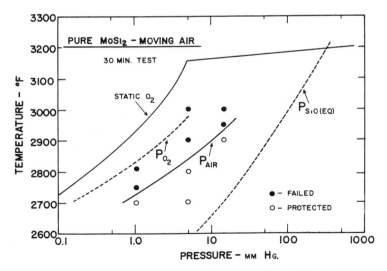

Fig. 2.20. Maximum temperature for a 30 minutes life of MoSi$_2$ - base coatings on molybdenum as a function of pressure - moving air.

Diffusion Coatings for Columbium and Columbium Alloys. Coatings for columbium are recent developments compared with those for molybdenum. Early efforts in columbium coatings was simply the application of coatings which had shown promise on molybdenum, and this was not generally successful. The major reason for specific columbium coatings development was the wider range of compositions in columbium alloys. Since the substrate becomes a reactive constituent of the coating in diffusion coating systems, the composition and properties of a coating on columbium would be quite different from the same elements diffused into molybdenum. Columbium and columbium compounds have thermal, physical and mechanical properties quite different from the corresponding molybdenum compounds. Columbium and columbium alloys, having an appreciable solubility for oxygen and nitrogen which embrittle the substrate, require a coating that will prevent these gases reaching the substrate in addition to providing gross oxidation protection.

Some of the most successful oxidation-resistant coatings result from the formation of columbium intermetallics by diffusing Si, Cr, Al, B, Ti, and Be, singly or in combinations into the substrate. Most coating system have rather complex compositions, and because of the limited information available about the exact composition, they are difficult to arrange as logically as those for molybdenum. Some of the coatings containing silicon which have shown promise will be discussed in more detail than in Table 2.15.

The Tapco Division of Thompson Ramo Woolridge developed the TRW Coating system for columbium. This is a Cr-Ti-Si coating applied by a pack process including KF to "activate" the coating. Apparently the presence of the halide causes the formation of a continuous $CbCr_2$; a layer of mostly Si + Cr also forms covered by an outer Si layer. The presence of the $CbCr_2$ layer improves the performance since it inhibits diffusion of oxygen inward and Cb outward. The Cr + Si layer just under the Si layer helps heal the thermal and mechanical cracks and supplies Si for the outer surface oxidation. Table 2.22 shows the protection provided for several columbium alloys by the TRW coatings (57). A total depth of penetration for the Cr-Ti-Si coating is about 4 mils, with 2.5 mils of silicon rich layers above the $CbCr_2$ layer. The thermal shock resistance of Cr-Ti-Si coatings and similar Cr-Ti-Si-Al coatings is excellent and specimens have survived 1000 cycles of torch heating to 2500°F and air blast cooling to 250°F in a 30 sec cycle. After 1000 cycles, some cracking was noted in the coating but the substrate was not embrittled and the cracks did not penetrate through the diffusion layer.

Chance Vought (59) is developing a Cr-Al coating for use on columbium. The composition is similar to "Vought IX" and is applied by

TABLE 2.22. PROTECTIVE LIFE OF ACTIVATED
Cr-Ti-Si AND Ti-(Cr-Ti)-Si COATINGS ON D-31,
F-48 AND UNALLOYED COLUMBIUM
AT 2300 AND 2500°F

Alloy	Oxidation Temperature	Protective Life,[a] hrs	
		Cr-Ti-Si[b]	Ti-(Cr-Ti)-Si[c]
Cb	2500	70–80	>90
F-48	2500	70–80	>90
D-31	2500	80–90	>90
Cb	2300	90–110	140–160
F-48	2300	90–110	240
D-31	2300	140–180	240

[a]Indicates point of initial failure. Minimum of two specimens
per condition. At 2500°F tests were terminated at 90 hrs with no
failures on any of the titanium-prealloyed specimens. Specimens
were cycled to room temperature eight times in every 24-hr period
and inspected thoroughly.
[b]Cr-Ti (KF activated), 8 hrs at 2300°F
  Si (KF activated), 12 hrs at 2150°F
[c] Ti (KF activated), 8 hrs at 2200°F
  Cr-Ti (KF activated), 8 hrs at 2300°F
  Si (KF activated), 12 hrs at 2150°F

pack cementation. Most of Vought's work has concentrated on two
cycle coatings similar to the "Vought II-IX" process for molybdenum.

Boeing Airplane Company (50) applies the "Disil-3" process to columbium alloys by a vacuum pack and by fluidized bed techniques. By
introducing the iodine into an evacuated retort containing the substrate
and the silicon composition, contamination problems are minimized.

Chromalloy Corporation has applied modified "W-2" coating to
columbium-base alloys. Some embrittlement of the substrate by the
residual air in the pack during heat-up is reported.

"Durak-Cb", a pack-applied coating, has been developed by Chromizing Corp. Its melting point and emittance are reported higher than
that of modified "W-2." Coatings on Cb-6Ti-0.75Al alloy showed some
oxidation after 1 hr at 2500°F, and failure at 2700°F. In other tests,
FS-82 sheet coated with "Durak-Cb" withstood 15 min at 2950°F in air.

Fansteel Metallurgical Corp. (60) has investigated a silicide coating,
designated S-2. Life at 2300°F was 20 hr. A second coating system,
designated M-2, was formed by dipping the substrate in liquid MoO_3
at 1470°F, reducing the oxide to molybdenum metal and siliciding the
outer molybdenum with S-2 coating. Protection of 40 hr at 2300°F was
achieved.

Pfaudler Company (51) has used single and multicycle pack cementation processes to coat columbium-base alloys. The first cycle consists
of a precoating cementation treatment, and the second cycle deposits
silicon and alloying elements simultaneously. Alloys such as D-31,

Cb-1Zr, FS-82, F-48, C-103 and columbium have been coated as shown in Table 2.23.

The Linde Company LM-5 coating (57) (40Mo-40Si-8Cr-2B-2Al) plasma sprayed or flame sprayed (detonation gun) protected columbium for 1000 hr at 2100°F and 100 hr at 2730°F. The coating was 4 mils thick. Self-healing and thermal-shock resistance was improved by a base coat of D-945 (44Cb-32Ti-15Cr-5V-4Al) under the LM-5.

Aluminide coatings have also received investigation for columbium protection and a number of coating techniques have been reported for applying the aluminum. Most popular of the techniques are molten baths at approximately 1900°F. The bath composition may be Al-15Si, Al-10Cr, Al-5Cr-5Ti, and other similar compositions. Diffusion may be achieved either in the molten bath, or by a post application treatment at 1700 to 2100°F for an hour or more. The aluminum coating can be applied by dipping in a water or organic liquid slurry of aluminum and other metal powders. The coated part is then diffused at 2000 to 2200°F to form the coating. General Electric LB-2 coating is an example of a "paint and sinter" aluminide-chromium coating. One to two hour protection for FS-82 exposed to 2700°F was reported (50).

Zinc-based coatings were developed by the Naval Research Laboratory in 1959 (60). Although the protection afforded by zinc on columbium alloys is limited to 2050°F, some unique characteristics of the

TABLE 2.23. PERFORMANCE OF SEVERAL EXPERIMENTAL
COATINGS (PFAUDLER CO.) FOR COLUMBIUM AND
COLUMBIUM-BASE ALLOYS

Substrate	Coating Designation	Oxyacetylene Torch Oxidation Test Life		
		At 2600°F[a]	At 2800°F[a]	At 3000°F[a]
D-31 (2 cycles)	PFR-1M-D-31	16.3 hr and 26.3 hr (Two samples tested)	5–11 hr	2–4 hr
FS-82 (1 cycle)	PFR-1S-FS-82	2–6 hr	. . .	. . .
FS-82 (2 cycles)	PFR-1M-FS-82	2–6 hr	. . .	0.5–0.75 hr
Cb-1% Zr (2 cycles)	PFR-1M-Cb-1Zr	3–4 hr	1–4 hr	0.5–4 hr
C-103 (2 cycles)	PFR-2M-C-103	Coated 5 mil-thick foil did not fail after 3 hr	0.5–1 hr	. . .
Cb (2 cycles)	PFR-2M-Cb	3.5–6 hr	. . .	0.5–1 hr
F-48 (2 cycles)	PFR-2M-F-48	. . .	. . .	0.25–1 hr

[a]Temperatures were measured with optical pyrometer assuming coating emittance of 1.0.

coating deserve mention. The coating may be applied to columbium by vapor distillation of zinc, hot dipping, electroplating, or cladding. The remarkable quality of this coating is its ability to heal large defects in itself. This is believed to be a result of the relatively high vapor pressure of zinc over the Cb-Zn intermetallic compounds.

When a defect occurs and Cb_2O_5 appears as an oxidation product, the Zn vapor from adjacent coated areas permeates the Cb_2O_5 and forms a protective layer of ZnO at the Cb_2O_5-air interface. The repair is complete when the zinc vapor reacts with underlying columbium metal to form a layer of Cb-Zn intermetallics. The temperature range in which healing occurs is limited by the vapor pressure of zinc at low temperatures, and 1800°F is the lower healing temperature. The upper healing temperature is 2048°F where CbZn decomposes.

Diffusion Coatings for Tantalum. Coating efforts on tantalum represent only recent work but significant results have been achieved. In some cases, columbium coating technology is also applicable to tantalum.

Of the aluminide coatings for tantalum, $TaAl_3$ forms an oxidation-resistant coating material, but some modifications offer further improvement. Aluminide coatings have been formed by roll cladding and a diffusion-anneal; hot dipping with diffusion treatment; spraying with powder slurry and diffusing; flame spraying and diffusing; pack cementation in powders; and fluidized bed techniques. Many of these coatings are similar in their chemistry, relying on the same protection mechanism. In most application techniques, the diffusion anneal is about 1900°F for several hours and about a 2 mil coating is desirable.

One promising coating is designated 34S (Sylvania-Corning Nuclear Corporation), and consists of a 2 cycle coating process where a suspension of powdered 50Sn-50Al composition is sprayed, diffused at 1900°F and the process repeated. Most promising results were obtained for the Ta-10W alloy however unalloyed tantalum performs similarly. The coating of $TaAl_3$ formed by diffusion may be fractured by sharp bends or twisting before oxidation exposure and will heal. Apparently enough Sn-Al coating remains unreacted to provide this additional protection. Upon exposure to temperatures above 1900°F, the $TaAl_3$ diffuses rapidly into the tantalum, converting to lower aluminides. Apparently, the best oxidation protection is provided by rapidly oxidizing a portion of the $TaAl_3$ at the surface before the diffusion to form Ta_2Al becomes significant.

Oxidation behavior for 34S coating on Ta-10W alloy is shown in Figure 2.21 (62). Other observations which have resulted from the investigation of aluminides indicate that some differences exist between the performance of samples heated in furnace, by flame and those which are self-resistance heated. Flame and self-heated exposures gave similar

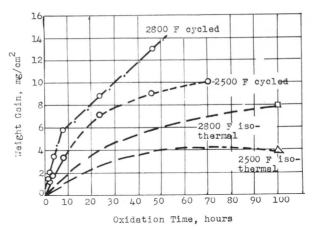

Fig. 2.21. Weight gains of 34S coated Ta-10W samples oxidized at 2500° and 2800°F.

failures, but coating life was shorter than that obtained in furance exposures. Self-resistance heating showed a tendency for the coating to migrate toward the negative electrode when dc was used. Cyclic heating materially shortened the coating life.

Sn-25Al coatings have shown slightly better performance than the Sn-50Al coating compositions. The aluminum diffuses rapidly through the liquid phase above 1200°F and is distributed in areas of localized depletion which may be caused by thermal gradients. This probably accounts for the healing characteristics of the Sn-25Al coatings. Protection of 100 hours at 2500°F and 29 hours at 2800°F was obtained. The addition of Ta and more Al to the Sn-25Al to form $TaAl_3$ in the composition (Sn-25Al) $10TaAl_3$ gave protection of Ta-10W alloy for 10 hours at 3000°F in furnace exposures. This coating was not as protective on Ta-30Cb-7½V alloy, but withstood 2800°F for 8 hours.

Even though Sn-Al diffusion coatings have a liquid phase, their resistance to oxidation in a rapidly moving gas stream is equal to that of solid coatings, and suggest that liquid phase coatings deserve further consideration (63).

Beryllide coatings for tantalum and Ta-10W alloy have been prepared by placing tantalum sheet between beryllium sheets and heating *in vacuo* at 1800 to 2200°F for 2 to 25 hr. The high vapor pressure of beryllium at this temperature readily forms a uniform 2-mil beryllide coating. The beryllide formed ($TaBe_{12}$) diffused rapidly into tantalum at 2500°F, but much more slowly in Ta-10W alloy. After 10 hr at 2600°F the coating had diffused from the original 2-mil thickness to a depth of 5 mils in Ta-10W alloys; the penetration was up to 9 mils after 15 hr at 2500°F in pure tantalum.

The oxidation resistance of beryllide-coated tantalum was inferior to that of Ta-10W alloy. The latter gave 10 hours protection at 2500 to 2700°F and under 10 cycles of stresses producing 1 to 15 per cent total elongation. At 2800°F mixed results were obtained but samples not subjected to thermal cycling lasted much longer than cycled samples. At lower temperatures, some early failures occurred around 2200°F but other samples lasted for over 64 hr. Further work on the beryllide coatings appears justified (64).

Significant oxidation protection can be achieved with silicide coatings on tantalum. Vapor deposition and pack processes have been used largely to apply the silicon. Aluminum, boron or manganese additions are often used to modify the silicide coating.

The alloy composition produces even more difference in the performance of silicide coatings than in the aluminides or beryllides. Siliciding tantalum provides a coating of $TaSi_2$ which is partially protective but allows controlled, continuous oxidation of the coating. Ta-30Cb-10V alloy, however, when silicided produces a coating which provides a protective glassy oxide film that exhibits excellent stability and limits further oxidation. Ta-10Hf-5W alloy yields similar silicide coating performance when a small amount of aluminum is included in the siliconizing treatment. The diffusion of the silicide coating at 2500 and 2700°F is shown in Figure 2.22 (65).

Modification of silicide coatings for tantalum and tantalum alloys by the addition of boron or manganese is also promising. Aluminum, boron, or manganese may be deposited prior to pack siliconizing or the manganese can be applied after pack siliconizing by a pack process. The latter has given excellent protection at 2700°F for 24 hr (no cycling)

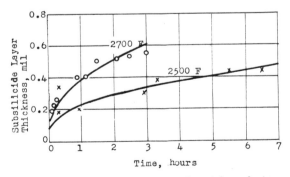

Fig. 2.22. Growth of subsilicide layer in coated tantalum during exposure to air at 2500° and 2700°F. Initial subsilicide layer thickness was 0.08 mil.

without signs of failure. The tantalum retained zero radius bend ductility after exposure.

Modification of the silicide coating and the oxide scale by additions to the coating or the substrate, significantly improve the coating performance at low and high temperatures. The results of various silicide coatings on tantalum alloys is shown in Table 2.24. It is apparent that both the silicide coating and the base alloy composition must be considered.

Tungsten Diffusion Coatings. Though tungsten has a very high melting point, its protection against oxidation and its high density have been major limitations to its usage. Summarizing diffusion coating progress for tungsten briefly, there are no reliable coatings for use above 3000°F for extended periods and most current coatings represent only laboratory efforts.

W-2 coated 50W-50Mo alloy has been reported to survive 60 hr at 2700°F (*51*). This diffusion coating has been described as a proprietary disilicide coating applied by pack cementation.

Other studies (*66*) of disilicide coatings for tungsten reveal disilicide "pest" failures similar to that experienced with molybdenum. Wires were coated by pack siliconizing at 1900°F and up to 10 hr protection at 3300°F has been obtained, but pinhole imperfections were common, and in some instances a liquid phase appeared at 3300°F that was not identified.

After a 10 hr exposure at 3300°F, the WSi_2 coatings were converted to W_5Si_3 and a glassy outer layer formed due to continued diffusion of the Si in the tungsten and surface oxidation (Figure 2.22). The thickness of coatings which could withstand cycling from 3300°F was found to be less than 2 mils.

Modifications in pack siliconized tungsten coatings have improved low temperature "pest" failure, but coating life even at 2000°F is unreliable and generally less than 10 hr for a 2 mil coating.

Recent investigations (*63*) into the failure mechanisms for silicide coatings of tungsten have shown that the "pest" failure can be explained by the silicon being initially oxidized to SiO_2 at the surface and depleting the surface of Si, forming W_5Si_3. At high temperatures a uniform layer of W_5Si_3 is formed, (Figure 2.23) but at "pest" temperatures, the attack is non-uniform and seems to follow grain boundaries or sub-grain boundaries in the disilicide (Figure 2.24). The next stage in the "pest" is the rapid growth and penetration of the complex oxide into the disilicide layer (Figure 2.25). This process ultimately consumes the disilicide, causing oxidation of the tungsten substrate.

The failure of a coated sample at the edges can be easily explained by the expansion which occurs due to the inward diffusion of the silicon and the outward diffusion of the metal. As the metal pushes outward,

TABLE 2.24. CYCLIC LIFE OF SILICIDE-COATED TANTALUM AND TANTALUM ALLOYS

Coating Composition, Atom Per Cent	Amount of Coating[a] mg/cm²	mil/side	Average Cyclic Life, hrs, at Temperature Indicated[b]						Average Cyclic Life, hrs, of Defected Coating At Temperatures Indicated[b,c]	
			1200°F	1500°F	1800°F	2200°F	2400°F	2700°F	2500°F	2700°F
Tantalum										
100Si	22.1	3.4	60	35	3	>100	7.5	2.5	<1	<1
Si-5Al	18.1	2.9	100	85	20	95	6.5	2	<1	<1
Si-3Mn	60.0	9.7	>100	25	3	100	11	4	<1	<1
Ta-10W										
100Si	36.0	5.8	100	15	3	50	10	4.5	4.5	<1
Si-5Al	22.0	3.5	>100	25	10	15	3.7	4.2	4.5	<1
Si-8Mn	44.9	7.3	40	15	3	70	>20	10	4.5	10
Ta-10Hf-5W										
100Si	19.6	3.2	85	15	35	55	8	2	9.5	<1
Si-6Al	17.5	2.8	100	>100	>100	55	9.5	4	4.5	<1
Si-5Mn	52.5	8.4	>100	10	1	95	15	7.5	4.5	<1
Ta-30Cb-5V										
100Si	26.2	4.2	>100	>100	>100	>100	>20	9	2	<1
Si-9Al	20.7	3.3	>100	>100	>100	95	>20	3.3	2	<1
Si-8Mn	57.1	8.9	>100	>100	>100	30	>20	4.8	10	10

a 100Si and Si-Al coatings were applied in two cycles, 4 & 12 hrs, at 2200°F. Si-Mn coatings were applied by depositing Mn for 4 hrs at 1800°F followed by siliconizing 12 hrs at 2200°F.
b Samples were exposed at 1200 to 2200°F for up to 100 hrs with cooling and examination twice daily. 2500°F and 2700°F samples were exposed for up to 20 and 10 hrs, respectively, with hourly cooling and examination.
c Defect consisted of 0.04 in. hole drilled halfway through each sample.

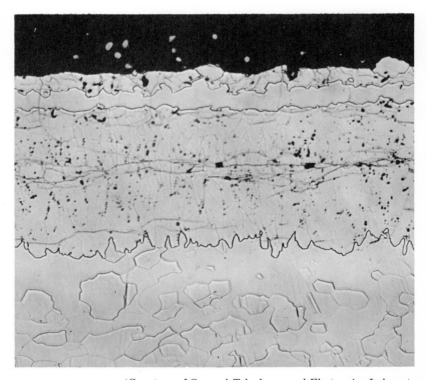

(Courtesy of General Telephone and Electronics Laboratory)
Fig. 2.23. Structure of the oxidation products formed on silicide coated tungsten at 3000°F. Dark outer coating is SiO_2, layers are W_5Si_3, WSi_2, W_5Si_3 and tungsten substrate. (250X)

any corner causes tensile stresses to be developed on the edge, and if continued, a crack may form at the corner, deepening as the diffusion continues. This edge effect is an inherent characteristic of diffusion coatings and can be minimized but not eliminated by rounding the corner.

The glassy film which forms on the surface must be sufficiently fluid to fill the edge cracks. Modifications in the coating which improve "pest" resistance usually improve the flow of glass in the edge cracks as well. In speculating on oxidation protective coatings for ultra-high temperatures, 3350°F and above, the conclusions of Nicholas, *et al.* (67) were:

(1) Coating defects such as pinholes and edge effects are only of importance when the system otherwise would be protective. Thus, they cannot be considered as a fundamental cause of failure.

(Courtesy of General Telephone and Electronics Laboratory)
Fig. 2.24. Structure of tungsten silicide coating oxidized at 2550°F for 76 hr. showing beginning of "pest" attack. A thin, dark layer of SiO_2 covers a W_5Si_3 layer at the upper interface; the thick layers is WSi_2 over W_5Si_3 and the tungsten substrate. (500X)

(2) Oxide films grown from a substrate or metallic reservoir have a much greater probability of being flaw-free than deliberately applied bulk oxide layers.

(3) With the exception of glasses, coatings that exhibit self-healing properties depend on a metallic reservoir from which the refractory protective oxide film can re-form when necessary.

(4) The maximum useful temperature of silica-bonded bulk oxides is limited by the properties of silica, particularly the viscosity and vaporization at high temperatures.

From a study of the vaporization rate and other characteristics of SiO_2 and the platinum group metals, Nicholas concluded that neither the silicides nor platinum group metals were adequate for ultrahigh temperature protection. Of the stable refractory oxides which offer some promise, HfO_2, ThO_2, UO_2 and ZrO_2, none form as slow self-heating coatings on stable metallic reservoirs. Methods must be found to grow this slow, protective oxide and the use of liquid phase coatings, similar to Sn-Al, to encourage protective oxide formation may possibly provide

(Courtesy of General Telephone and Electronics Laboratory)
Fig. 2.25. Structure of oxidation products formed near 2400°F. An unidentified oxide (dark) covers a mixed oxide-silicide layer which has penetrated the WSi_2 layer. A thin W_5Si_3 layer is present between the WSi_2 and tungsten base. (250X)

such an answer. At least the use of liquid phase coatings does not rule out the use of as many materials.

Coatings for Vanadium, Chromium and Rhenium Alloys. Only limited work has been performed on these alloys. No coatings which offer substantial protection above 2000°F have been reported for vanadium. The use of zinc diffusion coating to form a zinc intermetallic on vanadium resulted in 24 hr protection at 1800°F. Coatings of oxides or glass bonded oxides have offered little protection to vanadium.

Vanadium silicide coatings have shown no "pest" attack at low temperatures around 1800°F, and offer several hundred hours oxidation protection at 1200 to 1500°F. Flame spray coatings on nickel show some self-healing characteristics, or limiting of the oxidation at intentionally defected areas. Exposures of only 6 hr at 2000°F have caused some hardening of the base metal near the defects from diffusion of atmospheric contaminants. Electrodeposited nickel is less satisfactory than sprayed coatings due to blistering and peeling; however, improved deposition techniques could possibly eliminate this problem.

A flame-spray consisting of 70Si-30Ag provides some protection of vanadium alloy V-1Ti-60Cb. The coating is diffused into the base at 2000°F and forms an almost continuous silver-rich layer over the silicide layer as shown in Figures 2.26 and 2.27. This 70Si-30Ag coat-

(Courtesy of Armour Research Foundation)
Fig. 2.26. Flame-sprayed 70Ag-30Si coating on V-1Ti-60Cb alloy; as deposited (250X)

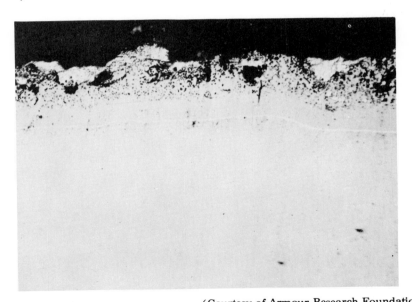

(Courtesy of Armour Research Foundation)
Fig. 2.27. Flame-sprayed 70Ag-30Si coating on V-1Ti-60Cb alloy; after 16 hr. diffusion at 2200°F in argon. (250X)

ing protected V-5Ti-20Cb alloy 16 hr at 2000°F and V-1Ti-60Cb alloy for 244 hr.

While extremely high temperature protection has not been achieved with vanadium alloys, research is in progress toward these goals. One difficulty encountered with vanadium alloys is the intense fluxing action of the vanadium oxide. The oxide reacts with coating oxides rapidly and produces a characteristic stain. This stain is evident in Figure 2.28 where intentional defects have been made in a flame-sprayed nickel coating and the sample exposed at 2000°F.

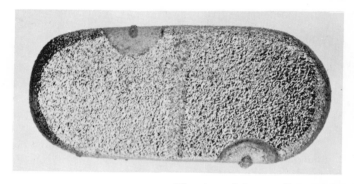

(Courtesy of Armour Research Foundation)
Fig. 2.28a. V-1Ti-60Cb alloy coated with flame-sprayed nickel, exposed to 2000°F air for 40 hours, intentionally defected, and reheated in air at 2000°F. Lower right defect was 0.005 inch wide by 0.012 inch deep, exposed for 6 hours in 2000°F air. Upper left defect was 0.010 inch wide by 0.025 inch deep, exposed for 2 hours in 2000°F air. The oxide growth and staining of the glassy coating layer are evident. 3X

(Courtesy of Armour Research Foundation)
Fig. 2.28b. Same specimen as shown in Fig. 2.28a, after 0.020 inch stock had been removed by surface grinding. Some attack of the base alloy is noted, especially after the 6-hour exposure, lower right. 3X

From these studies (68) of vanadium coatings it was also found that the vanadium silicide, VSi_2 and V_5Si_3, show oxidation resistance superior to that of columbium silicide, $CbSi_2$. A $(0.5V-0.5Cb)$ Si_2 also showed good oxidation resistance.

Further work on coatings for these alloys is indicated. Suitable intermetallic coatings or glass bonded coatings should be possible for all these alloys. Sheet materials of a number of these newer alloys should be available in sufficient quantity for coating development.

Metallic and Composite Coatings

The use of undiffused metal coatings at temperatures above 2500°F is limited since some diffusion always occurs at the coating interface. The coatings discussed further in the following paragraphs represent coatings where no diffusion heat treatment is used prior to exposure, and protection is offered only partially by the intermetallic formed at the interface.

The General Electric System 300 (55) could have been considered as a flame-sprayed coating, because it consists of an electroplated chromium coating on molybdenum with a coat of Al_2O_3 applied by flame spraying. The total thickness of the chromium coating is about 5 mils. The coating life of comparative oxidation tests is limited but generally consistent. The tolerance of the System 300 coating for mechanical strain is good. The diffusion of the Cr into the Mo substrate and some oxidation of the Cr to Cr_2O_3, and diffusion into the Al_2O_3 would be expected in high temperature exposure. The protection afforded the Cr or Cr-Mo interface by the Cr_2O_3 should be noted, since this same protection is apparent in other Cr-base coatings.

Coatings for Graphite

Graphite has the highest use temperature of the elements, and only vaporizes appreciably above 6000°F. Unfortunately, as with the refractory metals, graphite requires protection against oxidation (and sometimes erosion) at temperatures of 800°F and above. The coating technology for graphite presents several unique problems because of its low tensile strength, its surface characteristics and its inert nature at temperatures below about 2000 to 2500°F. Because of the expansion characteristics of graphite and its low tensile strength, coatings tend to fail at the coating-graphite interface. The inert nature and surface characteristics of graphite cause many materials to melt on its surface with almost complete non-wetting; this prevents the formation of continuous coatings.

As with the refractory metals, flame spray, diffusion and sintered coatings have found use with graphite. Early attempts to improve graphite in strength and oxidation resistance resulted in addition of silicon to the graphite, at the surface, internally or by gaseous diffusion. This type coating was based on the oxidation resistance of silicon carbide, and the resulting "siliconized" graphite exhibits improved oxidation resistance up to 3000°F and improved abrasion resistance for many applications. Addition of other materials, such as zirconium boride and silicon has given some improvement in the protective oxide coating which forms on the graphite.

Since the oxides of carbon are gaseous, the penetration of the coating by oxygen results in gas formation which may further disrupt the coating. Continuous coatings of glassy materials are difficult to achieve due to the poor wetting of the graphite. Any pinholes which remain cause failure rapidly. The addition of borides or other "hard metals" to a graphite coating often improves the reaction of the coating with the surface. Since many of the "hard metals" wet or react with carbon, these form a basis for other coating systems.

Vapor-plated titanium nitride coatings have shown good performance in non-erosive environments. Pyrolytic deposits of other materials such as tantalum carbide, hafnium carbide and columbium carbide have recently been investigated. Many of these coatings, though continuous and reacted well with the surface, are extremely brittle and oxidize without affording great protection.

Deposits of the refractory metals on graphite, while offering no improvement in oxidation behavior, have often found use in rocket nozzles and extremely erosive conditions.

Sintered coatings of complex carbides such as tantalum-tungsten-zirconium carbide have been applied by slurry coatings and sintering at temperatures above 5000°F. These coatings and other complex carbide coatings have not shown great promise for most applications.

A recent coating system which has received careful attention is the use of an electrodeposited chromium-zirconium boride coating in which the hard metal phase is occluded during electrodeposition of the chromium. The performance of this coating in nozzles for solid propellant rockets has been surprisingly good. While the mechanism of the protection achieved is not well understood, the oxidation and erosion of the graphite was extended up to 8 times by the use of 2½ mils of coating. The flame temperature is obviously above the melting point of chromium metal; oxidation of the chromium is evident from post-firing examinations, but the protection offered by this modified chromium coating is not achieved with standard chrome plating, so the physical state of the chromium and zirconium boride are probably most important.

In general, most coatings for graphite can be characterized as research-stage coatings not finding widespread usage at this time. The use of pyrolytic graphite on a common graphite substrate, appears to be the most popular commercial high temperature "coating." While this coating of pyrolytic graphite is the same as the graphite base chemically, its properties are quite different from those of the substitute.

Summary of Coatings

Coating technology stills falls far short of protecting the refractory metals from oxidation so that their full capability for structural uses can be achieved. This limitation can be partially overcome by a compromise of the structure weight and the use of thicker coatings, or the use of a coating which offers better oxidation protection with some sacrifice of the mechanical strength of the substrate.

Coatings and substrates are inseparable combinations at temperatures of 2500°F and above. The extensive interaction between coating constituents and alloy constituents at these temperatures requires a careful consideration of the constitution of both and the contributions of both to the coating system. Even alloy constituents in percentages less than 0.5 per cent are important; even the "inert" diluent of Al_2O_3 in the pack cementation process yields Al in the coating. These contributions are important and should be considered in the total coating system.

Coatings are currently developed for commercial alloys which show promising mechanical properties, forming and welding characteristics and "productibility" at the mill. Since the alloy composition is an integral part of the coating system, better performance could be achieved by developing the coating and alloy together, or developing an alloy for improved "coatability" or coated performance. A refractory alloy is of little value if it can not be protected against oxidation, and the coated performance is quite different from the properties of the uncoated alloy measured *in vacuo* or inert gas. In many applications, the uncoated performance is of little value for designing, and the entire alloy-coating system must be evaluated together.

Glassy, liquid phase, and other types of coatings must be sought for very high-temperature use (above 3500°F). Many alloys are useful in this temperature range and the lack of coatings still limits their application. Bold and resourceful approaches are indicated; basic thermodynamic data is available for initial use, but reaction rates can not be adequately predicted and must often be verified. Careful analysis of the environment to be encountered must include a careful consideration of pressure, since the oxidation rate may even be higher, as in the case of silicides, with reduced pressures.

ACKNOWLEDGMENT

The author would like to acknowledge the suggestions and helpful criticisms of A. L. Friedberg, and D. G. Moore. The assistance of Z. A. Post in proof reading this chapter is also acknowledged. The contributions of E. E. Childs on rare earth hard metals, R. J. Brown on BeO and P. J. Lare on alloy diffusion coatings are gratefully acknowledged. Data have been assembled from many sources which have not been referenced directly, and particularly from DMIC Report No. 162 (*14*). The reader is particularly directed to the latter and the annotated bibliography (*70*).

REFERENCES

1. Newsome, *et al.*, "Alumina Properties," Technical Paper No. 10, Second Revision, Aluminum Co. of American, Pittsburgh, Pennsylvania, 1960.
2. Campbell, W. J., and Grain, C., "Thermal Expansion of Alpha Alumina," Bureau of Mines Report RI 5757, College Park, Maryland, 1961.
3. Brown, Raymond, J., Personal Communication, August, 1962.
4. Wang, Ke-Chin, *et al.*, "Sublimation of Cr_2O_3 at High Temperatures," *J. Am. Ceram. Soc.*, 43, No. 10, 509 (1960).
5. Levin, E. M., and McMurdie, H. F., "Phase Diagrams for Ceramists," Part II, *Am. Ceram. Soc.*, Columbus, Ohio, 1959.
6. Brockris, J. O'M., *et al.*, Eds., "Physico-Chemical Measurements at High Temperature," New York Academic Press, Inc., 1959.
7. Yavorsky, P. J., "Properties and High Temperature Applications of Zirconium Oxide," *Ceramic Age*, (June, 1960).
8. Kohl, W. H., "Materials Technology for Electron Tubes," New York, Reinhold Publishing Corp., 1960.
9. Resnick, R., and Steinitz, R., "High Temperature Reactions Between Tungsten and Several Refractory Compounds," Paper Presented at Fifth Meeting of the Refractory Composites Working Group, Dallas, Texas, August, 1961.
10. Schwarzkopf, P., and Kieffer, R., "Refractory Hard Metals," New York, The Macmillan Co., 1960.
11. Schwarzkopf, P., and Kieffer, R., "Cemented Carbides," New York, The Macmillan Co., 1960.
12. Litz, L. M., "Graphite, Carbide, Nitride and Sulfide Refractories,"; Westbrook, J. H., "Silicides, Borides, Aluminides, Intermetallics and Other Unique Refractories," "Proceedings of an International Symposium on High Temperature Technology," New York, McGraw Hill Book Co., Inc., 1960.
13. Childs, E. E., Personal Communication, Melpar, Inc., August, 1962.
14. Krier, C. A., "Coatings for the Protection of Refractory Metals from Oxidation," DMIC Report 162, Defense Metals Information Center, Battelle Memorial Institute, Columbus, Ohio, 1961.
15. Nicholas, M. G., and Dickinson, C. D., "The Development of Improved Coating Systems for the Protection of Tungsten From Oxidation and a study of the Fundamental Factors Involved," "High Temperature Protective Coatings for Refractory Metals - Part II," Paper Presented at Sixth Meeting of the Refractory Composites Working Group, Dayton, Ohio, June, 1962.
16. Paine, R. M., *et al.*, "An Investigation of Intermetallic Compounds for Very High Temperature Applications," WADC Technical Report TR59-29, Part II, July, 1960.
17. Westbrook, J. H., Ed., "Mechanical Properties of Intermetallic Compounds," New York, John Wiley and Sons, Inc., 1960.
18. Brooker, J., *et al.*, "Investigation of Intermetallic Compounds for Very High Temperature Applications," WADD Technical Report TR 60-889, April, 1961.
19. Douglass, R. W., *et al.*, "High Temperature Properties and Alloying Behavior of the Refractory Platinum-Group Metals," Summary Report Contract NOrd-2547(00), NR 039-067, 1961.
20. Vines, R. F., and Wise, E. M., "The Platinum Metals and Their Alloys," New York, International Nickel Company, Inc., 1941.
21. Passmore, E. M., *et al.*, "Investigation of Diffusion Barriers for Refractory Metals," WADD Technical Report TR 60-343, August, 1960.

22. Byrnes, Thomas, R., Personal Communication, Aeronca Manufacturing Corp., Middletown, Ohio, June, 1962.
23. Batchelor, J. D., Personal Communication, Alexandria, Virginia, Atlantic Research Corp., June, 1962.
24. "Pyrolytic Graphite Property Data," and Data Sheets on "Pyrolytic Tungsten," "Boralloy" (Trademark for Pyrolytic Boron Nitride), High Temperature Materials, Inc., Boston, Mass., and Personal Communication from Daniel Schiff, August, 1962.
25. Hampson, R. F., Jr., and Walker, R. F., "Vapor Pressure of Platinum Iridium and Rhodium," *J. Research Natl. Bur. Standards,* 65A, 289-95 (1961).
26. Ault, N. N., and Wheildon, W. M., "Modern Flame-Sprayed Ceramic Coatings," Chapter in "Modern Materials," H. H. Hausner, Ed., New York, Academic Press, Inc., 1960.
27. King, B. W., *et al.,* "Nature of Adherence of Porcelain Enamels to Metals," *J. Am. Ceram. Soc.,* 42, No. 11, 504 (1959).
28. Lauchner, J. H. and Bennett, D. G., "Thermal Fracture Resistance of Ceramic Coatings Applied to Metal; I, Elastic Deformation," *J. Am. Ceram. Soc.,* 42, No. 3, 146 (1959).
29. Timoshenko, S., "Theory of Elasticity," New York, McGraw Hill Book Company, Inc., 1934.
30. Walton, J. D., Jr., "Study of Strains Between Enamel and Iron as Related to Physical Properties of Each," *J. Am. Ceram. Soc.,* 37, No. 3, 153 (1954).
31. Cowan, R. E., et al., "Effect of Temperature on Modulus of Elasticity of Porcelain Enameled Steels," *J. Am. Ceram. Soc.,* 39, No. 9, 293 (1956).
32. Krikorian, O. H., "Thermal Expansion of High Temperature Materials," UCRL-6132, University of California, September, 1960.
33a. Buessem, W. R., "Thermal Shock" in "High-Temperature Technology," I. E. Campbell, Ed., New York, John Wiley & Sons, 1956.
33b. Kingery, W. D., "Property Measurements at High Temperatures," New York, John Wiley & Sons, 1959.
33c. "Symposium on Thermal Fracture," *J. Am. Ceram. Soc.,* 38, No. 1, 1 (1955).
33d. "Symposium on Thermal Shock," *Trans. Brit. Ceram. Soc.,* 57, 591 (1958).
34. Krier, C. A., "Coatings for the Protection of Refractory Metals from Oxidation," DMIC Report 162, Defense Metals Information Center, Battelle Memorial Institute, Columbus, Ohio, 1961.
35. "Recent Ceramic Coatings for High-Temperature Alloys," *Natl. Bur. Standards (U.S.) Tech. News Bull.,* 35, 89 (1951).
36. Cook, T. E., and King, B. W., "Glass-Bonded Refractory Coatings for Iron or Nickel Base Alloys," DMIC Memo 16, April, 1959.
37. Bergeron, C. G., *et al.,* "High Temperature Electrical Insulating Inorganic Coatings on Wire," WADC Technical Report 58-12.
38. Bergeron, C. G., *et al.,* "Protective Coatings for Refractory Metals," WADC Technical Report 59-526, Parts I and II, January and August, 1960.
39. Pentecost, J. L., *et al.,* "The Effects of Sandblasting, Hydrogen Annealing and Ceramic Coating on Chromel-Alumel Thermocouples," Report No. 66, University of Illinois, Cer. Eng. Dept., Under U.S. AF Contract AF W33-038 ac-14520.
40. Hall, W. B., and Graham, J. W., "System 400 Coating for the Protection of Columbium," Report No. DM-60-97, Chemical Engineering Sub-Operation Materials Information Memorandum, Aircraft Gas Turbine Division, General Electric Co., April, 1960.
41. The Carborundum Co., Technical Data Sheets on Fiberfrax Ceramic Fiber Coating-Cement.

42. Eubanks, A. G., and Moore, D. G., "Investigation of Aluminum Phosphate Coatings for Thermal Insulation of Airframes," NASA Technical Note D-106, November, 1959.
43. Sklarew, S., "Reinforced Inorganic Refractory Ceramic Coatings," Paper Presented at the Sixth Meeting of Refractory Composites Working Group, Dayton, Ohio, June, 1962.
44. Moore, D. G. and Cuthill, J. R., "Protection of Low Strategic Alloys with a Chromium-Boron-Nickel Cermet Coating," *Am. Ceram. Soc. Bull.*, 34, No. 11, 375 (1955).
45. Ortner, M. H., Personal Communication, Vitro Laboratories, West Orange, N. J., and Vitro Data on the Electrophoretic Process and Coatings.
46. Southern Research Institute, "The Development of Heat-Resistant Paints for Metals," Birmingham, Ala., Final Report Under Contract NOw 61-0546-d, March, 1962.
47. Ault, N. N., "Characteristics of Refractory Oxide Coatings Produced by Flame-Spraying,"*J. Am. Ceram. Soc.,* 40, No. 3, 69 (1957).
48. Vogan, J. W., "Thermal Protective Surfaces for Structural Plastics," WADD Technical Report 60-110, January, 1960.
49. Rummler, D. R., *et al.,* "A Comparative Study of Several Commercially Available Oxidation Resistant Coatings on Mo-0.5Ti Alloy Sheet." Paper Presented at Sixth Meeting of Refractory Composites Working Group, Dayton, Ohio, June, 1962.
50. Klopp, W. D., "Review of Recent Developments on Oxidation Resistant Coatings for Refractory Metals," DMIC Memorandum 120, July, 1961.
51. Summary of Fifth Meeting of the Refractory Composites Working Group, DMIC Technical Report No. 167, March, 1962.
52. The Pfaudler Co., "Development of a Cementation Coating Process for High Temperature Protection of Molybdenum," 1961.
53. Aves, W. L., Jr., Private Communication, Chance Vought Corp., June, 1962.
54. Mathauser, E. E., *et al.,* "Investigation of Problems Associated With the Use of Unalloyed Molybdenum Sheet in Structures at Elevated Temperatures," NASA Technical Note, TN D-447, October, 1960.
55. Graham, J. W., and Hall, W. B., "Protective Coatings for Molybdenum Alloys," Final Report Navy Bureau of Weapons Contract NOas 59-6026-6, March, 1960.
56. Wilks, C., and Magalotti, H., "Evaulation of Coatings for Molybdenum," Final Report Under Contract NOw 60-0321c, June, 1961.
57. Jeffreys, R. A., and Gadd, J. D., "Development and Evaluation of High Temperature Protective Coatings for Columbium Alloys, Part I, Coating Development," ASD Technical Report 61-66, May, 1961.
58. Perkins, Roger A., "Oxidation Protection of Structures for Hypersonic Re-Entry," Lockheed Missiles and Space Co., Palo Alto, California, Paper Presented at Sixth Meeting of Refractory Composites Working Group, Dayton, Ohio, June, 1962.
59. "Diffusion Coating Process for Columbium-Base Alloys," Chance Vought Corp., 1962.
60. Lorenz, R. H., and Michael, A. B., "Oxidation Resistant Silicide Coatings for Columbium and Tantalum Alloys by Vapor Phase Reaction," *J. Electrochem. Soc.,* 108, No. 9, 885 (1961).
61. Brown, B. F., et al., "Protection of Refractory Metals for High Temperature Service," Progress Report 1, July 1, 1960, "The Zinc-Base Coating for Niobium," NRL Report 5550, November, 1960. Progress Report 2, NRL Report 5581, January, 1961.

62. Sama, L., and Lawthers, D. D., "Aluminide and Beryllide Protective Coatings for Tantalum," Paper Presented at Technical Conference on High Temperature Materials, Cleveland, Ohio, June, 1962.
63. Sama, L., "Protective Coatings for Columbium and Tantalum Alloys," Part I of "High Temperature Protective Coatings for Refractory Metals," Paper Presented at Sixth Meeting of the Refractory Composites Working Group, Dayton, Ohio, June, 1962.
64. Klopp, W. D., *et al,* "Development of Protective Coatings for Tantalum-Base Alloys," Paper Presented at Fifth Meeting of the Refractory Composites Working Group, Dallas, Texas, August, 1961.
65. Maykuth, D. J., *et al,* "Coatings for Tantalum-Base Alloys," Paper Presented at Sixth Meeting of the Refractory Composites Working Group, Dayton, Ohio, June, 1962.
66. Goetzel, C. G., and Landler, P., "Refractory Coatings for Tungsten," WADD Technical Report 60-825, March, 1961.
67. Nicholas, M. G., *et al,* "The Analysis of the Basic Factors Involved in the Protection of Tungsten Against Oxidation," Part I, ASD-TRD-62-205, General Telephone and Electronics Laboratories, Inc., Bayside, New York. 1961.
68. "High Temperature Oxidation Protective Coatings for Vanadium Base Alloys," Armour Research Foundation Report 2227-5 Under Navy Contract NOw 61-0806-c. 1962.
69. Ingram, J. C., Jr., Personal Communication, Advanced Systems Division, Wright Patterson Air Force Base, Ohio.
70. Huminik, J., Jr., and Wright, C. H., "Bibliography on Oxidation and Erosion Resistant Coatings," Contract DA-36-034-ORD-3270, August, 1960.
71. Ryshkewitch, E., "Oxide Ceramics," New York, Academic Press, Inc., 1960.

3

STRUCTURAL MATERIALS FOR HIGH-TEMPERATURE USE

H. P. WEINBERG

Director of Research and Development
Value Engineering Company
Alexandria, Virginia

Metals which are considered oxidation-resistant possess a natural and very thin protective oxide film which forms rapidly on the surface and thereby protects the metal from further oxidation. The structural refractory metals do not form this natural oxide film and therefore require processed coatings for protection. Other materials scale badly or melt in certain environments if not protected by a coating.

Figure 3.1 shows the melting points of conventional and high-temperature materials; it also indicates the maximum serviceable temperature. Of the materials shown on this chart, only the refractory metals can be utilized at temperatures above 2500°F and yet have the advantage of being fabricated into complex shapes, by welding, forging, rolling, etc.

A concentrated research and development effort to produce improved elevated-temperature materials was begun in the middle 1940's. During this period and in the early 1950's the nickel and cobalt alloys were developed. These alloys survived high-velocity gas temperatures up to 1500°F. Cermets were developed in an attempt to compromise the poor high temperature properties of metals and the poor mechanical properties of the ceramics. When it became necessary to have materials operate above 2000°F, the cermets were considered. These materials, which are mixtures of metals and ceramics, are more oxidation-resistant than most metals. However, the cermets are brittle and sensitive to mechanical and thermal shock; in short, they behave like ceramics.

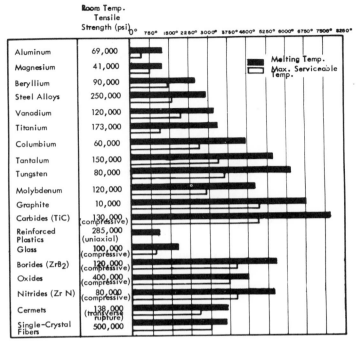

Fig. 3.1. Typical materials characteristics at current state of the art (1).

From Figure 3.2 it can be seen that at temperatures above 1500°F, there are very few alloys which have good stress rupture properties. It is above this temperature that the refractory metals are outstanding.

On the basis of tensile strength, most of the nickel and cobalt alloys fall below 50,000 psi at 1000°C, whereas molybdenum alloys exhibit 50,000 psi tensile strength up to 1400°C. Here it is important to bear in mind that the nickel and cobalt alloys have strengths of 150,000 psi and higher in the temperature range of 500 to 800°C. In this temperature range pure molybdenum and tungsten exhibit tensile properties of approximately 60,000 to 70,000 psi while columbium and tantalum exhibit less than 50,000 psi.

Recent coating research has largely concentrated on the refractory metals because of their good mechanical properties at high temperature. Also, since molybdenum, tungsten, tantalum, and columbium are relatively abundant, they have a favorable outlook for any production requirements.

All that is necessary to solve many high-temperature problems is to prevent these metals from oxidation at these temperatures. They have

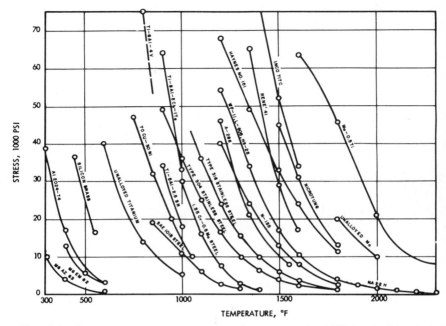

Fig. 3.2. Stress vs temperature curves for rupture in 1000 hours for selected alloys (2).

the desired high-temperature strength if they can be properly protected from oxidizing.

In the following pages there are presented pertinent data on many of the structural materials in wide use today, or on materials being considered for certain applications. Some materials which are in the developmental stage, but show great potential, are also discussed.

THE REFRACTORY METALS

The so-called refractory metals are those with very high melting points. In general, only the metals melting above 3000°F are considered to be in this category. On the basis of this definition there are actually twelve refractory metals. Because of their availability, only tungsten, tantalum, molybdenum, columbium, vanadium, rhenium, and chromium are considered practical at the present time for large-scale use. However, only the first four and their alloys are now used for structural applications. Table 3.1 reviews the presently available refractory metal alloys. These metals are being used for such ultra-high temperature applications as rocket nozzles, leading edges, re-entry vehicle structures, electronic com-

TABLE 3.1. LISTING OF MOLYBDENUM, COLUMBIUM, TANTALUM, TUNGSTEN AND VANADIUM ALLOYS

Alloy	Nominal Alloy Composition, weight per cent (Balance Refractory-Metal Base)									
	W	Mo	Ta	Cb	Hf	Ti	Zr	V	C	Other
Molybdenum-Base Alloys										
Mo-0.5Ti						0.5			0.02–0.05	
TZM						0.5	0.08		0.02–0.08	
TZC						1.25	0.15		0.15	
Mod. TZC						1.27	0.29		0.3	
Mo-0.05Zr							0.054		0.024	
Mo-0.5Zr							0.5		0.02	
Mo-1.5Cb				1.5					0.25	
Mo-25W	25						0.11		0.05	
Mo-0.5TiO$_2$										0.5 TiO$_2$
Columbium-Base Alloys										
F-48	15	5				1			0.1	
F-50	15	5			5	1			0.05	
Cb-7	28				7					
Cb-16	20				10		3			
Cb-65					7	0.8			0.075	0.11 O, 0.02 N
Cb-74	10					5			0.03	0.12 O, 0.02 N
FS-80						0.75				
FS-82			33			0.75				
D-31		10			10				0.06	0.05 O, 0.07 N
D-41	20	6			10					
15–20	15		20							
20–20	20		20							
Cb-Ta-W-Zr	10		24				1			
C-103					10	1	0.5			
Cb-Mo-Hf		5			5					
Cb-W-Zr	10						5			
Cb-Ti					8					
Cb-V-Al								3		3 Al
Tantalum-Base Alloys										
Ta-10W	10									
Ta-10Hf-5W	5				10					
Ta-30Cb-7.5V				30				7.5		
Tungsten-Base Alloys										
W-1ThO$_2$										1 ThO$_2$
W-2ThO$_2$										2 ThO$_2$
W-10Mo		10								
W-15Mo		15								
W-25Mo		25								
W-0.38 TaC										0.38 TaC
Vanadium-Base Alloys										
V-50Cb				50						
V-20Cb-5Ti					5					

ponents, gas turbines, ramjet engines, electrical contacts and chemical processing equipment.

The usefulness of the refractory metals is restricted by their poor oxidation resistance. For example, tungsten oxidizes in air about 1000 times too rapidly for service at 1800°F. Consequently, protective coatings are usually required. In fact, the primary limiting factor in the use of the refractory metals is the availability of coatings which protect the metals from oxidation at high temperatures. It should be emphasized that until such coatings are developed for each of the refractory metals, full advantage cannot be taken of the useful strength of these materials. Other chapters of this book cover the coatings currently in use.

The oxidation behavior of the refractory metals as compared to other metals is shown in Figure 3.3. In some cases oxidation results in a weight loss because the oxide melts or volatilizes and in other cases an oxide scale is formed and builds up.

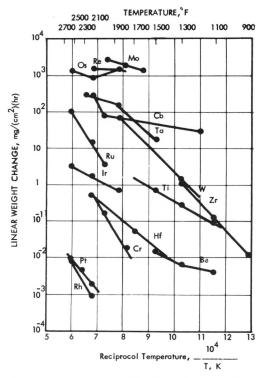

Fig. 3.3. Oxidation of some metals (5). Data for Mo, Re, Os, Ru, Ir, and Rh are weight-loss rates.

Table 3.2 lists nineteen metals which are currently being used or show potential for applications at 1500°F or above. The table gives an insight into the oxidation behavior as well as listing the present uses of these metals. The scaling characteristics at 2000°F of the four most common refractory metals are shown in Figure 3.4.

A comparison of the mechanical properties of typical alloys of tungsten, tantalum, molybdenum and columbium is shown in Table 3.3. These data indicate that tantalum-10W exhibits the highest strength at room temperature and also surpasses the other alloys at 2200°F.

Molybdenum

This refractory metal has a melting point of 4730°F. Because it is relatively abundant in the United States, it was the first of the refractory metals utilized for high temperature structural applications. Molybdenum

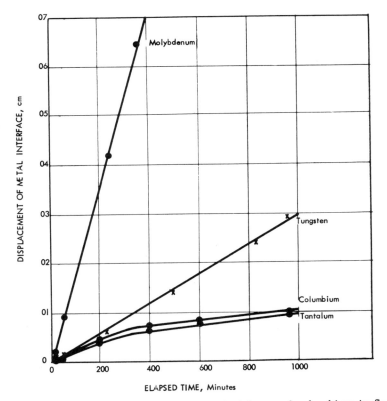

Fig. 3.4. Scaling of molybdenum, tungsten, tantalum and columbium in flowing air at 2000°F.

TABLE 3.2. METALLIC ELEMENTS THAT ARE USED OR SHOW PROMISE
AS HIGH-TEMPERATURE METALS (5)

Metal	Melting Point, °F	Temperature Range of Usefulness, °F	Density, lb/cu in.	Oxidation Behavior in Air[a]	Major Uses of Metal at Elevated Temperatures
Tungsten	6170	3000–4000	0.697	Resistant to 750°F	Rocket nozzles, lamp filaments
Rhenium	5755	...	0.756	Rapidly oxidizes above 600°F	Thermocouples, contact points
Osmium	5432	...	0.815	Resistant	Pivots, contact points
Tantalum	5425	3000–4000	0.600	Resistant to 500°F	Alloying element
Molybdenum	4730	2000–3000	0.369	Rapidly oxidizes above 900°F	Rocket and ramjet components
Columbium	4474	2000–2500	0.310	Resistant to 1200°F	Nuclear reactors
Iridium	4449	...	0.813	Resistant	Glass dies, hardener for Pt
Ruthenium	4082	...	0.441	Resistant	Hardener in Pt and Pd alloys
Hafnium	4032	...	0.473	Resistant to 1300°F	Nuclear reactor control rods
Rhodium	3571	...	0.447	Resistant to mp	Contact points, reflectors
Vanadium	3450	2000	0.220	Oxidizes at elev. temp	Alloying element
Chromium	3407	2000	0.260	Resistant to 1700°F	Alloying element
Zirconium	3366	...	0.234	Resistant to 400°F	Nuclear reactors
Platinum	3217	...	0.775	Resistant to mp	Thermocouples, heating elements, contact points, glass dies and bushings
Palladium	2826	...	0.434	Resistant to mp	Contact points, as alloy for heating elements
Iron	2798	to 1600	0.284	Resistant to 1600°F	Fe-alloys for boilers, furnaces, chem processing equipment, turbine rotors and buckets
Cobalt	2733	to 2000	0.322	Resistant to 2000°F	Co-alloys for turbine buckets, turbo-superchargers
Nickel	2647	to 2000	0.322	Resistant to 2000°F	Ni-alloys for furnaces, chem. processing equipment, heating elements and thermocouples
Beryllium	2332	to 1500	0.067	Rapidly oxidizes above 1400°F	Heat shields

[a]Oxidation behavior is only relative and varies greatly with alloy content and testing method. Information relates primarily to pure metals except for iron, cobalt, and nickel, for which information applies to oxidation-resistant alloys.

TABLE 3.3. MECHANICAL PROPERTIES OF COMMERCIAL ALLOYS
OF REFRACTORY METALS

Alloy & Condition	Property Value at Indicated Temperature, °F						
	75	1800	2000	2200	2400	2600	3000
W-15Mo, arc cast							
Tensile strength, 1000 psi	41		30				25
Elongation, per cent	0		14				17
Ta-10W, recrystallized							
Tensile strength, 1000 psi	180	94		67		21	
Elongation, per cent	4	4		4		17	
Mo-0.5Ti, stress relieved							
Tensile strength, 1000 psi	97	63			20		
Elongation, per cent	1	6			30		
100-hr rupture stress, 1000 psi		50	35	18	10		
Mo-0.5Ti-0.07Zr (TZC), stress relieved							
Tensile strength, 1000 psi	130		102	63			
Elongation, per cent	0		15	6			
10-hr rupture stress, 1000 psi				35			
100-hr rupture stress, 1000 psi				28			
Cb-32.5Ta-0.75Zr (FS-82) worked							
Tensile strength, 1000 psi	80		30		12		
Elongation, per cent	3		2		...		
10-hr rupture stress, 1000 psi			25				
100-hr rupture stress, 1000 psi			18				
Cb-15W-5Mo-1Zr (F-48) hot worked							
Tensile strength, 1000 psi	125		65	48	31		
Elongation, per cent	25		19	21	...		
10-hr rupture stress, 1000 psi			44	25			
100-hr rupture stress, 1000 psi			35	16			
Cb-10Mo-10Ti (D-31), worked							
Tensile strength, 1000 psi	100		35	25	20		
Elongation, per cent	22		12	14	8		

oxidizes rapidly in air at elevated temperatures. Therefore, the use of molybdenum and its alloys at elevated temperatures requires protective atmospheres, vacuum systems or coatings.

Despite its lack of oxidation resistance, molybdenum, when properly protected, has many advantages for ultra-high temperature structural applications. It has a high modulus of elasticity, low coefficient of expansion, high thermal conductivity, and good electrical conductivity and corrosion resistance.

Molybdenum is much less expensive than tungsten. Although it has lower strength at high temperatures, it is more widely used because of its low cost. In the electronic industry, for example, grids for power tubes are generally made from molybdenum wire, which has sufficient ductility to permit cold drawing.

Molybdenum has an additional advantage over tungsten in that it is more readily fabricated into sheets, and it can be drawn into cups and other shapes. Rocket nozzle liners, heat shields, corona shields, special furnace parts and miscellaneous supporting structures are frequently made of molybdenum. A large nozzle of molybdenum is shown in Figure 3.5.

Molybdenum is used to a large extent in high-temperature electric furnaces as heater elements and heat shields, but a neutral atmosphere must be utilized to prevent oxidation. This refractory metal is also suitable for welder tips on spot welders and for thermocouple protection tubes.

For increased strength and creep resistance, molybdenum is alloyed with titanium, zirconium and tungsten. Molybdenum-rhenium alloys containing 40 to 50 per cent rhenium are also available. They have excellent ductility and can be readily cold worked.

Very recently, there has been considerable interest in the solid-solution strengthened molybdenum-25W alloy. Test data for this alloy have

(Courtesy of The Pfaudler Co.)
Fig. 3.5. A molybdenum alloy nozzle coated by the pack cementation process. (part size is 15 inches long x 14 inches diameter)

indicated that it has outstanding tensile strength up to 2400°F, although its stress-rupture strength at 2400°F is not as great as that obtained in some of the dilute Mo-Ti-Zr-C alloys.

Structure and Mechanical Properties. Pure molybdenum and its alloys are generally used in the hot cold-worked condition, in which they have fibered microstructures. The strain hardening from fabrication improves strength, and the fibered structure is more ductile at lower temperatures than the recrystallized structure.

The advantages of adding alloying elements to molybdenum is that they raise the recrystallization temperature so that properties developed from strain hardening are retained at higher temperatures.

The mechanical properties of molybdenum are affected primarily by the degree of working, the amount and distribution of impurities, and the annealing temperature. As the annealing temperature is increased, the tensile and yield strength are decreased. Annealing above 2500°F frequently causes low ductility at room temperature, since it results in the recrystallized structure previously mentioned. The response to annealing is affected by the impurities in the molybdenum. Arc-melted molybdenum, for example, is severely embrittled by as little as 0.0025 per cent oxygen.

Several investigators have suggested that a strengthening phenomenon, such as strain aging, is responsible for the very attractive high-temperature properties of molybdenum.

Room temperature tensile properties of unalloyed molybdenum are shown in Table 3.4.

Table 3.5 presents data on seven currently produced commercial alloys, and compares stress relieved properties with those in the recrystallized condition.

TABLE 3.4. ROOM-TEMPERATURE TENSILE PROPERTIES
OF UNALLOYED MOLYBDENUM (6)

Thermal Treatment	Tensile Strength, psi	Yield Strength, psi	Elongation, per cent	Reduction of Area, per cent
5/8-In. Rod				
As rolled	102,000	78,800	40	61.1
Stress relieved	97,200	82,900	42	69
Recrystallized	68,200	55,900[a]	42	37.8
1/12-In. Sheet				
Stress relieved[b]	91,300–105,500	79,700–90,800[a]	20–27	...
Stress relieved[c]	91,500–106,200	82,700–95,800[a]	16–24	...
Recrystallized[b]	62,200–66,500	45,500–61,300[a]	40–58	...
Recrystallized[c]	58,200–66,000	43,700–58,500[a]	16–57	...

[a]Yield strength based on drop in load
[b]Parallel to rolling direction
[c]Transverse to rolling direction

TABLE 3.5. SUMMARY OF PROPERTIES OF COMMERCIAL OR SEMICOMMERCIAL MOLYBDENUM-BASE ALLOYS (6)

Composition, weight per cent	Elastic Modulus, 10^6 psi	Recrystallization Temperature, °F	Room Temperature Hardness, VHN	Condition	Temperature, °F	Tensile Properties				Stress-Rupture			Transition Temperature, °F		Melting Temperature, °F
						Yield Strength, 1000 psi	Tensile Strength, 1000 psi	Elongation, per cent	Reduction in Area, per cent	Temperature, °F	Time, hrs	Stress 1000 psi	Impact	Tensile	
Mo-30W	50(a)	...	198(b)	Stress relieved	Room	106.9	121.5	26	40	1800	1.0	60.0	...	...	5160
				Recrystallized	Room	69.1	83.8	12	10	1800	28.1	50.0	...	...	
				Stress relieved	1800	...	65.7	25	77	...	...	...	...	...	
				Recrystallized	1800	...	32.4	83	90	...	...	...	...	...	
Mo-50W	...	...	232(b)	...	Room	95% of breaking load	180% of molybdenum wire and 60% of tungsten wire of the same diameter	8-14	...	...	...	...	...	...	...
Mo-0.5Ti	45	2450	270(d)	Stress relieved	Room	103.4	112.9	36	62.1	1800	227.9	50.0(a)	600 to 725(e)	-35 to -30(a)	4730
				Recrystallized	Room	63.7	77.5	36	34	1800	93.3	12.0(c)	575 to 590	-35 to -15(c)	
				Stress relieved	1800	...	67.8	...	...	2000	261.6	20.0(a)	...	...	
				Recrystallized	1800	...	37.0	...	...	2000	5.3	12.0(c)	...	...	
				Stress relieved	2400	8.5	18.6	70	94.6	...	...	...	...	...	
				Recrystallized	2500	...	24.4	...	75	...	...	...	...	...	
Mo-0.5Ti-0.08Zr (TZM)	47	2600	172(b)	Stress relieved	Room	120.5	134.3	20	35	1800	72.0	79.0(a)	...	-11 to -2(a)	...
				Recrystallized	Room	77.6	80.3	32	33	1800	256.5	37.0(c)	...	-11 to +60(c)	
				Stress relieved	1800	...	85.5	18	73	2000	132.6	50.0(a)	...	...	
				Recrystallized	1800	17.9	41.7	35	62	2000	213.0	27.0(c)	...	...	
				Stress relieved	2400	...	53.9	31	96	...	...	...	...	...	
				Recrystallized	2400	...	23.4	69	96	...	...	...	...	...	
Mo-0.5Zr	...	2850	280(d)	Stress relieved	Room	80.8	118.7	33	55.6	1800	53.8	60.0(a)	...	-54 to -4(a)	...
				Recrystallized	Room	63.4	85.0	49	50.1	1800	42.2	35.0(c)	---	+7 to +61(c)	
				Stress relieved	1800	62.8	72.7	10	34.3	1800	53.8	60.0(a)	...	...	
				Recrystallized	1800	...	47.0	40	88.0	1800	42.2	35.0(c)	...	...	
				Stress relieved	2400	24.0	26.6	27	24.6	2400	3.1	15.0(a)	...	...	
				Recrystallized	2400	10.9	23.0	81	93.2	2400	37.3	10.0(c)	...	...	
Mo-0.05Zr	47	2450	291(d)	Stress relieved	Room	111.0	121.9	26	58.9	...	...	...	...	+10 to +15(a)	...
				Recrystallized	Room	59.3	75.6	23	18.9	...	...	...	...	+60 to +50(c)	
				Stress relieved	1800	55.3	78.7	32	65.0	1800	209.1	55.0(a)	...	...	
				Recrystallized	2000	...	69.8	15	76.0	1800	150.7	25.0(c)	...	...	
				Stress relieved	2400	25.2	31.8	33	91.6	2400	147.3	10.0(a)	...	...	
Mo-1.25Ti-0.15Zr-0.15C (TZC)	...	2800	293(d)	Stress relieved	Room	104.6	112.9	22	34	...	...	...	...	...	...
				Stress relieved	1600	60.9	63.4	17.6	74.7	2200	322.0	20.0(a)	...	...	
				Stress relieved	2400	35.0	38.9	16.8	80.7	2500	67.0	17.0(a)	...	...	
				Stress relieved	2800	14.3	14.9	30.0	93.4	...	...	...	...	...	

(a) Stress relieved
(b) As cast
(c) Recrystallized
(d) As rolled
(e) Estimated from graph

Tungsten

Because of difficulties in fabrication, the development of tunsten alloys has, to some extent, lagged behind that of the other refractory metals. However, tungsten has the highest melting point (6170°F) of the metals, indicating that it could be used structurally at higher service temperatures than any of the other metals. The modulus of elasticity of tungsten (58×10^6) is higher than that for columbium, molybdenum or tantalum.

Tungsten is also one of the most dense metals (19.3 g/cc), being exceeded only by rhenium, gold and some of the platinum group metals. Hence, tungsten components must be kept to a minimum in airborne hardware since low weight is an important factor. Figures 3.6 and 3.7 illustrate hardware fabricated of tungsten.

(Courtesy of Super-Temp Corp.)

Fig. 3.6. Combination pure tungsten blast tube and nozzle assembly, fabricated and welded from thin-wall pure tungsten sheet.

Tungsten, like the other refractory metals, will readily oxidize in air at elevated temperatures. Consequently, all sintering, melting, heating and welding must be performed in vacuum, in hydrogen or in an inert gas. Commercial tungsten is forged in air, since the oxide formed acts as a lubricant in the forging operation. Commercially pure tungsten is relatively hard, brittle and difficult to form and machine. However, on an experimental scale, tungsten has been produced with sufficient ductility to permit cold rolling at room temperature.

Alloy Composition. Several alloys have been developed which show excellent strength at temperatures up to 3500°F. They include the thoriated grades; the W-0.38 TaC alloy, which must be produced by powder metallurgy; and the W-Mo binary alloys, which can be arc-melted. The W-15 Mo alloy retains a strength advantage over pure tungsten

(Courtesy of Super-Temp Corp.)

Fig. 3.7. Pure tungsten insert liner spun from .160 inch tungsten sheet x 22 inch diameter disc. Gauge thicknesses up to .375 or 3/8 inch and heavier are possible with diameters up to 36 inches.

to about 4000°F. At high temperatures, the W-1 ThO_2 and W-2 ThO_2 alloys have a significant strength advantage.

Mechanical Properties. With increasing temperatures, the tensile strength of wrought tungsten decreases steadily up to the recrystallization range. As recrystallization occurs, the strength drops off rapidly. A great amount of alloy development has been directed toward the prevention or delay of recrystallization so that strength may be maintained above 3000°F.

Mechanical properties of pure tungsten are shown in Table 3.6. It should be noted that representative properties are difficult to obtain because mechanical properties of tungsten reflect to an unusual extent, details of composition, microstructure, fabrication history and testing procedures.

Since tungsten has been primarily a lamp and electron tube material, there is a large amount of information on wire, but little on sheet.

Comparative properties of two commercial tungsten alloys are shown in Table 3.7. These alloys retain their room temperature strength to temperatures up to 2600°F, with a considerable increase in ductility.

Figure 3.8 indicates the strength of several tungsten alloys in the temperature range of 2500 to 6000°F.

TABLE 3.6. MECHANICAL PROPERTIES OF TUNGSTEN (*1*)

Property		Values	
Density, g/cc	Presintered at about 1500 °C (2700 °F)		10.0–13.0
	Sintered at up to 3000 °C (5400 °F)		16.5–17.5
	Swaged		18.0–19.0
	Drawn		19.0–19.3
Lattice structure	Body centered cubic parameter, 3.158 A		
Hardness, VPN	Sintered bar		200–250
	Swaged bar		350–500
	Cold-rolled sheet		450–500
	Recrystallized sheet		260–380
		T.S.	Elong.
Tensile strength, 1000 psi, and elongation, per cent	Sintered bar	18	...
	Swaged bar	50–213	...
	Wire .04-in.-diam	256	1–4
	.02-in.-diam	284	1–4
	.008-in.-diam	355	1–4
	.004-in.-diam	427	1–4
	.0008-in.-diam	582	...
	Wire .004-in.-diam, annealed (recryst)	156	...
	Single crystal (containing Th)	156	20
Yield point, 1000 psi	Wire 0.02 to 0.04-in.-diam		
	Annealed		99–113
	Unannealed		213
		T.S.	Elong.
Hot tensile strength, 1000 psi, and corresponding elongation, per cent	Wire .025-in.-diam		
	400 °C (750 °F)	170–227	2–3
	800 °C (1470 °F)	113–142	4–5
	1200 °C (2200 °F)	57–85	5–6
	1800 °C (3270 °F)	14–42	n.d.
Young's modulus, 10^6 psi	20 °C (70 °F)	59	
	1000 °C (1830 °F)	47	
Torsion modulus, 10^6 psi	20 °C (70 °F)	24	
Compressibility, cm^2/kg	Swaged bar	$2.93 \cdot 10^{-7}$	
	Drawn wire	$3.15 \cdot 10^{-7}$	

Columbium

The melting point of columbium is 4470°F, 265 degrees lower than that of molybdenum. The development of columbium and its alloys for high temperature structural applications was started later than that of molybdenum and tungsten, but considerable progress has been made in the last few years.

Here again, the tendency for columbium to oxidize in air at elevated temperatures is a serious disadvantage. Alloy development programs

TABLE 3.7. COMPARATIVE PROPERTIES OF
TWO TUNGSTEN ALLOYS (*1*)

Composition, Weight per cent:	85W–15Mo	98W–2Mo
At 70 °F:		
Ultimate tensile strength, psi	45,000	25,000
Elongation, %	0	0
Reduction of area, %	0	0
At 600 °F:		
Ultimate tensile strength, psi	42,000	28,000
Yield strength, psi	28,000	18,000
Elongation, %	5	1.5
Reduction of area, %	5	0.9
At 800 °F:		
Ultimate tensile strength, psi	50,000	33,000
Yield strength, psi	22,000	15,000
Elongation, %	6	4
Reduction of area, %	6	...
At 1000 °F:		
Ultimate tensile strength, psi	50,000	37,000
Yield strength, psi	20,000	...
Elongation, %	20	9
Reduction of area, %	20	7
At 1500 °F:		
Ultimate tensile strength, psi	45,000	...
Yield strength, psi	20,000	...
Elongation, %	15	...
Reduction of area, %	20	...
At 2000 °F:		
Ultimate tensile strength, psi	50,000	30,000
Elongation, %	...	26
At 2600 °F:		
Ultimate tensile strength, psi	42,000	...

have been unsuccessful in promoting better oxidation resistance, without increasing fabrication problems. Those alloys which have satisfactory oxidation resistance are unsatisfactory as structural materials because of inadequate strength, very poor fabricability, low recrystallization temperature, or other undesirable characteristics.

Pure columbium is very ductile and can be cold-worked easily at room temperature. However, columbium has a tendency to seize and gall in such processes as wire drawing, spinning and threading. Working and forming are usually conducted at room temperature to avoid oxidation.

The density of columbium (0.310 lbs/cu in.) is only slightly greater than that of steel and considerably less than that of the other refractory metals. This characteristic coupled with favorable nuclear properties has resulted in extensive development of columbium-base alloys for airborne nuclear reactors. High strength columbium alloys have many of the same processing problems connected with them as with molyb-

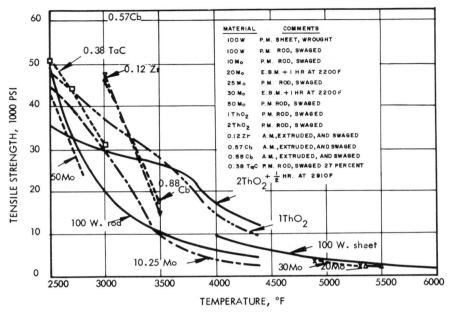

Fig. 3.8. Effect of temperature on the tensile strength of tungsten alloys (9).

denum. Since there are generally more alloying elements in the columbium alloys than in molybdenum alloys, it is more difficult to arc cast
homogeneous ingots.

Alloy Composition. The compositions of the columbium alloys in use
today are shown in Table 3.8. In general, the low strength alloys such
as FS-80 have superior fabricability and weldability, and have a low
transition temperature similar to pure columbium. These alloys contain
a low percentage of zirconium for strengthening by dispersion hardening.

Tantalum additions improve hot strength and oxidation resistance.
Tungsten and molybdenum are solid solution strengtheners and produce even greater strengths. The strongest columbium alloys contain
zirconium and carbon as well as tungsten and molybdenum. It should
be noted that improvements in strength are offset by increased difficulties
in fabrication and decreased ductility at low temperatures.

Mechanical Properties. Pure columbium is very ductile even at very
low temperatures. The addition of alloying elements to improve strength
raises the transition temperature considerably. Recrystallization affects
the columbium alloys to a much lesser degree than in the molybdenum
alloys. The tensile strength of the F-48 alloy decreases only about 10

TABLE 3.8. TODAY'S COLUMBIUM ALLOYS (7)

Name or Code	Nominal Composition	Developer or Producer	Status
FS-83	28% Ta, 11 W, 1% Zr	. . .	Laboratory
FS-82	33% Ta, 1% Zr	Fansteel Metallurgical Corp.	Commercial
FS-80	0.75-1% Zr	Widely studied*	Commercial
F-48	15% W, 5% Mo, 1% Zr	General Electric Co.	Pilot prod.**
F-50	15% W, 5% Mo, 1% Zr, 5% Ti	General Electric Co.	Pilot prod.**
D-31	10% Ti, 10% Mo	DuPont Co.	Pilot prod.
Cb-7	28% W, 7% Ti	Union Carbide Metals Co.	Laboratory
Cb-16	20% W, 10% Ti, 3% V	Union Carbide Metals Co.	Laboratory
Cb-65	7%, Ti, 0.8% Zr	Union Carbide Metals Co.	Pilot prod.
Cb-74	10% W, 5% Zr	Union Carbide Metals Co.	Laboratory
15-20	15% W, 20% Ta	. . .	Laboratory
20-20	20% W, 20% Ta	. . .	Laboratory

*Alloys containing 0.75 to 1.04% Zr have been evaluated by most concerns working in this field. The alloy was originally discovered because of zirconium's occurrence in columbium ore and its carry-over into the reduced metal.

**Alloys in pilot production have been arc melted in 4 to 6 in. diameter ingots and converted to bar and sheet. Mill products of General Electric's alloys have been produced for internal consumption.

per cent on complete recrystallization, whereas the molybdenum alloys lose up to 50 per cent of their strength when recrystallized.

The mechanical properties of pure columbium have been evaluated up to 2500°F and some alloys have been examined for tensile properties up to 4000°F. Most of the columbium alloys are currently in the development or pilot production stage and consequently mechanical property data is considered preliminary.

Typical test data are shown in Table 3.9 and Figure 3.9.

TABLE 3.9. PHYSICAL PROPERTIES OF SOME COLUMBIUM ALLOYS (7)

Alloy	Melting Point, °F	Temperature, °F	Elastic Modulus(a)	Coefficient of Thermal Expansion(b)	Thermal Conductivity(c)	Specific Heat(d)	Density(e)
F-48	4500*	70	25	3.4	24*	. . .	0.34
		2000	18*	4.0	34*	. . .	. . .
F-50	4400*	70	24	. . .	20*	. . .	0.33
		2000	16.5	. . .	. . .	. . .	. . .
D-31	4100	2000	8.5	4.1	. . .	0.074	. . .
FS-80	4350	70	15.1*	. . .	32	0.065	0.313
FS-82	4550	70	16.5	. . .	. . .	. . .	0.366
Cb (unalloyed)	4480	70	15.1	. . .	30	0.065	0.313

*Estimated data
(a)Psi × 10^6
(b)In. per in. per °F × 10^{-6}

(c)Btu per sq ft per hr per °F per ft
(d)Btu per lb per °F
(e)Lb per cu in.

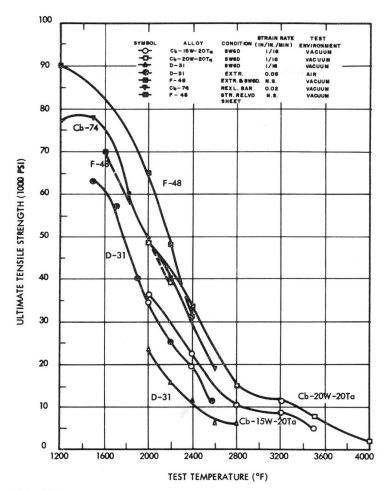

Fig. 3.9. Ultimate tensile strength for selected columbium alloys between 1200 and 4000°F (9).

Tantalum

Tantalum has a melting point of 5430°F. Only tungsten, rhenium, and osmium melt at higher temperatures. The development of tantalum and its alloys has not advanced as rapidly as that of molybdenum and columbium. Tantalum has a high density and low strength, and it is not as plentiful as the less dense molybdenum and columbium. Since tantalum is present in columbium ores as a sister element, increasing amounts of tantalum have become available with the increased demand for columbium. Pure tantalum oxidizes in air at high temperatures even more rapidly than tungsten. Therefore, it must be utilized in a vacuum or must be protected by oxidation resistant coatings.

Tantalum has exceptional resistance to most corrosive media below 300°F. Consequently, it is used in many applications involving exposure to corrosive environments in the chemical industry. In applications involving both corrosion and high temperature, an inexpensive coating would be desirable.

Another application of tantalum has resulted from a surface oxide film which has important dielectric properties. With this film, tantalum is being used for electrolytic capacitors and rectifiers. It is also used extensively in electron tubes and as implants in human surgery.

Composition. The only tantalum alloy considered commercially at the present time is the Ta-10W alloy. Two other alloys which are in the advanced development state are Ta-10Hf-5W and Ta-30Cb-7.5V. Strength comparisons indicate that the Ta-10Hf-5W alloy has an advantage over both Ta-10W and Ta-30Cb-7.5V, up to 300°F. Up to 3000°F, strength to weight comparisons indicate that the Ta-30Cb-7.5V alloy has the advantage due to its lighter weight. This alloy retains its ductility in tension at temperatures as low as –320°F.

Mechanical Properties. Tantalum and some of its alloys have better ductility and toughness than the other refractory metals and can be rolled and fabricated easily at room temperature. It even retains its ductility as low as –423°F. Tantalum also does not work harden as rapidly as many other metals.

A comparison of the low-temperature ductility and tensile strength of tantalum with the other important refractory metals is shown in Figure 3.10. Room temperature tensile properties of tantalum are shown in Table 3.10. The range in ultimate tensile strength from 27,500 to 180,-000 psi is indicative of the large effect of purity and thermal-mechanical history on the strength properties of tantalum.

Table 3.11 indicates the high-temperature tensile properties of the most promising tantalum alloys.

Vanadium

Vanadium melts at 3450°F, about 1000°F lower than columbium. Consequently there has not been a great deal of interest in the use of vanadium for high-temperature applications.

Until recently, pure vanadium was not available in quantities great enough for complete studies of its physical and mechanical properties. Pure vanadium is relatively ductile and can be worked easily at room temperature. Because it oxidizes rapidly at elevated temperatures, it must be protected during hot working or hot forging. Hot rolling is usually accomplished with the ingot sheathed in a jacket of stainless steel. Pure

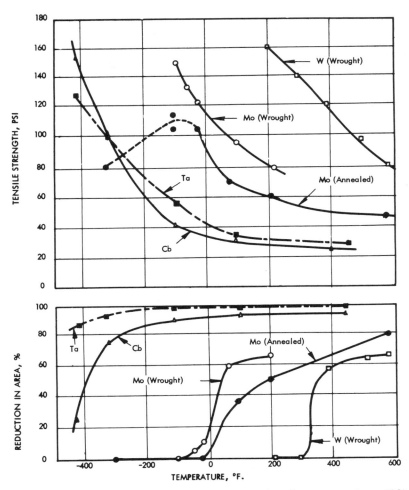

Fig. 3.10. Strength and ductility of refractory metals at low temperatures (10).

vanadium can be machined, extruded, drawn and stamped by conventional methods provided it is not heated to the temperature at which oxidation starts. The pure metal is also weldable with the use of argon shielding or other protective atmospheres.

Currently, vanadium has few commercial applications other than its use as an alloying element. Vanadium foil is used as a bonding material in the manufacture of titanium-clad steel sheet. Vanadium may

TABLE 3.10. TENSILE PROPERTIES OF TANTALUM AT
ROOM TEMPERATURE (*9*)

Condition	Ultimate Tensile Strength, 1000 psi	Yield Strength, 1000 psi	Elongation, per cent	Reduction in Area, per cent
Recrystallized	27.5		38	89
Recrystallized high-purity sheet (1 hr at 1200 C 0.040 in. thick)	29.4	26.3	36	...
Recrystallized rod (1 hr at 2600 °C)	33.4	...	50	...
Recrystallized sheet	40.0/50.0	30.0/40.0	30/40	...
Recrystallized rod (1 hr at 1700 °C)	49.8	39.3	45	86
Annealed sheet (0.010 in. thick)	50.0	...	40	...
Cold-worked high-purity sheet (cold reduced 95%; 0.040 in. thick)	60.5	49.0	...	...
Recrystallized sheet (0.010 in. thick)	67.1	57.4	25	...
Annealed wire (0.002 in. diameter)	100.0	...	11	...
Cold-worked sheet	100.0/120.0	95.0/105.0	3	...
Cold-worked sheet (0.010 in. thick)	110.0	...	1	...
Hardened plate (0.010 in. thick)	145.0	...	18	...
As-drawn wire (0.002-in. diameter)	180.0	...	2	...

have potential use as a structural material for reactors because of its low-neutron capture cross section, useful strength at elevated temperatures and high thermal conductivity.

Alloy Composition. No commercial alloys of vanadium are available at present. However, many alloy development programs are being pursued involving additions of columbium, yttrium, titanium and the rare-earth metals. Recent investigations have shown that ternary refractory metal additions of columbium, molybdenum, tantalum and tungsten to a vanadium-titanium binary base material produce alloys with attractive elevated temperature strength properties.

Mechanical Properties. Room temperature mechanical properties of pure vanadium are shown in Table 3.12. Table 3.13 indicates the properties of a variety of experimental vanadium sheet alloys at room tem-

TABLE 3.11. TENSILE PROPERTIES OF TANTALUM ALLOYS (9)

Tensile Properties

Alloy	Approximate Recrystallization Temperature, °F	Test Temperature, °F	Ultimate Tensile Strength, 1000 psi	Yield Strength, 0.2 Per cent Offset, 1000 psi	Strength-To-Weight Ratio, 1000 psi/lb/in.³
100 Ta(a)	2000–2300	2145	14.7	13.9	24.5
		2190	7.4	(3.8)(b)	12.3
		2190	11.4	. . .	19.0
		2400	10.0	8.4	16.7
		2600	4.6	. . .	7.67
		2700	5.3	(3.8)	8.84
		2860	3.3	. . .	5.50
		3040	3.6	. . .	6.00
Ta-7.5W(a)	2500–2700	. . .	. . .	. . .	. . .
Ta-10W(a)	2500–2800	1500	103.2	97.8	170
		2500	22.25	19.85	36.7
		3000	12.1	11.8	19.9
		3500	7.48	7.26	12.3
		4000	4.35	4.30	7.17
		4500	2.06	2.06	3.39
		5000	0.645	0.645	1.06
Ta-10W (Modified)(c)	. . .	. . .	. . .	. . .	. . .
Ta-15W	2600–2900	2190	47.5	32.5	77.4
Ta-20W	2800–3200	2190	49.6	45.1	80.3
Ta-30Cb-7.5V	2300–2500	2190	60.6	47.6	142
		2600	36.1	22.3	84.7
		3000	10.2	6.2	23.9
Ta-10Hf-5W	2500–2900	2190	63.8	. . .	108
		2415	41.4	30.6	70.3
		2605	37.0	25.0	62.8
		3045	17.8	12.1	30.2

(a)C = Commercial, others in advanced development stage.
(b)Values in parentheses are estimated.
(c)Strength data at moderate strain rates not available.

TABLE 3.12. MECHANICAL PROPERTIES OF
UNALLOYED VANADIUM (9)

	Yield Strength, 0.2 Per cent Offset, psi	Ultimate Tensile Strength, psi	Elongation, %	Reduction in Area, %	Hardness, R_A	Grain Size, mm
Iodide V vanadium (99.9 + V)	13,200	28,700	38.3	95.0	21	0.20
Ca-reduced vanadium (99.7 + V)	23,000	37,600	33.7	36.7	38	0.04

TABLE 3.13. TENSILE PROPERTIES OF SOME EXPERIMENTAL VANADIUM SHEET ALLOYS (9)

[Annealed 0.50 hr at 1830°F (1000°C), Water Quenched]

Alloy Addition, Wt %	Room Temperature			1200°F (650°C)			1800°F (980°C)		
	Ultimate Tensile Strength, psi	Yield Strength, psi	Elonga-tion, %	Ultimate Tensile Strength, psi	Yield Strength, psi	Elonga-tion, %	Ultimate Tensile Strength, psi	Yield Strength, psi	Elonga-tion, %
10 Ti	73,500	65,200	29	46,700	34,800	32	35,800	34,000	36
20 Cb	107,000	105,500	6	81,700	61,200	13	55,100	41,500	22
50 Cb	168,000	163,500	2	151,500	130,300	3	85,300	75,400	5
20 Ti-10 Mo	114,000	104,500	23	90,800	67,800	17	43,500	39,900	42
20 Ti-20 Cb	113,500	108,500	21	96,500	78,500	12	44,200	41,300	56
5 Ti-40 Cb	129,000	112,700	20	97,900	84,200	7	...	...	...
5 Ti-5 W	73,600	57,000	23	58,500	39,800	...	28,900	24,800	7
20 Ti-20 W	112,000	105,200	21	108,000	82,000	12	46,400	41,600	52

perature, 1200°F, and 1800°F. Stress rupture data on V-20 Cb alloy are shown in Table 3.14.

THE REACTIVE METALS

Zirconium and titanium are referred to as the "reactive" metals because they combine so readily with oxygen, sulfur, nitrogen and other nonmetallic elements to form very stable compounds. Very brief coverage will be given to these metals, since they are utilized at moderate temperatures, as compared with the refractory metals.

Zirconium

Zirconium, which melts at 3370°F, is primarily used in nuclear reactor applications. It resists oxidation at temperatures only up to 400°F. In general, pure zirconium loses strength rapidly above 1300°F. Consequently, it is considered inferior to the refractory metals for high-temperature applications.

The mechanical properties and corrosion resistance of zirconium can be modified by alloying. The alloys known as the "Zircaloys" are produced by either arc melting or by powder metallurgy processes. The ingots or compacts may be hot forged and rolled without protective atmospheres. "Zircaloy-2" contains about 1.5 per cent tin and "Zircaloy-3," about 0.25 per cent tin. Both alloys also contain small amounts of iron, chromium, and nickel. These alloys have improved room tem-

TABLE 3.14. STRESS RUPTURE DATA OF VANADIUM ALLOYS
AT 2000°F IN HELIUM (*9*)

Alloy Addition to V-20CB Binary, (Wt %)				1/2 Hr Heat Treatment, °F	Stress, psi	Time, hr	Elong, %
Element							
Ti	ZR	Hf	Other				
5				2,000-WQ	46,000	0.0375	14
					40,000	0.075	18
					30,000	1.5	22
					20,000	2.1	16
					8500	4.1	20
					2500	17.8	45
5			0.25Y	2,400-WQ	20,000	1.4	22
5			0.1B	As cold rolled	20,000	1.1	44
				2,800-FQ-1 hr-2,000	20,000	1.4	22
	2		0.05C	2,800-FQ-1 hr-2,000	20,000	1.4	22
		2	0.1C	2,800-FQ-1 hr-2,000	10,000	4.1	95
		2	0.03C	2,800-FQ-1 hr-2,000	10,000	2.1	60
5			0.25C	2,800-FQ-1 hr-2,000	20,000	1.3	...
				2,800-FQ-1 hr-2,000	10,000	40.7	55
				2,800-FQ-1 hr-2,000	8000	21.7	64
				2,800-FQ-1 hr-2,000	6000	105.7	70
	2		0.1C	2,800-FQ-1 hr-2,000	20,000	0.9	19

perature and elevated temperature strength, and superior corrosion resistance compared with unalloyed zirconium. They could be considered to be moderately oxidation-resistant.

In addition to nuclear reactor components, zirconium is used for special corrosion-resistant equipment for the chemical industry, in photo-flash bulbs, and for surgical applications. If the cost of zirconium production were lowered substantially, it could replace tantalum for some applications involving corrosion by acids. In these applications zirconium would be more desirable due to its lighter weight.

Titanium

Titanium has a melting point of 3040°F and its density is only 57 per cent that of iron. A large number of titanium alloys have been developed. Many of these have excellent mechanical properties, and offer considerable weight savings at intermediate temperatures up to about 1000°F. Since the titanium alloys lose strength rapidly above that temperature, they are more competitive with the alloy steels than with the superalloys or the refractory metals.

The large number of titanium alloys which have been produced can be classified in three categories, based on their crystalline structure at room temperature, as follows: (1) alpha alloys, (2) alpha-beta alloys, and (3) beta alloys. The best known and most widely used alloys of each type are: Alpha: Ti-5Al-2.5Sn, Alpha beta: Ti-6Al-14V, Beta: Ti-13V-11Cr-3Al. The alpha-beta and beta alloys may be heat-treated to improve their strength.

Titanium is used primarily in aircraft structures which are subjected to temperatures considerably above those which aluminum alloys can withstand. It is also used for special chemical equipment and in marine applications.

CARBON AND GRAPHITE

Carbon and graphite have many desirable properties, particularly at high temperatures. These materials have low coefficients of thermal expansion which result in dimensional stability at elevated temperatures. Carbon and graphite also have low elastic moduli and high thermal conductivities which result in high resistance to thermal shock.

The difference in structure between carbon and graphite is in the ordering of the crystals, graphite being heated to temperatures high enough to remove the strains and imperfections which permit crystal ordering and growth.

Table 3.15 indicates the difference in properties between carbon and graphite.

The properties of carbon and graphite can vary depending upon the sizes of the particles bonded together by the pitch or tar, the type of

TABLE 3.15. TYPICAL PROPERTIES OF CARBON AND
GRAPHITE AT ROOM TEMPERATURE (*12*)

	Carbon	Graphite
Young's modulus, psi $\times$ 10^6	2.3	1.3
Compressive strength, psi	7500	5000
Specific gravity	2.10	2.26
Resistivity, ohm-cm	0.0041	0.00102
Thermal conductivity		
Cal sec^{-1}, Cm^{-2}, Cm C^{-1}	0.0124	0.310

petroleum coke used, the type of lampblack, and baking temperature.
Carbon and graphite exhibit increasing temperatures up to 4500°F.
Plastic flow in graphite begins at approximately 4200°F under a stress
of 1000 psi.

The greatest use of carbon and graphite is in the production of electrodes for electric furnaces. A more recent application has been for
rocket nozzles and nozzle liners or inserts. In this application, an oxidation and erosion-resistant coating is frequently required in order to
derive maximum benefit from the graphite. The material is also useful
as a back-up heat sink material in rocket propulsion systems as seen
in Figure 3.11.

A much greater range of applications for graphite could be anticipated
if improvements could be made in its oxidation resistance, strength, and
hardness. Some research has been conducted recently in an attempt to
improve the properties of graphite by the use of additives. The resultant materials are primarily composites formed by hot pressing. The
materials are powdered blends of coke or graphite, pitch, and the additives. In general, the process is carried to a point where a liquid

(Courtesy of Super-Temp Corp.)

Fig. 3.11. A.160 gauge pure tungsten elbow liner (fabricated, welded and final
machined) encased within an ATJ graphite heat sink. An overlay of pyrographite
is then fitted, cured, bonded and final machined.

phase appears in the system due to the melting of the additives. Compression then forces the liquid phase into the pores of the solid phase.

Additives which have been investigated are Ta, Hf, Cb, Si, ZrC, B_4C, TiB_2 and ZrB_2. Figure 3.12 illustrates the improvement in oxidation resistance imparted by the TiB_2 and B_4C additives.

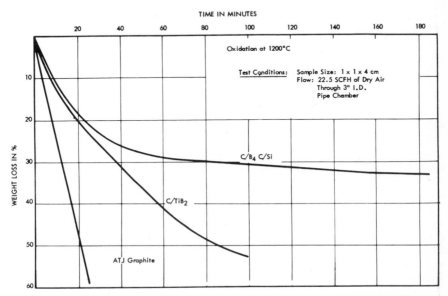

Fig. 3.12. Effect of additives on oxidation characteristics of graphite (17).

Work on the graphite base composites is continuing with the goal of producing a machinable material which will withstand oxidizing atmospheres up to 4000°F.

Pyrolytic Graphite

This form of graphite can be utilized either as a coating or a free-standing shape. Pyrolytic graphite is formed by depositing pure carbon atoms layer by layer on a suitably prepared substrate. This deposition occurs in a closely controlled vacuum furnace operating at 1900 to 2500°C. The layers of graphite are highly ordered and are oriented parallel to the surface of the substrate. The material deposited in this manner is spectroscopically pure carbon; it approaches theoretical density, is monolithic, free of voids, and has relatively high strength. More details on this material are given in Chapter 2.

It appears that the greatest advantage of pyrolytic graphite over conventional graphite is its freedom from voids. The conventional graphite process by its nature presents difficulties in attaining either the preferred orientation or density which has been attained in pyrolytic graphite.

STEELS FOR HIGH TEMPERATURE SERVICE

The stainless and high-alloy steels were probably the first to be used under extreme operating conditions of high temperatures and pressures. These steels are still widely used in the chemical process industry, in steam and gas turbines, and in missiles and aircraft. Figure 3.13 illustrates a low alloy steel, coated to resist high temperatures.

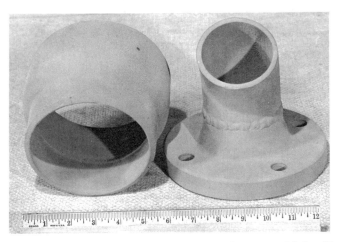

(Courtesy of Solar Aircraft Co.)

Fig. 3.13. Aluminum-ceramic "Alcermet" coating applied to heavy pipe sections. Low-alloy steels are protected up to 1100°F.

Some of the stainless steels resist oxidation to temperatures up to 2000°F, and maintain substantial strength up to 1500°F. The elevated temperature strength of chromium-nickel stainless steels is affected by additions of molybdenum, tungsten, vanadium, titanium, and columbium. Chromium increases the oxidation resistance and nickel increases the high temperature creep resistance. Table 3.16 lists most of the conventional stainless steels and indicates the maximum temperature each can withstand without excessive scaling.

SUPERALLOYS

High strength metal alloys for use at elevated temperatures are often referred to as "superalloys." These are divided into three groups, nickel, cobalt, and iron-base alloys. Applications for superalloys generally fall in the range of 1200 to 1800°F and extend occasionally up to 2000°F.

TABLE 3.16. CONVENTIONAL STAINLESS STEELS MAXIMUM
TEMPERATURE WITHOUT EXCESSIVE SCALING (*15*)

Alloy Nominal Analysis	Type No.	Maximum Temp, °F, Without Excessive Scaling
4-6 Cr-2 Mo	502	1150
8-10 Cr	. . .	1200
10-14 Cr	410	1250
12-14 Cr	420	1200
14-18 Cr	440	1400
14-18 Cr	430	1550
23-30 Cr	446	2000
18 Cr-8 Ni	302	1650
18 Cr-8 Ni	303	1600
18 Cr-8 Ni	304	1650
25 Cr-12 Ni	309	2000
25 Cr-20 Ni	310	2000
18 Cr-8 Ni-2 Mo	316	1650
18 Cr-8 Ni + Ti	321	1650
18 Cr-8 Ni + Cb	347	1650

The iron-base alloys will not be discussed since they are primarily used for applications below 1500°F.

Nickel-Base. The first superalloys were the nickel-base alloys. These have been in existence for a little over 20 yr. Their excellent high temperature mechanical properties are a result of the precipitation of a finely dispersed second phase.

Although research and development has been recently concentrated on the refractory metals, the nickel-base superalloys are widely used for present high-temperature structural applications. They are the most important of the superalloys in the 1500 to 1800°F range. For conventional aircraft, these alloys have been used for turbine buckets, speed brakes, nozzle guide vanes, rotor discs, afterburners, thrust reversers, and fasteners. For space vehicles, nickel alloys have been used for the structural framework and as shingles on the outer surfaces.

Most of the nickel-base superalloys for elevated temperature service contain from 5 to 30 per cent chromium. Chromium adds increased strength, oxidation resistance and resistance to the harmful effects of sulfur.

Other elements that act as solid-solution strengtheners for nickel are molybdenum and tungsten. Cobalt is also present in many nickel alloys. Boron and zirconium are added in small, controlled amounts to improve creep rupture properties and hot workability. Vacuum melting has been responsible for much of the recent progress made in the development of nickel-base alloys. Table 3.17 lists the nominal composition of typical nickel-base alloys in current use.

Heat treatment is of extreme importance to the nickel-base superalloys. Because of the complex composition of these materials, wide variation

TABLE 3.17. PROPERTIES AND APPLICATIONS FOR NICKEL-BASE SUPERALLOYS (16)

Alloy	Nominal Chemical Composition, %													Characteristic Rupture Strengths, 1000 Psi†						Typical Applications
	C	Mn	Si	Cr	Ni	Co	Mo	W	Cb	Ti	Al	Fe	Other	1200 °F 100 Hr	1200 °F 1000 Hr	1500 °F 100 Hr	1500 °F 1000 Hr	1800 °F 100 Hr	1800 °F 1000 Hr	
G-157	0.06	1.25	0.40	27	Bal.	...	1.5	1.5	...	2.0	0.75	6.0*	...	...	...	14.5	10.5	...	...	Sheet alloy
J-1500, M-252	0.15	0.5	0.5	20	Bal.	10	10	...	...	3.0	1.0	...	...	102	88	37	23	...	...	Gas turbine buckets, parts, sheet
GE-B-129(c)	0.06	0.4	0.4	5	Bal.	...	15	...	2	...	6.0	4	0.5 B	...	...	47	29	...	...	High-temperature structural parts
M-600	0.08	...	...	19	55.5	...	7	...	...	2.3	1.1	13	...	...	...	28	17	...	...	High-temperature structural parts
I-1360(c)	0.10	...	...	10	70.5	...	5	...	2	...	6.0	4.5	0.3 B	...	...	40.5	27.3	9.4	4.8	High-temperature structural parts
DCM	0.08*	0.10*	0.15	15	Bal.	...	5.25	...	...	3.5	4.6	5.0	0.08 B	...	...	...	20	...	11.5	Aircraft gas turbine blades, parts
René 41	0.09	...	...	19	Bal.	11	10	...	...	3.1	1.5	...	0.01 B	110	102	45	29	11	...	Aircraft gas turbine parts, sheet, bolting
Astroloy	0.06	...	...	15	Bal.	15	5.25	...	...	3.5	4.4	...	0.03 B	...	...	50	...	...	...	Jet engine components, forgings, castings
GMR-235(c)	0.15	0.25*	0.60*	15.5	Bal.	...	5.25	...	...	2.0	3.0	10	0.06 B	...	...	38	29	11	...	Jet engine parts
GMR-235D(c)	0.15	0.10*	0.30*	15.5	Bal.	...	5.0	...	...	2.5	3.5	4.5	0.05 B	110	100	56	39	17.5	...	Jet engine parts
Hastelloy B	0.10	0.8	0.7	0.6	Bal.	2.5*	28	...	...	...	...	5	0.30 V	50	36.5	16.5	10.4	...	...	Corrosion-resistant alloy. Service under oxidizing conditions limited to 1400°F.
Hastelloy C	0.07	0.8	0.7	16	Bal.	2.5*	17	4	...	...	...	5	...	54	42.5	18.5	14.5	...	...	Engine parts, collector rings, combustion chambers
Hastelloy D(c)	0.12	1.0	9.0	...	Bal.	2.5*	...	...	...	...	...	1	3.0 Cu	...	...	...	...	...	...	Corrosion-resistant alloy
Hastelloy N	0.06	0.8*	0.5*	7	Bal.	0.5*	16.5	...	...	...	...	5*	0.01 B	42	29	13	6.8	...	...	Resistant to hot fluoride salts
Hastelloy R-235	0.15	...	...	15.5	Bal.	2.5*	5.5	...	...	2.5	2.0	10	...	85	63	40	30	8	5	Gas turbine and jet engine parts, sheet

(Continued)

TABLE 3.17. (Continued)

Alloy	C	Mn	Si	Cr	Ni	Co	Mo	W	Cb	Ti	Al	Fe	Other	1200°F 100 Hr	1200°F 1000 Hr	1500°F 100 Hr	1500°F 1000 Hr	1800°F 100 Hr	1800°F 1000 Hr	Typical Applications
				Nominal Chemical Composition, %										Characteristic Rupture Strengths, 1000 Psi†						
Hastelloy W	0.12*	1.0*	1.0*	5.0	Bal.	2.5*	24.5	...	...	...	...	5.5	0.6 V*	...	...	...	...	...	...	Jet engine turbine rings; joining dissimilar metals
Hastelloy X	0.10	0.5	0.5	22	Bal.	1.5	9	0.6	...	...	...	18.5	...	43	32	14.3	9.5	5.2	3.0	Jet engine parts, good oxidation resistance.
Inconel (Inconel Alloy 600)	0.04	0.20	0.20	15.8	76.0	...	...	...	...	...	...	7.20	...	23	14.5	8.0	5.6	2.8	1.8	Combustion liners, manifolds, good oxidation resistance
Inconel "M" (Inconel Alloy 721)	0.04	2.25	0.12	16.0	71.0	...	...	...	...	3.0	...	7.20	...	55	35	17	10	...	...	Valves for aircraft engines
Inconel "W" (Inconel Alloy 722)	0.04	0.55	0.20	15.0	75.0	...	...	...	...	2.40	0.6	6.50	...	74	54	19	11.5	3.2	...	Sheet metal components, after burners
Inconel "X" (Inconel Alloy X-750)	0.04	0.70	0.30	15.0	73.0	...	...	...	0.85	2.50	0.80	6.75	...	80	68	28	16	3.3	2.3	Jet engine and structural parts, bolting
Inconel "X 550" (Inconel Alloy 751)	0.04	0.70	0.30	15.0	72.5	...	...	...	1.00	2.50	1.20	6.75	...	...	...	34	21	3.3	3.3	Jet engine and structural parts, bolting
Inconel Alloy 700	0.12	0.10	0.30	15.0	46.0	28.5	3.75	...	...	2.20	3.00	0.70	...	100	87	43	30	6.0	3.4	Gas turbine parts
Inconel Alloy 702	0.04	0.05	0.20	15.6	79.5	...	...	...	...	0.70	3.40	0.35	...	54	41	15	9	3.1	2.5	Excellent oxidation resistance to 2400°F.
Inconel Alloy 713C (Inconel Alloy 713)(c)	0.12	0.10	0.30	11.5	74.0	...	4.5	...	2.0	0.6	6.0	1.0	...	101	92	68	47	20	15	Jet engine blades, parts
Inconel Alloy 718	0.04	0.20	0.20	19	52.5	...	3.0	...	5.2	0.8	0.6	18	0.006 B	100	85	...	...	...	...	High-temperature structural parts
Waspaloy	0.07	0.7	0.4	19	Bal.	14	4.3	...	...	3.0	1.3	1	...	110	86	40	25	6.5	...	Jet engine blades, parts
Waspaloy Mod.	0.05	...	...	19	Bal.	11.5	7	...	...	2.5	1.2	1	...	...	...	...	...	...	...	Jet engine blades, parts
Udimet 500	0.08	0.75*	0.75*	19	Bal.	19.5	4.0	...	...	2.9	2.9	4*	0.01 B	94	46	33	12	...	...	Gas turbine parts, sheet, bolting

TABLE 3.17. (Continued)

Alloy	Nominal Chemical Composition, %													Characteristic Rupture Strengths, 1000 Psi†						Typical Applications
	C	Mn	Si	Cr	Ni	Co	Mo	W	Cb	Ti	Al	Fe	Other	1200°F 100 Hr	1200°F 1000 Hr	1500°F 100 Hr	1500°F 1000 Hr	1800°F 100 Hr	1800°F 1000 Hr	
Udimet 520	0.05	...	...	19	Bal.	12	6	1.0	...	3.0	2.0	...	0.005 B	...	...	48	33	...	...	Properties equal to Udimet 500; improved workability
Udimet 700	0.15*	...	...	15	Bal.	18.5	5.2	...	...	3.5	4.25	1*	0.1 B	100	...	58	43	16	...	Jet engine parts
Unitemp AF1753	0.24	0.05	0.10	16.25	Bal.	7.2	1.6	8.4	...	3.2	1.9	9.5	0.008 B; 0.06 Zr	115	98	47	34	10	6.5	Gas turbine components, buckets, wheels, fasteners, rings and spacers
Nicrotung(c)	0.10	...	...	12	Bal.	10	...	8	...	4	4	...	0.05 B; 0.05 Zr	...	...	68	45	22	13	High-strength parts
TRW 1800(c)	0.09	...	...	13	Bal.	...	...	9	1.5	0.6	6.0	...	0.07 B; 0.07 Zr; 1.0 V	...	...	...	...	24	15	Turbine blades
IN-100, PDRL 100(c)	0.18	...	...	10	Bal.	15	3	...	...	5	5.5	1.0*	0.015 B; 0.05 Zr	...	...	75	59	25	16	Turbine blades

*Maximum
†For rupture in 100 and 1000 hr
(c)Denotes cast alloy

in properties can be obtained in any given alloy by use of different heat treatments. Most commercial alloys are available with a recommended heat treatment that provides an optimum compromise of properties.

Different solution and aging treatments are used on the same alloy, depending on whether it is being heat treated to obtain optimum stress-rupture or tensile properties. Maximum stress-rupture strength is usually obtained with a relatively large grain size, whereas maximum tensile strength is obtained with relatively fine grain sizes. Typical stress rupture values are reviewed in Figure 3.14.

Cobalt-Base Alloys. For several years the cobalt-base alloys were considered superior for service between 1600 and 2000°F, because of their high strength and excellent oxidation resistance in that range. However, continued development of the precipitation-hardenable nickel-base alloys resulted in alloys with a higher strength than the cobalt-base alloys in most of this temperature range, the latter having the advantage only above 1900°F.

Cobalt-base alloys depend upon solid solution hardening and often on a dispersion of stable carbides for their strength at high temperatures. In addition to nickel and chromium, the alloying elements most often used in these alloys are molybdenum, columbium, tantalum, and particularly tungsten. Boron additions have been used to give the alloy improved high temperature mechanical properties. Some alloys also utilize titanium. Table 3.18 lists the nominal composition and the stress rupture values of typical cobalt base alloys in current use.

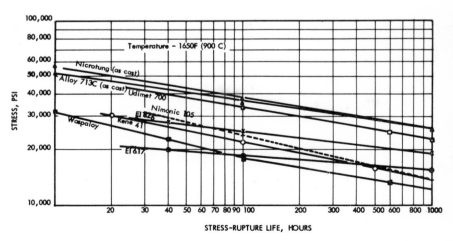

Fig. 3.14. Typical stress-rupture properties of some nickel-base superalloys at 1650°F (4).

TABLE 3.18. PROPERTIES AND APPLICATIONS FOR COBALT-BASE SUPERALLOYS (16)

Alloy	Nominal Chemical Composition, %												Characteristic Rupture Strengths, 1000 Psi†						Typical Applications
	C	Mn	Si	Cr	Ni	Co	Mo	W	Cb	Ti	Al	Fe	1200°F 100 Hr	1200°F 1000 Hr	1500°F 100 Hr	1500°F 1000 Hr	1800°F 100 Hr	1800°F 1000 Hr	
S-816	0.38	1.20	0.40	20	20	Bal.	4	4	4	...	...	4	60	46	25	18	...	...	Jet engine buckets, bolting, springs
S-816(c)	0.38	1.20	0.40	20	20	Bal.	4	4	4	...	...	3	56	44	28	21	11	6.5	High-temperature castings
S-816 + B(c)	0.40	1.00	0.40	20	20	Bal.	4	4	4	...	...	3	86	78	44	32	14.5	7.8	High-temperature castings
V-36	0.27	1.00	0.40	25	20	Bal.	4	2	2	...	...	3	...	...	23	18	8.5	5	High-temperature sheet uses
AF-94	0.12	1.20	...	15	10	56	5	10	1	...	...	2	...	...	30	...	10	...	High-temperature bar alloy
WF-11, L605, HS-25	0.10	1.50	0.50	20	10	Bal.	...	15	...	1.0	...	...	70	54	24	17	7	3.8	Jet engine parts, good sheet alloy
WF-31	0.15	1.42	0.42	20	10	Bal.	2.6	10.7	...	1.0	...	...	...	...	25	18	...	...	High-temperature sheet alloy
J-1570	0.20	...	...	20	28	38	...	7	...	4.0	...	2	95	78	33	24	...	...	Gas turbine parts
J-1650	0.20	...	...	19	27	Bal.	...	12	2.0 Ta	3.8	...	...	...	82	46	33	13	...	Jet engine parts; one of strongest wrought alloys
X-40, HS-31(c)	0.50	0.50	0.50	25	10	Bal.	...	7.5	...	...	...	1.5	56	51	28	22	11.3	9.8	Gas turbine blades, parts
X-63(c)	0.40	...	...	23	10	58	6	...	...	...	...	1.0	54	45	24.3	17.7	8	...	Gas turbine blades, parts
HS-30, 422-19(c)	0.45	0.60	0.60	26	15	Bal.	6	...	...	...	...	1.0	...	...	28.6	21.7	10	7.1	Gas turbine parts
HS-36, L251(c)	0.40	1.2	0.50	19	10	Bal.	...	15	...	...	...	1.0	...	...	29	25.5	10.5	7.2	Gas turbine parts
HE-1049(c)	0.40	0.8	0.8	26	10	Bal.	...	15	...	...	...	3.0*	...	...	45	35	...	11.5	Gas turbine parts
Haynes No. 151(c)	0.50	1.0*	1.0*	20	...	Bal.	...	12.7	...	...	...	...	73	68	37	33	14	11.5	Gas turbine blades, vanes, integrally cast turbine wheels
W152(c)	0.45	0.50*	0.50*	21	1.0*	Bal.	...	11	2.0	...	...	2.0	...	...	...	...	11.5	7.8	Gas turbine parts
Nivco-10	0.05*	0.35	0.15	...	22.5	Bal.	...	...	...	1.8	0.22	1.0*	54	43	...	...	...	...	Steam turbine blades, high damping
HS-21(c)	0.25	0.60	0.60	27	3	Bal.	5	...	...	...	...	1.0	52	42	20	13.5	9.4	7.0	Gas turbine blades, parts

*Maximum.
†For rupture in 100 and 1000 hr
(c)Denotes cast alloy.

REFERENCES

1. Gatzek, L. E., and Peck, J. L. H., "Trends and Future Development in Aerospace Materials," Report by Aerospace Corp., Inglewood, Calif., December, 1961.
2. Moon, D. P., and Simmons, W. F., "Stress-Rupture Strength of Selected Alloys," DMIC Memorandum No. 92, March, 1961.
3. Simmons, W. F., "What Alloy Shall I Use For High Temperature Applications (Above 1200°F)?" *Metal Prog.*, 80, No. 4, 84 (October, 1961).
4. Lund, C. H., "Physical Metallurgy of Nickel-Base Superalloys," DMIC Report No. 153, May, 1961.
5. Campbell, J. E., *et al.*, "Introduction of Metals for Elevated Temperature Use," DMIC Report No. 160, October, 1961.
6. Houck, J. A., "Physical and Mechanical Properties of Commercial Molybdenum Base Alloys," DMIC Report No. 140, November, 1960.
7. Barth, V. D., "Physical and Mechanical Properties of Tungsten and Tungsten Base Alloys," DMIC Report No. 127, March, 1960.
8. Barth, V. D., "Review of Recent Developments in the Technology of Tungsten," DMIC Memorandum No. 127, September, 1961.
9. Tietz, T. E., and Wilson, J. W., "Mechanical, Oxidation and Thermal Property Data for Seven Refractory Metals and Their Alloys," Special Report, Lockheed Missile and Space Division, September, 1961.
10. Ogden, H. R., and Perlmutter, I., "A Metal for Service at Both Cryogenic and Ultrahigh Temperatures," *Metal Progr.*, 80, No. 5, 97 (November, 1961).
11. Barth, V. A., "Review of Recent Developments in the Technology of Tantalum," DMIC Memorandum No. 108, May, 1962.
12. Jahnke, L. P., *et al.*, "Columbium Alloys Today," *Metal Progr.*, Part I, 77, No. 6, 69 (June, 1960) and Part II 78, No. 1, 76 (July, 1960).
13. Krier, C. A., "Coatings for the Protection of Refractory Metals From Oxidation," DMIC Report No. 162, November, 1961.
14. Hampel, C. A., "Rare Metals Handbook," New York, Reinhold Publishing Corp., 1954.
15. Anon., "Steels for Elevated Temperature Service," U.S. Steel Corp., 1961.
16. Campbell, I. E., "High Temperature Technology," New York, John Wiley & Sons, 1956.
17. Zeitsch, Karl J., "Oxidation Resistant Graphite Base Composites," National Carbon Co., June, 1962.

4

METHODS FOR APPLYING COATINGS

J. C. WITHERS

Manager of Materials Division
General Technologies Corporation
Alexandria, Virginia

Coatings occupy the key position in the successful use of many materials in high-temperature applications. The selection of a coating system is usually quite dependent upon the method and techniques employed to produce it. A technique is herein understood to represent one of the possible variations on a given method of application. Numerous methods are available for applying coating materials to a given base material to form a potential coating system. The purpose of this chapter is to consider these methods, the various application techniques and their respective merits for producing optimum coating systems.

For a given coating system, such as the molybdenum disilicide system on a substrate of molybdenum, each method of application has certain advantages and disadvantages depending on the end application, the substrate's size and geometry, and the "art" and/or experience of the workers involved.

Most of the methods and techniques which have been used to produce coating systems for high-temperature applications may be briefly summarized as follows:

(1) Electrodeposition methods
    (a) Aqueous solution
    (b) Fused salts
    (c) Organic solvents
    (d) Electrophoresis
(2) Spraying methods
    (a) Oxyfuel flame spraying
    (b) Arc plasma spraying

(3) Cladding methods
    (a) Roll cladding
    (b) Gas pressure bonding
(4) Vapor (gas) deposition methods
    (a) Pack cementation technique
    (b) Chemical and pyrolytic reaction
        (1) Vapor phase
        (2) Fluidized bed
(5) Enamelling methods
(6) Vacuum metallizing method
(7) Hot-dipping method
    (a) Molten metals
    (b) Selective freezing (desolutionizing)
    (c) Fused salts
(8) Slurry method
    (a) Painting technique
    (b) Trowelling technique
(9) Exothermic reaction method

PREPARATION OF SUBSTRATES

The preparation of the substrate prior to the application of the coating is most important to the achievement of maximum coating effectiveness and reliability. The surface of the base material must be mechanically and chemically clean in order to properly receive the coating. The cleaning procedure depends on the base material, the coating composition, the method of applying the coating, and the size and geometry of the part to be coated. Since procedures for preparing the base metal are so numerous and many of these are proprietary with the coating producer, only a few procedures which are known to produce good results for effectively removing surface oxides will be presented.

Rounding of the corners and edges is common to the preparation of all base materials, before any coating is applied. Diffusion-type coatings, when applied to a part having too small a radius on an edge, will result in an imperfect, cracked coating. This is illustrated in Figures 4.1 and 4.2. It is generally accomplished by a hand sanding or abrading operation. Although rounding is beneficial, the hand operation is costly and, more important, is not reproducible, especially with changing geometrics and base metal thicknesses. A much improved technique for rounding edges is effected by rotating the component in a drum (barrel finishing or ball milling) with 240 mesh silicon carbide and other materials to maintain good agitation. Aluminum oxide particles (60 to 325 mesh) and various sizes and types of agitation materials, such as copper nuts and bolts, have been used effectively for this purpose. The edges are rounded with all mesh sizes of the aluminum oxide and the

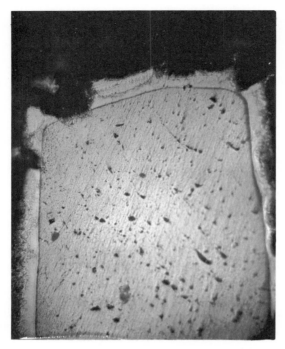

Fig. 4.1. Incorrectly rounded corners resulting in edge failure.

agitating material need only be large enough to provide adequate agitation as determined by experience. Other preferred materials are 60-mesh aluminum oxide and small water-washed gravel pebbles varying in size from about 1/10 to 3/8 in. in diameter. Milling times of 24 to 60 hr, depending on the thickness of the base material, are required to obtain adequate rounding. The milling produces a surface condition similar to that produced by sand blasting. The larger, 60-mesh aluminum oxide minimizes this latter effect.

Preliminary results published by the Structures Research Division at NASA, Langley Field (1), have shown that coatings applied by a variety of manufacturers to specimens rounded by the ball-milling technique last longer at high temperatures than specimens whose edges are prepared by shearing or machining. This is also true when rounding edges with various sizes of aluminum oxide and agitation materials. Some typical results are shown in Table 4.1. Although there is a wide statistical variation in these data, the average improvement of the ball-milled over the unmilled samples was 33 per cent and 51 per cent, respectively, for the molybdenum and columbium coatings.

Fig. 4.2. No edge failure on correctly rounded corners.

Some of the common chemical cleaning compositions which are known to be effective for removing the oxides from base metals prior to coating are given in Table 4.2. All materials are first degreased, followed by suitable chemical pickling or electrolytic etching; the parts are then thoroughly rinsed, dried, and coated. It is preferable not to heat the specimens for drying, as most of the metals that require coating for high temperature oxidation protection readily form a thin oxide layer which interferes with coating applications and the subsequent coating life. Drying is commonly accomplished by dipping in acetone and then allowing a few minutes for the acetone to evaporate in air. However, it has been shown that acetone leaves a very thin film upon drying (2), which could decompose and form a carbide if the coating application is carried out at a high temperature in a closed system. A methyl alcohol rinse after the acetone does not leave such a film (3).

ELECTRODEPOSITION

Electrodeposition is probably the most widely used method of applying a protective metal coating to another material. It is only natural that this method was the first to be investigated for applying high-

TABLE 4.1. COMPARISON OF SILICIDE COATING* PROTECTIVE
AT 2500°F OF 0.020 BASE METALS WITH AS-SHEARED EDGES
VERSUS BALL MILLING FOR FORTY HOURS

Base Metal	Specimen No.	Protective Life in Hrs		% Increase in Life
		As Sheared	Ball Milled	
Molybdenum	12	200	205	2.5
	17	225	395	76
	26	105	125	19
	33	360	450	25
	58	296	300	1.7
	61	75	90	20
	63	125	144	15
	67	100	199	99
Columbium	4	66	125	89
	9	78	94	20
	15	145	190	31
	107	92	102	11
	111	80	86	7.5
	117	79	200	153
	118	60	75	25
	130	50	100	100
	131	112	136	21

*General Technologies Corporation, NOX-1 for Molybdenum and NOX-2 for Columbium

temperature protective coatings. The first major work on electrodepositing coatings for high-temperature applications was for the protection of molybdenum. This work began about 1945 and developed in the early and mid-1950's. Two of the more systematic approaches to this probelm were conducted at the National Bureau of Standards (5, 7, 8), and at the Battelle Memorial Institute (6, 8). A wide variety of metal coatings including aluminum, chromium, cobalt, gold, iridium, nickel, platinum, palladium, rhodium, and cobalt-tungsten, among many others, have been plated onto the refractory metals in both single and multiple layers for protective purposes. These metals and alloys, for the most part, have been applied by electrodeposition from aqueous solutions. However, some plated coatings worth noting have been deposited from fused salts, organic solvents, and by electrophoretic techniques.

Aqueous Solutions

Few metals are applied as coatings by electroplating that do not rely on the aqueous solution techniques. The major emphasis has been on electroplating nickel and chromium in multiple layers for the protection of molybdenum. Chromium is first applied to molybdenum to obtain an adherent underlay whose thermal expansion coefficient more closely matches that of molybdenum than does the expansion coefficient

TABLE 4.2. CLEANING PROCEDURES FOR REMOVING SURFACE
OXIDES PRIOR TO APPLICATION OF COATING (*4*, *5*, *6*, *10*)

Metal	Chemical Pickle	Electrolytic Etch
Molybdenum	1 : 1 HNO_3	Anodic at 200–400 asf in 70% H_2SO_4 for 2–3 min.
	25% HNO_3 25% HF 100–300 g/1 potassium ferricanide	Anodic at 20–100 asf in 1 : 1 H_2SO_4-H_3PO_4 for 2–3 min min.
	100 g/1 potassium hydroxide 180–190° F	Anodic in 100 g/1 CrO_3 10 g/1 $Na_2Cr_2O_7$ at 350 asf for 2 min.
	$3HNO_3 : 2HF : 2H_2O$	100–300 asf 60 cycle a.c. in 10–50% HF for 2–3 min. Dip in alkali or HNO_3 to remove smut. 100–300 asf 60 cycle a.c. in 1 : 1 H_2SO_4-H_3PO_4 for 2–3 min. Dip in alkali or CrO_3 to remove smut.
Columbium	$3HNO_3 : 2HF : 2H_2O$	a.c. etch as for molybdenum.
Tantalum	$3HNO_3 : 2HF : 2H_2O$	a.c. etch as for molybdenum.
Tungsten		a.c. etch as for molybdenum. 1-5V 60 cycle a.c. in 5– 25% NaOH for 1–30 min.
Titanium	10–20% HNO_3, 2% HF	
Superalloys Co or Ni Base	$3HNO_3 : 2HF : 2H_2O$	1 : 1 H_2SO_4-H_3PO_4 as for molybdenum.

of nickel. The difference in thermal expansion between nickel and molybdenum alloys is quite large. Nickel forms a molybdate which is quite
oxidation-resistant and stable to the Ni-Mo eutectic (2400°F). A drawback to using nickel is that the molybdate spalls on cooling.

Chromium can be electroplated onto molybdenum with greater adherence than most other metals; chromium also alloys with molybdenum
forming an alloy that melts at about 3100°F. This alloy has good oxidation resistance and acts as a diffusion barrier to both the inward
diffusion of oxygen and the outward diffusion of molybdenum.

There are several reliable procedures which can be used to provide
adherent electroplates of chromium to molybdenum (*4–8*). Probably
the best is that developed by Brenner and Associates (*5, 8*). This involves anodically etching the molybdenum in equal volumes of sulfuric
acid and phosphoric acid at 20 to 100 amps/ft^2 for two to three minutes, followed by water rinsing and soaking for at least three minutes
in a solution composed of 6 per cent chromic acid, 15 per cent sul-

furic acid, and 15 per cent hydrochloric acid, followed by water rinsing again, and then plating in a conventional chromium bath. After the anodic etch, which effectively removes molybdenum trioxide and other surface scales, the soak in the chromic-sulfuric-hydrochloric acid pickling bath completely removes the viscous film left by the anodic etch. This step is necessary for obtaining reliable adhesion of the chromium plate to molybdenum.

The plating potential is applied to the cleaned molybdenum part prior to placing it in the chromium plating solution which minimizes the formation of undesirable surface deposits prior to plating. The point of electrical contact should be hastily rotated every fifteen seconds for the first minute, then once every minute for the next five to ten minutes, and then as necessary to obtain a uniform deposit (9). This rotation of the contact is necessary to obtain complete coverage of the base material and to prevent spotting which causes premature failure.

Chromium is best plated from a standard sulfate catalyzed chromic acid solution. A recommended concentration is 250 g/1 chromic acid and 2.5 g/l sulfuric acid which should be operated at 700 to 1200 amps/ft^2 and at 80 to 100°C. In general, the commercial, self-regulating type chromium plating solutions are not well suited for chromium plating molybdenum. Apparently, oxides are deposited from those solutions and this results in blistering either during the chromium plating process or, subsequently, during heating of the coated specimen. These latter types of chromium deposits are more difficult to plate with adherent nickel deposits than are conventional chromium deposits.

Although chromium itself is quite oxidation-resistant, chromium electrodeposits alone do not appear to provide reliable protection to molybdenum. The reason is not readily apparent, possibly because of the porosity of thin deposits, or because of the inherent cracked structure. However, the favorable aspects of the chromium-molybdenum system has led to many studies on the use of chromium as an intermediate layer in other electrodeposited coatings. Nickel has received by far the most attention as an outer coating. Metallurgically, a duplex coating of chromium on molybdenum with a nickel overcoat has many advantages over either material used above. Also, costs do not seem to be prohibitive.

In the early investigations of chromium-nickel coatings, difficulty was encountered with the formation of blisters between the chromium and nickel layers during heating and cooling. This has been overcome by Reid and Ogburn (8) with a procedure that provides improved adhesion of nickel plate to chromium. It consists of anodically etching the chromium-plated molybdenum in a 15 per cent sulfuric acid solution utilizing glacial acetic acid as the solvent at 30 to 70 amps/ft^2 until the surface of the chromium is covered with a dark brown film. A five-minute etch at about 40 amps/ft^2 was considered best. The specimen is then rinsed, given a Woods nickel strike and plated to the desired thickness in any nickel plating solution. Nickel may be plated from any desired solution that deposits a relatively stress-free, minimum-porosity coating. Generally, the Watts plating formulations are used.

Gold, platinum and palladium have been investigated as diffusion barriers for the chromium-nickel system. Sound chromium-nickel coatings on molybdenum have been known to fail in short time periods. This has been attributed to diffusion of the molybdenum through the coating and volatilizing as MoO_3. A diffusion barrier of gold will reduce this problem (6). Palladium has also been used for this purpose but appears to be no better than chromium. Gold has been applied to molybdenum over a chromium strike (6). The gold was plated from a modified cyanide solution. It seems likely that gold could also be plated directly on molybdenum from a citrate or chloride bath after the molybdenum has been prepared for plating by the sulfuric-phosphoric acid etch. Palladium can be plated directly onto molybdenum from the chloride bath after using the above cleaning procedure. Rhodium has been plated directly on tungsten and on intermediate layers of chromium and silicon from the sulfate solution.

Platinum may be plated on molybdenum by first applying a platinum flash from a fused cyanide plating bath and then building up a deposit using periodic reverse currents of five seconds cathodic and two seconds anodic. A deposit of two mils can be built-up which is protective up to one hr at 2500°F (11). Failure is due to pin holes and cracks in the deposits. However, deposits formed with the periodic reverse current cycling are superior in corrosion and high-temperature resistance to platinum plated by more conventional means.

Rhodium plated from many commercial preparations is highly stressed, usually cracked, quite porous and difficult to obtain in thicknesses over one mil thick. A plating bath containing 50 g/l rhodium chloride and 300 g/l hydrochloric acid operated at 70°C and 25 amps/ft^2 yielded deposits seven mils thick (11). Although no test data on this coating are available, deposits in these thicknesses would be expected to offer long term oxidation resistance to extreme temperatures. The cost of such deposits may prohibit any wide scale usage, however.

Cermet Electrodeposition

Electrodeposition of cermets from aqueous solutions has been investigated for high-temperature coating applications on metals and graphite (11—13). Hirakis (14) has cursorily investigated the electrodepositing of nickel-base cermets for protecting columbium. The technique of depositing cermets consists of suspending small ceramic particles less than 325 mesh in an agitated electroplating bath. As the metal is deposited, particles are occluded in the deposit. Any combination of an electroplatable metal and particles that do not react with the plating solution can be deposited by this technique. A typical photomicrograph of a chromium-tantalum boride cermet. so deposited, is shown in Figure 4.3. The particles are maintained in suspension by air agitation or by mechanical stirring. Particle size can range down from about 44 micron size to as small as desired. In most applications, a 3 to 25 micron diameter particles are preferred.

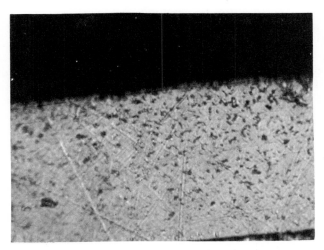

Fig. 4.3. Chromium-tantalum boride cermet.

The concentration of particles in a deposit varies with the plating metal matrix, particle size, and the operating conditions of the plating solution, and is limited to about 20 weight per cent when only mechanical agitation is used. However, if the particles are ball-milled with organic additive agents such as zein or benzoic acid prior to their addition to the plating bath, particle concentrations in the metal matrix may be increased.

Chromium-base cermets (*12, 13*), using zirconium and tungsten borides, zirconium nitride, and molybdenum carbide as the particulate materials, may be readily plated on the refractory metals and graphite. The substrate must be cleaned by the procedures outlined in Table 4.2 prior to application of the coating. Coatings up to 5 mils thick offer oxidation protection to graphite and the refractory metals for short-time operation (15 to 40 min), above 3000°F.

Metal-ceramic coatings containing a variety of oxide and hard metal particles have been prepared. Nickel, chromium, platinum, rhodium and cobalt-tungsten have been used as the metallic phase (*11*).

Cermet deposits suffer from the same drawbacks as many other electrodeposits, i.e., they can be porous and cracked. However, cermet electrodeposits do offer potential in high-temperature applications where the exposure times are short, when erosion conditions are severe, and where a thermal expansion match between a base metal and a pure ceramic outer coat constitutes a problem. The ceramic content of a cermet electrodeposit can be graded from a low to high concentration. Interest in this type of deposition technique is increasing due to the low cost of the process and its adaptability to production.

Fused Salts

Plating from fused salt solvents is commonly used for the electrowinning of metals. Very little effort has been devoted to electrodepositing coatings from fused salts for high-temperature use. Hirakis (*14*) has electrodeposited titanium, chromium, and aluminum for the protection of columbium and molybdenum from the following formulations:

SOME FUSED SALT COMPOSITIONS

For Titanium Deposition

K_2TiF_6	160 g	$1740^\circ F$
NaCl	840 g	720 amps/ft^2
Ti	200 g	steel anode

For Aluminum Deposition

$2NaF \cdot AlF_3$	450 g	$2010^\circ F$
NaF	500 g	144 amps/ft^2
Al_2O_3	150 g	
Al	40 g	

For Chromium Deposition

$KCl \cdot NaCl$ (equimolar)	242 g	$1380^\circ F$
Cr	40 g	72 to 216 amps/ft^2

Hirakis found that coatings of titanium and aluminum were easily obtained, but that the complete coverage of the specimen with chromium was impossible, particularly in the area of cathode contact. In an area already coated with chromium, cathode contact resulted in redissolution of the chromium layer in that area. Aluminum plating of columbium resulted in a columbium-aluminum compound, presumably $CbAl_3$, which was ductile but which developed fine cracks on deformation. These coatings were not oxidation-resistant at 2500°F.

Aluminum has been plated from fused chloride and bromide baths and from fused cryolite baths. The best (*7, 15*) chloride bath consisted of:

900 **g** aluminum chloride
200 g sodium chloride
Temperature 320-360°F
Tungsten anodes
Current density 10 to 40 amps/ft^2

The limiting thickness for smooth deposits from this plating bath is 0.001 in. After plating aluminum on nickel from this solution, heating from 1000 to 1400°F is required to form the nickel-aluminum alloy.

Optimum conditions for the chloride bath are (16):

440 g sodium chloride
560 g potassium chloride
150 g cryolite
Temperature 1832°F
Current density 100 to 200 amps/ft^2

Aluminum plated under these conditions alloys with nickel as deposition proceeds. It was found that at least two mils of aluminum were required to significantly improve the oxidation resistance relative to that provided by chromium-nickel plated molybdenum. The entire coating consisted of 1 mil of chromium, 7 mils of nickel, and 2 mils of aluminum diffused in the nickel.

Aluminum has also been deposited (16) on nickel-plated molybdenum from a eutectic mixture of 75 per cent cryolite with 25 per cent NaF at a temperature of 1840°F with a graphite anode. As aluminum was depleted by plating, it was recharged with the addition of aluminum oxide. The saturated concentration of aluminum oxide in the plating bath at 1800°F is 15 per cent. Deposition rates of 150 amps/ft^2 produced a deposit of 1.8 mils in 15 minutes.

The platinum group metals have been deposited from fused cyanide solutions for the protection of the refractory metals. Rhode (18) has investigated electroplating the platinum group metals from molten cyanide electrolytes. A eutectic mixture of sodium cyanide and potassium cyanide was operated at 932 to 1292°F. Rhodium, iridium, platinum, and platinum-rhodium alloys have been successfully deposited in coherent ductile deposits up to 10 mils thick (17, 18). The cyanide mixture is brought into a molten state under an argo atmosphere and the metal complex is formed by a.c. electrolysis at about 10 amps/ft^2 for one hr. The metal complex can be formed by plating in a normal fashion and the anode will dissolve to form the complex; however, the initial rate of metal deposition at the cathode will be rather slow until a reasonable metal concentration is built up in the solution. About 0.3 per cent metal complex in solution is the equilibrium concentration (18).

Rhodium baths are unstable; platinum-rhodium alloys can be plated, but the solution will decompose over a long period of time. A platinum-rhodium alloy will plate out at the cathode in the approximate concentration they are comprised in the anode. The preferred plating condition is an anode-to-cathode ratio of about 2 to 1 and a cathode current density of 5 to 25 amps/ft^2, 10 being optimum at a temperature of 1060 to 1112°F. Table 4.3 gives data on the various metals plated.

TABLE 4.3. OXIDATION RESISTANCE OF PLATINUM GROUP
METAL COATINGS PLATED FROM FUSED CYANIDES
ON THE REFRACTORY METALS

Metals	Thickness of Plate, Mils	Base Metal	Temperature of Test, °F	Protective Life, hrs
Platinum	1	Molybdenum	2000	48
Platinum	1.9	Molybdenum	2500	1.2
Platinum	5	Tungsten	3000	5
Iridium	2	Molybdenum	1832	0.5*
Platinum — 10% rhodium	2	Molybdenum	2500	24

*Sample still good after ½ hr

Presumably, nonporous coatings of platinum, rhodium, iridium, and their alloys would offer some high-temperature protection to the refractory before diffusion causes difficulty. These cyanide plating formulations may be used to apply adherent initial electrodeposits on molybdenum or tungsten. The base metals are degreased, edges prepared, and then placed in the fused cyanide plating baths. They may either be allowed to soak for 1 to 5 min. or be given a reverse current etch at 10 to 25 amps/ft^2 for 1 to 3 min. before a platinum group metal is deposited over them. A flash deposit may be applied and then the desired subsequent coat applied or a thickness may be built up for the particular application. The fused cyanide electroplating process is presently the only one that can be used to build up thick, ductile, crack-free deposits of the platinum group metals and their alloys.

Organic Solvents

Little effort has been devoted to applying coatings from organic solvents by electrodeposition for high-temperature applications. Brenner (*19–22*) and associates have investigated deposition of a variety of metals from organic solvents, but the only significant success has been the electrodeposition of aluminum from a diethyl ether solvent (*19, 20*). The bath consists of 265 to 400 g/l AlCl$_3$ and 4 to 8 g/l LiAlH$_4$ or LiH operated in a closed container at 5 to 50 amps/ft^2. Moisture and oxygen must be excluded from the bath to prevent its decomposition. This bath can be used to plate aluminum over nickel deposits and subsequently heated to 1000 to 1392°F to form the nickel-aluminum alloy for improved oxidation resistance. An alloy of beryllium and boron has also been deposited from an ether solvent (*23*). Although this coating was not investigated for high-temperature applications, it has potentials since the borides, and particularly the beryllides, have excellent oxidation resistance at very high temperatures (*24, 25*).

The Bureau of Mines (*26*) has reported excellent deposits of tin-nickel from a variety of organic solvents. Acetamide, and ethylene glycol were found to be best for depositing the tin-nickel alloy. The deposits were less stressed and afforded a general improvement over those obtained from an aqueous solution. This could provide an idea for electrodepositing more reliable coatings, because the characteristic stress and porosity of platings from aqueous solution are often a significant factor in reliability.

Platinum may be deposited from a cyanide alcohol solution. Although the efficiency is quite low, such deposits are potentially useful at high temperatures. The advantages of depositing metals from organic solvents are worthy of additional investigations.

Electrophoresis

Although electrophoresis is not the same as electroplating, it is akin to it and is therefore treated here as an electrodeposition technique. The electrophoretic deposition technique consists of suspending particles generally less than 325 mesh in size in an organic dielectric solvent, and impressing a direct current of 50 to 500 volts between two electrodes, thus causing the particles to deposit on one of the electrodes. The most effective voltage gradient depends upon the solvent, particle size distribution, and the materials being used, and must be determined empirically and by practical experimentation for each case. The particles are either negatively or positively charged depending on the particle, the solvent, and addition agents used. Electrophoretic deposits are a reasonably firm, compact coating, but care must be exercised in handling them because the individual particles are loosely bound to each other and are easily dislodged. As an example, strong running water may ruin an electrophoretic deposit.

Electrophoretic deposits require a series of posttreatments to obtain high-density, well-bonded coatings as shown in Figure 4.4 which covers the method developed by the Vitro Corporation. Densification is accomplished generally by sintering the as-deposited coating, and even higher densities can be obtained by pressing before sintering. Pressing can be accomplished by isostatic means, by mechanical pressing, by ball burnishing, or gas pressure bonding (*50*). Electrophoretic deposition and the treatment of the subsequent deposit have been covered in detail by several authors (*27–31*).

A variety of organic solvents can be used as the suspension medium, but pyridine, nitromethane (propane), isopropyl alcohol, and petroleum ether are most frequently used. One method of preparing the suspension is by ball milling 2 g of particles to 100 ml of solvent with appropriate

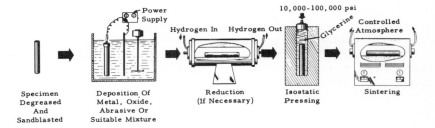

ADVANTAGES OF VITRO PROCESS

- Excellent Uniformity Is Obtained.
- Coating Thickness Can Be Readily Controlled.
- Process Is Versatile. Alloys, Cermets, Etc. Of Controlled Composition Can Be Deposited.

- Coating Is Metallurgically Bonded And Impervious.
- Heavy Coatings Can Be Deposited Rapidly.
- Power Consumption Is Low.
- Process Is Readily Applicable To Irregularly-Shaped Articles.

Fig. 4.4. Vitro electrophoretic coating process.

addition agents for a few hours, and then electrolyzing at the selected operating voltage while stirring to keep the particles in suspension.

For metals, 2 g of –325 mesh or smaller metal particles per 100 ml of isopropyl alcohol are ball milled for 2 to 16 hrs. The alcohol is decanted, 10 ml of acetone added for each 2 g of metal, and the mixture ball-milled for an additional period of at least 30 minutes. Additions of 1 g/100 ml benzoic acid, 1/2 g/100 ml zein and 1 ml/100 ml of buty-tamine, and ball milling a few minutes for good mixing completes the preparation. The dispersion is transferred to a suitable plating container and electrophoretically deposited at the selected voltage while agitating to maintain suspension. Each metal or combination of metals (alloy composition) will deposit most effectively at a particular voltage and this voltage must be determined for each set of conditions. Example of an electrophoretically coated tap is shown in Figure 4.5.

Nonmetals are ball-milled in isopropyl alcohol as in the case of metals: the alcohol is decanted, 10 ml of nitromethane per 2 g of particles added and the mixture ball milled for about 15 minutes. Addition of 1 g/100 ml of benzoic acid, 1/2 g/100 ml of zein, and a final ball milling of the entire mixture for about seven minutes completes the preparation.

Many attempts to deposit metals and nonmetals simultaneously by various combinations of the above procedures have been unsuccessful. However, Werner (29) deposited mixtures of metals and nonmetals simultaneously from a mixed solution of isopropyl and nitromethane with zein as an addition agent. Some examples are superalloys, tantalum-chromium, tantalum-tungsten, $BeO-Al_2O_3$.

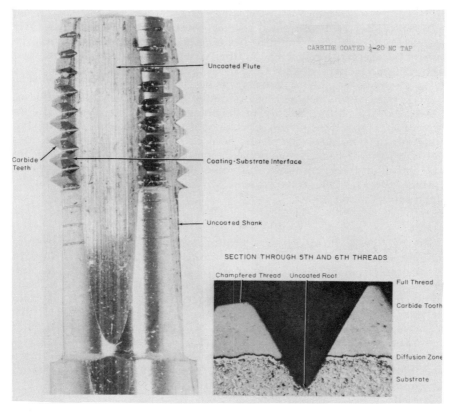

Uncoated Flute

Carbide Teeth

Coating-Substrate Interface

Uncoated Shank

SECTION THROUGH 5TH AND 6TH THREADS

Champfered Thread   Uncoated Root

Full Thread

Carbide Tooth

Diffusion Zone

Substrate

(Courtesy of Vitro Laboratories)
Fig. 4.5. Example of an electrophoretically coated tap.

An "as-deposited" electrophoretic deposit is referred to as a "green" coating. Many commercial firms have proprietary addition agents to improve the green strength of electrophoretic deposits in order to lessen the chance of damaging the powdery deposit. Polymeric materials such as ethyl cellulose and cellulose acetate have been used to improve the green strength of electrophoretic deposits (*31*). An effective method to permit handling of electrophoretic deposits prior to densification is to spray it (encapsulate it) with an acrylate-type resin.

Prior to sintering an electrophoretic deposit, it is advisable to press it to achieve densities in excess of about 80 per cent of the theoretical density. Isostatic pressing is commonly used. This is accomplished by bagging the deposit in a natural rubber or other suitable bag (*29*), and pressing at 40 to 100 tons/inch^2. After pressing, the deposit is sintered at the appropriate temperature of the coating material. Densities on the order of 97 per cent theoretical can be obtained by this technique. The new technique of gas pressure bonding (*50*) can be used to achieve essentially theoretical density. In this case, pressing and sintering are accomplished simultaneously.

The electrodeposition of cermets was described in the aqueous solution section. However, if the particles are ball-milled and an organic addition agent used, the charge density of the particles is increased and the concentration of particles in an electrodeposited matrix can be doubled. Although no conclusive proof has been shown that electrophoresis does occur in a highly conductive solvent of an electroplating bath, evidence indicates that there are electrophoretic effects since the particle concentration increases when the charge on the particles suspended in the plating bath increases.

SPRAYING METHODS

The two basic processes of spraying materials for high-temperature coatings are flame spraying and arc plasma spraying. Regardless of the process used, spraying involves three stages: (1) heating the material to be sprayed to form molten or semimolten droplets in a flame or plasma, (2) projecting these heated particles at a high velocity onto the part being coated, and (3) the collision of the hot particles with this part, where they adhere to the part to form the final coating. No other treatment is needed except possibly machining if a smooth surface is desired. The methods whereby the spraying material is supplied to the heating zone of the gun or torch and the methods of heating the material for impingement on the parts are quite diverse.

The spray materials are supplied to the hot zone of the spray gun in wire, rod and powder form. The spray material is fed into a flame or arc for heating and propelled to the object being coated. The flame guns use oxygen as the oxidizer and generally acetylene, hydrogen, or propane, as the fuel, while the arc plasma spray gun generally employs a controlled arc between two electrodes to ionize a flowing gas such as argon or nitrogen, causing a liberation of much heat. These various processes and techniques for spraying coatings and the properties of the coatings so produced have been described many times (*32—41*). Galli (*42*), for example, has presented a critical review and examination of the processes of flame spraying, including a bibliography through 1958. However, no such critical review of plasma arc spraying has come to the author's attention.

Flame Spraying

The commercially available flame-spraying equipment are either of the wire or powder type. The wire or rod is fed into the cone of the flame where droplets melt, are atomized, and are propelled by the flow of the gases to the substrate. One of the advantages of this type of spray gun is that the propelled material must become molten before it can be released from the wire and projected to the object being coated. Molten particles striking this object will obviously produce coatings that are superior to those formed by powder particles which are incompletely melted before striking the part. The limitations are that spray materials must be capable of being drawn into wires or made into rods and often large droplets melt off the wire without being completely atomized. These droplets result in rough, uneven, and poorly bonded coatings.

General Mills (*43*) has developed a flame spray gun that employs the expulsion of burning gases from a rocket nozzle to melt a wire and propel the molten particles onto the base material at velocities greater than the speed of sound. Its advantages are the higher temperatures that can be achieved as the fuel (propane) and oxygen expand through the nozzle and ignite, and higher velocity particles impinge on the substrate. The higher initial temperature and higher velocity cause a greater portion of the particles to reach the substrate in a molten state. The higher velocity also increases the flow of the particle at the surface, resulting in a denser sprayed coating.

Powder-type spray guns employ the same principle as the wire gun, except that powder (about 200 to 325 mesh) is fed into the cone of the oxygen-gas flame. With this type of gun, the particles may not become completely molten while they are in the flame. Galli (*42*) measured the residence time of a particle in the flame and the time in transit from the flame to a substrate 20 cm away. The maximum time in the flame is about 4.6 milliseconds and transit time is about 1.6 milliseconds. Thus, large particles with poor thermal conductivities and/or low total hemispherical emissivity are unlikely to be completely molten on striking the substrate. The outstanding advantage of the powder-type spray technique is that coatings with practically any desired composition can be made by blending several powders. Multifeeders can also be used to grade or blend materials for producing a better thermal expansion match with the substrate material, and other desired properties.

The Linde Company's "flame plating" apparatus operates on a different principle from that just described. Powder and a carrier gas are fed into an oxygen-acetylene gun chamber which detonates about four times a second and propels the particles in each detonation front at 9600 ft/sec at 8000°F and at a pressure of 47 atm. The particles impact on the substrate, however, at about 2400 ft/sec. The rate of deposition is about 1/4 mil over a one in. circular area for each detonation or about a mil a sec.*

---

*Although this spray gun is not commercially available, it is available on a contractual basis at the Linde Company facilities.

Arc Plasma Spraying

The principles of arc plasma spraying are the same as for powder flame spraying. The high temperatures (about 10,000 to 20,000°K) created in the plasma arc potentially assures that all particles are in a molten state, with consequently improved coating characteristics. Any material that will melt without decomposition can be sprayed by the arc plasma process. In addition, oxygen-sensitive materials can be sprayed, since the carrier gas in the plasma can be neutral or reducing. Coatings obtained by plasma spraying are much denser than comparable flame-sprayed coatings. This is primarily because hotter particles impinge on the substrate. Figure 4.6 illustrates a plasma gun that was developed into a compact hand tool for use by skilled personnel.

Materials that are frequently used in coating for high temperature applications are best sprayed by the plasma process in a neutral or reducing atmosphere. As an example, aluminum or silicon sprayed by the flame process forms a thin oxide layer around each particle, which results in powdery, loosely adherent coatings which cannot be further compacted by heating and will not react metallurgically to form a desired alloy or intermetallic system. On the other hand, these dense coatings are not always desired. The thermal shock resistance of porous

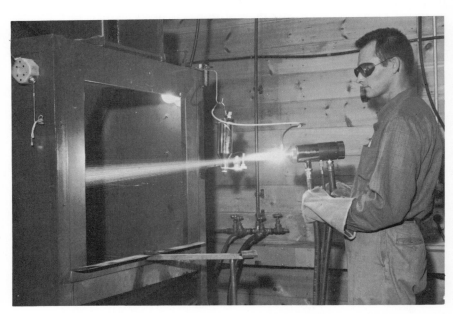

(Courtesy of Thermal Dynamics Corp.)
Fig. 4.6. Compact aimable plasma gun.

coatings is much better, and often erosion protection or thermal insulation is more important than high density since all sprayed coatings are slightly porous. Materials can also be readily sprayed with the arc process by using a neutral or reducing atmosphere rather than argon or nitrogen, providing the spraying materials react favorably to this environment.

The Schoop Electro-Pistole (44) is an arc spray gun that works on a different principle from that of the more conventional arc plasma guns. The "nozzle" end of the gun consists of two wires composed of the materials to be sprayed which are used as the electrodes for the arc discharge. As the electrodes form an arc, the tips of the wires become molten and are atomized and propelled to the substrate by an inert gas stream. The frequency of discharge and deposition rate is controlled by the feed rate of the wires.

Sprayed coatings produced by any of the techniques described are restricted to substrates of simple, regular shapes because coverage can only be achieved along the line of sight to the spray gun. Internal and deeply recessed surfaces sometimes cannot be effectively coated and excess thicknesses tend to build up on corners and edges if the operator is not careful. Attachments have been developed that allow for the spraying of internal shapes.

Sprayed coatings by all processes are porous, although plasma-sprayed coatings are the least so. Post-treatments, such as glass impregnation (45) or hot dipping in aluminum (14), are frequently employed to overcome this difficulty. Another way of overcoming it is to have the coatings made quite thick (about 10 mils or more). However, this creates a weight problem in many cases and results in poor adhesion or high stress in the coatings.

The adhesion of a sprayed coating is generally rather poor. The bond of the coating to the substrate and between the particles in the coating is almost entirely mechanical. In some cases, particularly with plasma-sprayed coatings, chemical bonds are believed to exist. There are two excellent treatments on the adhesion of sprayed coatings (32, 41).

In spite of these noted limitations, sprayed coatings for the protection of molybdenum (46–49) have been investigated extensively. There also has been some interest shown in protecting columbium by sprayed coatings (14, 45).

The application of a sprayed coating is relatively simple. It generally consists of grit-blasting the parts to be coated to provide a rough surface for improved mechanical adhesion, which is the principal adhesion mechanism. The parts are then chemically pickled or vapor-blasted to produce a chemically clean surface. The desired coating composition is then sprayed by a flame or arc process. Post-treatments, such as heating to fuse and/or densify, and impregnation, are generally accomplished on the sprayed coating before service or test.

The actual spraying operation is performed in short intervals so as not to overheat the substrate, which causes oxidation during coating. The distance between the gun and substrate varies but is on the order of 4 to 18 in. Continual spraying can be accomplished if the substrate is cooled with an inert atmosphere blast or maintained in an inert atmosphere. There is a good deal of "art" involved in applying spray coatings, and the reliability of these coatings depends on this art and the experience of the spray operator. Coating compositions that are sprayed as coatings for the protection of substrates at high temperatures are covered in Chapter 2.

CLADDING METHODS

Cladding is one of the early methods used in developing coatings for molybdenum. It is an ideal method for reliably applying a continuous chemically and metallurgically sound coating layer of metal to sheets, rods, and other objects of simple shape. The paramount limitations of cladding are: the simple shape requirement; the metallurgical problems of diffusion, bond strength, and the formation of low-melting alloys or brittle intermetallics; and the problem of protecting corners, ends, and edges after a clad sheet or rod has been cut.

There are two principal techniques by which cladding is accomplished. The most common one is to capsulate the base metal with the cladding material and roll or forge while hot. A recently developed technique in which gas pressure bonding of cladding layers to a base material is used, has shown great promise (50).

Roll Cladding

In roll cladding, one starts by building a frame, sometimes called a yoke, that fits around the core material to be protected, and then cutting the cladding sheet to fit over the core and frame as illustrated in Figure 4.7. The assembly is then heated in an inert or reducing atmosphere and rolled while hot to effect bonding. A reduction in over-all thickness of

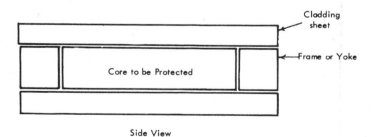

Side View

Fig. 4.7. Core with frame and cladding sheet ready for bonding.

about 20 per cent per rolling pass is common practice. On the first pass, a reduction of up to about 40 per cent is often used to insure bonding (51). It is common practice to weld the frame and cladding sheets before heating and rolling. This decreases the chance of internal oxidation during heating and rolling. This technique is commonly known as "canning." However, some cladding materials that form stable surface oxide films prevent bonding from taking place during this rolling. This problem has been experienced even on assemblies that have been "canned" prior to the heating and rolling operation. This has been prevented (51) by welding a tube on the edge of the assembly, pressure testing under water for defects in the welding, evacuating the air in the assembly, and sealing the tube under vacuum. The assembly can then be heated in air and rolled with more success, since no atmospheric contamination of any materials would be present.

Electroplating the cladding material to prevent oxide formation has also been done effectively. In addition, the electroplated layer, if of the proper material, may serve a useful function to promote bonding between the cladding and base metal and act as a diffusion barrier. This technique has been used to bond stainless steel to molybdenum (51). Nickel was electroplated on the stainless prior to heating and roll-cladding. Forging is sometimes used, but is not as effective as rolling. It should be noted that though cleaning of all materials is necessary before the process is started, cotton gloves are used for handling to prevent contamination.

Clad sheets must be cut to manufacture hardware components. Protection of the edges must then be accomplished to prevent oxidation of the core. For core sheets greater than about 40 mils thick, a narrow cladding material strip or wire can be welded to the overlay clad sheets. On thinner core sections as well as on thick sections, a technique was developed (51) for chemically or electrolytically dissolving out the core material from between the cladding sheets to a desired depth. A filler wire may then be inserted in the cavity left by the dissolved core. It may be welded directly in place or the claddings lapped over before welding.

As stated earlier, cladding is an ideal coating technique for protecting parts of simple shape. The reliability of roll clad coatings is well established. In some cases, it is advantageous to form an intermetallic bridge between the cladding and base metal to serve as a bond between them, to retard diffusion of the two metals, and to act as an oxygen diffusion barrier. Experimentally, such a system has shown promise (52). In this case, aluminum was applied as a barrier prior to roll-cladding of platinum on molybdenum. Another possibility is the use of chromium for cladding columbium systems.

Roll cladding of powder deposits applied to a core may also be accomplished to achieve a clad layer composition that is not already available in sheet form. Complex, idealized metallurgical systems could be accomplished by this technique. Powder deposits can be applied to core materials by spraying, painting, slurry dipping, or electrophoresis. The aluminum-clad steel which has recently become available is made by electrophoretically depositing aluminum to steel with successive rolling and heating treatments (*53*).

Metal Cladding by Gas-Pressure Bonding (*50*)

Gas-pressure bonding has been found ideal as a cladding technique. Cladding by this technique consists of preparing the assembly in the same manner as for roll cladding, except that the clad must be evacuated and sealed around the base metal. The assembly is then heated to an elevated temperature in an autoclave containing an inert gas at high pressure. The pressure and temperature are maintained long enough to permit solid state bonding between the cladding and the base material. By the gas-pressure bonding technique, the cladding material can be conveniently applied to the core as a powder; the coated core is then placed in an evacuated expendable container. The isostatic pressure in the autoclave is uniformly transmitted throughout the container, and the particles are bonded into a solid sheet on the core material. Gas-pressure bonding has the advantage that no deformation is required. For this reason, and because of the uniformity of pressure, very brittle base materials and objects of complex geometrical shapes may be clad. Cladding by gas pressure bonding obviously holds great promise for overcoming many of the difficulties inherent in roll cladding. The major limitations of this process are the cladding of closed cavities that would collapse under high pressure and the part size limitation imposed by reasonable autoclave sizes.

Vapor (Gas) Deposition Method

Vapor or gas deposition, for the purpose of the following discussion, is defined as any technique in which the coating material is carried in the gaseous state to a heated substrate whereon the coating material is deposited, the gas vehicle going off as a waste product. The mechanisms by which the coating element is deposited are chemical reduction, condensation, pyrolysis or thermal decomposition, and displacement.

Pack Cementation Technique. One of the most important types of coating on both the research and the commercial scale is the diffusion coating formed by the vapor deposition of a coating from a granulated or powdered pack of solid materials onto a heated substrate. At the coating temperature the deposited elements interdiffuse with the substrate forming the coating system.

This vapor deposition technique is commonly called pack cementation (*54—58*). It consists of first packing the substrate to be coated in a retort with a powder mixture of the coating elements to be deposited and an activator, carrier or gaseous transport agent, as seen in Figures 4.8, 4.9, 4.10. The retort, which may or may not be sealed, is then heated either in a vacuum or an inert reducing atmosphere, to a predetermined reaction temperature, and held at that temperature until a sufficient coating thickness is deposited. Usually, the pack powder composition contains 50 to 90 per cent of an inert powder material such as Al_2O_3 or SiO_2 in order to prevent sintering (or cementation) of the pack. The inert filter also makes the pack technique more economical. The activator or carrier is generally a halide salt which reacts with the elements to be deposited to form a volatile compound; this is transferred to the surface of the substrate where it reacts in accordance with one of the reaction mechanisms given above to deposit the coating element. The halide gas either volatizes or reacts with another coating element.

As an example, the pack process is typified by the siliconizing or siliciding process. The substrate to be coated can be cleaned by one of the methods mentioned above. The pack mixture is prepared by thor-

(Courtesy of The Pfaudler Co.)

Fig. 4.8. Packing five molybdenum alloy samples prior to pack cementation coating.

(Courtesy of Chromalloy Corp.)
Fig. 4.9. View of line of furnaces and some typical retorts.

(Courtesy of Chromalloy Corp.)
Fig. 4.10. Loaded retort being removed from gas-fired furnace.

oughly mixing silicon powder, aluminum oxide, and a halide salt such as NaF. The many coating applications vary the particle sizes used and the ratios of coating elements, inert filler, and activator. A nominal composition ratio is 20 g of silicon powder to 80 g of aluminum oxide with 2 g of sodium fluoride. The particle sizes may vary from about 20 mesh to 325 mesh, but the larger sizes are generally preferred. The activator is varied from about 1/2 to 10 per cent by weight. The cleaned parts are embedded in the powder mixture in a retort which may or may not be sealed (Figure 4.8). The packed retort is then heated to a temperature of 1800 to 2200°F in a vacuum or in an inert or reducing atmosphere for 2 to 16 hours. Both the temperature and the heating time required depend on the substrate being coated. After the retort has cooled to room temperature, the coated substrate is removed and the pack powders simply brushed from it.

As an alternative, and perhaps better approach, the metal powder and aluminum oxide are mixed together without the halide activator salt. The activator is sprinkled in the bottom of the retort, the metal powder and filler are added, the substrates packed therein, and then the retort is sealed and vented with a small hole at the top. The activator volatilizes up through the pack, forming the coating metal halide, which, in turn, deposits the coating metal on the substrate. This variation has recently been shown to provide a more uniform coating that provides longer-term protection and greater stability. For further economy in the pack process, which is a factor of considerable importance in coating parts that are several feet in a given dimension, the coating element (used singularly or diluted with a filler, with or without an activator salt) is suspended in a vehicle such as lacquer, water, etc., and is applied to the substrate by dipping, brushing, or spraying. The coated part is then packed in a retort of Al_2O_3 containing a layer of activator in the bottom. The retort is then heated, wherein the coating element forms the halide as before and is deposited and diffused into the substrate. This latter technique can represent a substantial economy because the cost of filling a retort several feet in size can run to several thousand dollars (as much as $25,000 or more).

Chromizing and siliciding are the most common of the coatings applied by the pack technique. These will be used as examples to indicate the possible mechanisms of deposition; however neither the theoretical formulas nor the available data are sufficient to establish all the reactions that may occur in applying coatings by the pack technique. Three reaction mechanisms that can be used to illustrate the process of chromizing iron, using a chloride activator, are (*54*):

Displacement $\quad\quad\quad\quad Fe_{(alloy)} + CrCl_2 \longrightarrow FeCl_{2(g)} + Cr_{(alloy)}$

Reduction (hydrogen) $\quad H_{2(g)} + CrCl_2 \longrightarrow 2\ HCl_{(g)} + Cr_{(alloy)}$

Thermal decomposition $\quad CrCl_2 \longrightarrow Cl_{2(g)} + Cr_{(alloy)}$

One well-used technique for chromizing iron is to pack chromium powder, ammonium chloride, and aluminum oxide in a retort with an iron alloy. The exact chemistry has not been documented, but reaction steps which could occur are as follows (54):

(1) $NH_4Cl_{(g)} \longrightarrow NH_{3(g)} + HCl_{(g)}$

(2) $2NH_{(g)} \longrightarrow N_{2(g)} + 3H_{2(g)}$

(3) $Cr_{(powder)} + 2HCl_{(g)} \longrightarrow CrCl_{2(g)} + H_{2(g)}$

(4) $CrCl_2 + Fe_{(alloy)} \longrightarrow FeCl_{2(g)} + Fe\text{-}Cr_{(alloy)}$

Several thermodynamic and kinetic requirements must be fulfilled for the reactions to proceed as shown. First, the vapor pressure of the activators or carriers must be sufficiently high at the coating temperature for the reaction to proceed. The activator should have a boiling point slightly above the temperature of coating to provide a reservoir for reaction without volatilizing away too rapidly (55). The coating element halide should have a boiling point below the coating temperature to saturate the pack. This involves reactions (1) and (3). The volatility of the by-product of the coating reaction must be high; fast removal prevents the formation of a barrier to continued deposition for the coating element, and also avoids contamination of the coating.

In addition, the thermodynamic stability of the carriers must be slightly greater than the stability of the formed coating element halide to maintain a reservoir of halide activator for continued reaction (55). The coating element halide must be more stable than the substrate halide formed to prevent an exchange reaction at the surface. In the case of chromizing an iron alloy, a double displacement or exchange reaction can occur (54).

Coating proceeds by the transport of the gaseous halides between the activator, coating element powder, and the susbstrate. Consequently, as stated earlier, the particle size of the pack powders should be relatively large to prevent packing and sintering (cementation) of the pack to impair the diffusion rates of the gases.

In the reaction cited above, hydrogen is evolved in reaction (2), which can reduce the chromium chloride in reaction (4). However, since hydrogen is quite volatile at reaction temperatures, displacement is the main reaction. In the case of chromizing coating temperatures are generally too low for any applicable thermal decomposition to occur in the case of chromium halides. However for some less stable materials, some thermal decomposition may occur.

According to the reactions that occur in using the ammonium halide carriers presented for chromizing iron, these carriers could not be used in applying coatings to columbium and tantalum. Both hydrogen and nitrogen gas are formed, and it has been shown (57) that these gases are absorbed interstitially in Cb and Ta, causing severe embrittlement. Consequently, ammonium halides should be avoided when coating columbium and tantalum.

Klopp (55) presented reactions for the siliconizing of tantalum which is basically an oxidation-reduction reaction, with the coating element, after deposition, being continually removed through diffusion into the substrate. Sodium fluoride was used as an activator. The reactions are:

$$(1) \ 6NaF_{(g)} + 2Si \xrightarrow[\text{(powder)}]{} Si_2F_{6(g)} + 6Na_{(g)}$$

$$(2) \ 2Si_2F_{6(g)} \longrightarrow 3SiF_{4(g)} + Si(TaSi_2)_{(g)}$$

$$(3) \ 3SiF_{4(g)} + Si \xrightarrow[\text{(powder)}]{} 2Si_2F_{6(g)}$$

These reactions can be generalized as follows:

$$(1) \ MX_{(g)} + C \xrightarrow[\text{(powder)}]{} CX_{(g)} + M_{(g)}$$

$$(2) \ CX_{(g)} + S_{(g)} \longrightarrow C(SC)$$

where

M is the cation of the halide salt
X is a halide (Cl, F,)
C is the coating element
S is the substrate

If the rules for volatilities and thermodynamics of the halides (as stated earlier) are followed, the reaction can be used for aluminizing, siliciding, or chromizing and similar processing. In the selection of the best halide activator for depositing a given coating element, reference should be made to the accumulated thermodynamic and vapor pressure data given in references (55) and (56).

High-temperature coatings applied by the pack technique are generally complex and involve more than one coating element. It is not uncommon in silicide coatings for the refractory metals to contain three to five coating elements other than silicon. In the simultaneous deposition of such multicomponent coatings, it is frequently possible to use a mixture of halide carriers such as sodium chloride, potassium iodide, and ammonium chloride which are made up of the best selected carrier for each element. In some cases, it is necessary to compromise and select a carrier which has some favorable properties for each element being deposited. The deposition of complex coatings is influenced by the relative vapor pressure of each coating element halide with respect to the other coating elements halides, and by the rate of diffusion of the coating element in the substrate alone and in conjunction with the other elements.

In practically all diffusion type coatings applied by this technique, the rate of diffusion of the coating element in the substrate is the rate-controlling step. Diffusion of the deposited element into a substrate may be expected to be high for elements forming compounds with the substrate and to decrease with increasing melting points of the coating elements. However, in the case of chromium, deposition rates are slow, probably because of the stability of chromium halides. Chromium forms compounds with columbium and molybdenum, but deposition rates are rather slow. Gadd (56), in a simultaneous deposition of titanium and chromium in a vacuum pack, has shown the influence of the titanium vapor on the deposition of chromium on columbium alloys.

Chemical and Pyrolytic Reaction Techniques

Pyrolysis involves the passing of a coating element compound, in the gaseous state, over a substrate contained in a chamber through which the atmosphere can flow freely. The substrate is heated to a temperature at which the coating compound is chemically reduced or is thermally decomposed to form an adherent coating. Reduction is commonly accomplished with hydrogen; however, stronger reducing agents such as zinc, magnesium or sodium may be used. Coating by displacement may be accomplished, but this is most commonly done by the pack technique.

Any material may be deposited as a coating by this technique if it forms a compound that can be vaporized at a relatively low temperature without decomposition and yet is sufficiently unstable to be chemically reduced or thermally decomposed at a coating temperature. This temperature is higher than the vaporization temperature of the material, but the material should not have appreciably high vapor pressure at the coating temperature. The requirements and details of vapor plating by this technique has been treated in detail by Powell, Campbell and Gonser (59) and in a Defense Metal Information Center Report (54). Chemical and pyrolytic deposition are commonly carried out in a vapor-phase reaction chamber and, most recently, in a fluidized bed.

Vapor Phase Reactions

A typical vapor-phase deposition chamber is illustrated in Figure 4.11. There are a great many variations in such a deposition chamber that are dictated by the characteristics of the material being deposited, by the temperature of deposition, and by the substrate being coated. If the compound being deposited is a gas at room temperature, there is no need for a vaporization chamber or for passing a gas through the chamber to carry the coating compound vapors into the deposition chamber. Gaseous coating compounds can be bled directly into the deposition chamber. For compounds that are thermally decomposed on the heated substrate, there is no need for a reducing gas. Substrates that cannot be heated by induction must be heated by radiation— a fact which affects both the design and materials of construction of a deposition chamber. Often the plating gases are not just passed through an

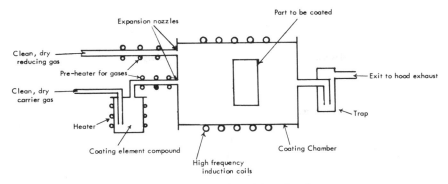

Fig. 4.11. Vapor deposition chamber.

expansion nozzle into the chamber, but rather are directed over the part being coated through tubes, in a manner similar to a sprinkling system. However, such a system, as shown in Figure 4.11, is typical in concept and can easily be modified to meet individual requirements.

Vapor deposition of high-temperature coatings in a free-flow chamber has been centered around the silicide systems. Molybdenum silicide coatings have been formed on molybdenum by the hydrogen reduction of silicon tetrachloride at 2000 to 3200°F (*60, 61*). Molybdenum silicide coatings have also been vapor-deposited on columbium and tantalum (*55, 61—63*). An apparatus similar to that shown in Figure 4.11 was used. These types of coatings are generally deposited with a $H_2/SiCl_4$ ratio of 1 to 3. The vaporization temperature of the silicon tetrachloride is about 150°C. At the deposition temperature, the deposited silicon diffuses into the base metal and forms the silicide. Coating times range from 1/2 to 4 hrs in which about 1/2 to 3 mils of silicon is deposited. This rapid deposition rate of silicon is faster than the rate of diffusion of silicon into the substrate. Consequently, the excess silicon build-up on the surface is frequently brittle, cracked, and nonadherent. In addition, the high deposition temperature frequently recrystallizes the refractory base metals. The use of hydrogen as the reducing gas is subject to the embrittlement of the columbium and tantalum. However, Fansteel (*62*) reports that embrittlement does not occur at temperatures above 2300°F as hydrogen has a very low solubility in tantalum at this temperature.

Fansteel has vapor-deposited molybdenum silicide on columbium and tantalum by two methods (*62, 64*): (1) simultaneous hydrogen reduction of silicon from the tetrachloride and molybdenum from the pentachloride at 1300 to 1500°C to form $MoSi_2$; (2) deposition of MoO_3 by immersion of the substrate in liquid MoO_3 at 1470°F reducing the

MoO_3 with hydrogen at 1470°F and siliciding the molybdenum coating by the deposition of silicon from the hydrogen reduction of silicon tetrachloride. The author has used a similar approach for forming molybdenum and tungsten silicide coatings on columbium.

Molybdenum or tungsten is first applied to a columbium or tantalum substrate by the hydrogen reduction of molybdenum or tungsten fluoride to a thickness of 1 to 5 mils. The coated substrates are then given a modified silicide coating by the pack technique. These coatings, although still in the initial development stages, appear quite promising, since the molybdenum and tungsten silicides are appreciably more protective than the corresponding silicide on tantalum and columbium, and form excellent diffusion barriers which prevent the coating from diffusing with the base metal. Investigations are in progress to deposit the molybdenum and tungsten from a fluidized bed-iodide chamber to avoid the hydrogen embrittlement problems inherent in the hydrogen reduction of the molybdenum and tungsten fluoride.

Vapor deposition of a Cr-Ti-Si* coating, which is presently applied by the pack technique at reduced pressure, is currently being studied (65). Preliminary results have shown that it is difficult to obtain a deposit of Cr-Ti on columbium by this technique. The vapor deposition of zirconium oxide from the isopropyloxide to form an oxidation-resistant coating is currently being investigated (70).

Fluidized Bed

The fluidized bed technique has recently attracted considerable interest for applying coatings for high-temperature use. Several organizations are currently investigating this technique, which is somewhat of a cross between pack cementation and vapor deposition in free-flow chambers. The state-of-the-art of fluidized beds in the petroleum industry is well established (72, 73) and beds 50 feet in diameter are not uncommon. The rapid heat transfer and temperature uniformity in fluidized beds has led to the investigation of this method for applying high-temperature coatings to large objects of diverse shapes. It is quite difficult to coat such objects uniformly by other presently used means.

A fluidized bed consists of a mass of finely divided solids, contained in a column, that has been brought into a fluidized state by the lifting action of a gas on the solids as it rises through the column. The velocity of the gas in the column must be sufficient to overcome the aerodynamic drag on the particles, for fluidization to occur. A schematic of a fluidized bed is shown in Figure 4.13.

There are several variations in the operation of a fluidized bed. Its operation is shown in Figure 4.12. The vaporized halide is carried by a gas into the fluidized bed where it reacts with the coating metal powder

---

*Coating developed by Thompson-Roma Wooldridge Corp.

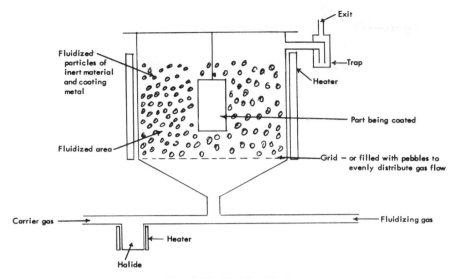

Fig. 4.12. Fluidized bed.

to form the coating element halide, which then thermally decomposes and deposits the coating metal. Alternatively, the metal coating particles may be fluidized prior to entering the bed. In this case, the halide gas is passed through the fluidized metal particles to form the coating metal halide gas, which is passed into a bed of inert particles where it is thermally decomposed to deposit the coating metal. There are other variations, such as fluidizing the halide in the bed with the metal and inert particles. However, most beds are operated like that shown in Figure 4.12 in which the bed consists of inert particles and the coating element or elements.

The most outstanding characteristics of a fluidized bed are its high heat transfer coefficient and its turbulence, which result in a high degree of temperature uniformity throughout the bed. Rapid and uniform heating of the parts placed in the bed to be coated is obtained. This is possible because the solid particles in the bed act as heat reservoirs and carriers. They almost completely overshadow the gas convection and radiant heat energy transfer mechanisms. Consequently, the rate of heating is essentially independent of the emissivity (absorptivity) of the sample being heated. The turbulent motion of the particles enables them to absorb heat in one part of the bed and release it in another, thus equalizing temperature and eliminating hot and cold spots which are a common problem of other heating methods. It is not unusual in the petroleum industry to operate a fluidized bed 50 ft in diameter at temperatures of 1200°F with no more than a 5°F variation at any point in the bed.

Often the heat transfer coefficient of a fluidized bed is as high as 180 Btu/hr/ft^2/°F. The surface area of a fluidized bed, because of the many particles, is on the order of 15,000 sq ft/cu ft of bed area. This combination of very large bed area and high heat transfer coefficient encourages rapid equalization of temperature between the bed, the fluidizing gas passing through it and the objects being coated. Rapid heating of the incoming gas is important, as the halide gas must (1) react with the fluidized coating elements to form the coating metal halide, which (2) must then be raised to the bed temperature, and which (3) thermally cracks or decomposes them to deposit the coating prior to being passed out of the fluidized section of the system. After the metal halides are formed, the reactions are the same as those given previously for vapor deposition in the pack technique. The primary differences are that the halide vapors are flowing instead of diffusing and that the carrier particle density is much lower in the bed than in the pack.

Molybdenum has been silicide-coated by the following procedure in a 4-inch diameter experimental bed. Iodine is used as the halide and argon as the carrier and fluidizing gas. The bed consists of 60-mesh aluminum oxide and 10 per cent by weight of silicon powder that has passed through a 40-mesh screen. A system similar to that shown in Figure 4.12 was used. The bed was heated to 1800 to 2000°F and molybdenum parts suspended in the bed with tantalum wires. Dense molybdenum silicide coatings were formed in two to four hours. These coatings have shown good oxidation resistance but are brittle compared to modified coatings formed in a pack. The DuPont Company (66) has formed tungsten silicide coatings on columbium by using a mixture of tungsten and silicon powder in the bed.

Further investigations of the fluidized bed technique are expected to result in the deposition of complex coatings (more than one coating element) with performance equal or superior to the pack technique. It should be borne in mind, however, that hardware with deep recesses may still represent a problem in using the bed technique. The halide vapors will not flow as freely into deeply recessed areas as over regular surface areas, resulting in thinner coatings in such recesses. Because of the turbulence in the bed, this problem is somewhat mitigated, but not completely eliminated.

ENAMELING METHODS

Enamels are mixtures of oxides smelted into glasses and fritted by quenching in water (67). After the glass is broken into small pieces by quenching, it is referred to as a frit. The enamel frit is ball-milled, usually with water with or without addition agents to form a slip or suspension. The slip is applied to the substrate to be coated by dipping, painting, or spraying. An example of dipping is shown in Figure 4.13. The coated part is normally air dried to remove the water and then fired to form a glassy coating. This is referred to as an enamel coating. It may be pure glass or a glass binder containing crystalline additives such as ZrO_2, Al_2O_3, TiO_2 or zircon.

Enamel coatings are prepared by proportioning the frit composition, mixing, and heating to melting. The melt is then poured into water or quenched rapidly, and is thus broken into small fragments. The frit is then ready to blend for a coating and may be used above or with crystalline materials added to make a more refractory coating. Common additions are ZrO_2, Al_2O_3, Cr_2O_3, Cr and clays (*52, 67—69*). The frit, with or without crystalline additions that can range from 10 to 80 per

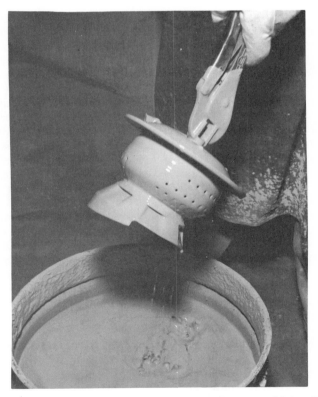

(Courtesy of Solar Aircraft Co.)

Fig. 4.13. A pot burner for a small gas turbine is being dipped into a slurry of ceramic and aluminum prior to drying and firing.

cent, is wet ball-milled to a particle size of about 200 to 325 mesh. The milling time varies from a few hours to as long as 24 hrs. Frequently, small amounts of salts such as barium chloride, citric acid, chromic acid, magnesium sulfate are added to stabilize the slip or increase the "set." "Set" is the term used to describe the formation of the coating film upon dipping or spraying. Sodium pyrophosphite is added to decrease the set (67).

The coating is applied by dipping the substrate in the slip or painting or spraying the slip on the substrate. The substrate is prepared for coating by removing all foreign matter and grease and roughening the surface by light sand-blasting or pickling. The rough surface improves adhesion of the substrate. Bubbles or foreign particles that enter a coating material during application or at any time prior to firing may cause failure of the coating. Enamel coatings in some cases are rather thick, in excess of five mils, and are applied in two or three layers.

After the slip is applied to the substrate, it is air-dryed and sometimes further dried by heating up to 500°F. The coating is then vitrified by firing to a temperature which depends on the coating composition for periods of 1 to 30 min. The time of firing depends on the thickness, substrate mass and viscosity of the glass coating. Thick coatings perform better if they are applied in thin layers (1 to 5 mils) and fired before the next layer is applied. Multicycle coatings generally give the best performance, as the application of successive layers seals imperfections of previous layers. However, thick ceramic coatings have poorer thermal shock resistance and less deformation than thinner coatings.

All-glass coatings are less refractory than coatings using glass as a binder for refractory crystalline particles. The all-glass coatings are fired from 1050 to 1600°F, while those containing a high percentage of crystalline material may require firing as high as 1500 to 2850°F (69). Enamel coatings for superalloy materials are normally fired in air. Those for the refractory metals are regularly fired in an inert atmosphere or vacuum to prevent oxidation of the substrate during firing. Glass coatings are frequently used to seal flame-sprayed coatings. One such coating system uses a glass-to-seal flame-sprayed Al_2O_3 (45).

The phosphate-bonded coatings are very similar to enamels except that aluminum phosphate is used as a binder for crystalline solid additions, rather than glass. The aluminum phosphate can be made by a variety of techniques. A survey of these are included in Ott's study (71) of aluminum phosphate coatings. One of the most convenient methods, developed by Eubanks and Moore (78), consists of ball milling 150 g of -325 mesh hydrated alumina with 700 g of 85 per cent orthophosphoric acid for one hour. After this, 150 g of hydrated alumina is added and milled for two hours. This is followed by an addition of 750 g of water and milling for fifteen minutes. The milled solution is removed from the ball mill and is allowed to stand for 24 hrs. The clear solution is decanted and 12 g of CrO_3 100 ml. is added. This solution is a suitable binder for practically any filler material desired.

Fillers such as ZrO_2, CeO_2, MgO, or Cr_2O_3, are added to the phosphate binder material until a creamy consistency is obtained. The coating is then applied by dipping, painting, or spraying, and cured to at least 400°F for 2 hr. High curing temperatures, up to 1200°F, are preferred. After curing, the phosphate binder is stable to about 3000°F. Modification of the binder by the addition of fluorine and other proprietary materials produces coatings with a higher temperature stability (79).

Phosphate-bound coatings, after curing, contain little glass and are very hard. Some glass may result from P_2O_5 (which forms a glass almost as readily as SiO_2) reacting with other coating compounds. These coatings are relatively porous and are not as oxidation-resistant as enamels. They are presently used primarily as insulation coatings (79) rather than for oxidation resistance.

VACUUM METALLIZING

This method is widely used to apply thin films, for decorative and optical purposes, to substrates that are essentially at low temperatures; however, poor adherence occurs at low deposit temperatures. The evaporation is performed in a chamber with the pressure reduced to 10^{-3} to 10^{-6} mm Hg (Figure 4.14). The coating metal is heated on a spiral helix (or in a boat of a refractory metal, a ceramic crucible, or by other suitable methods) to a temperature at which its vapor pressure is significant. The vapor then condenses on any cool substrates placed in the vacuum chamber. The coatings produced are generally quite thin, stressed, and porous. Evaporated coatings have been investigated for the protection of molybdenum without achieving a measurable degree of success. Other investigations (69) included the evaporation of SiO onto tungsten with subsequent heating in air to convert to SiO_2. These coatings rapidly failed at 2000°F.

Adherence is usually poor unless the substrate is heated during evaporation. The method is very inefficient, because the evaporating metal is condensed onto all areas of the coating chamber and only a small amount falls on the substrate. Diffusion of the evaporating metal into the heated substrate does occur if the substrate is sufficiently hot during evaporation. Chromium and aluminum have shown some promise when evaporated onto heated substrates of molybdenum and columbium. However, the substrate must be heated to about 2000°F and the rate of deposition and diffusion of the evaporated metal into the substrate at this temperature is rather slow. This is especially true with aluminum, since aluminum vapor is more likely to re-evaporate as it strikes the heated substrate, than to remain and diffuse into the substrate. The

Fig. 4.14. Chamber used for vacuum metallizing.

main problem with this technique is to maintain a sufficient concentration of metal vapors in contact with the substrate. This might be achieved by heating a supply of coating metal in a small chamber which contains the heated substrate. To avoid condensation of the coating metal into the chamber walls if they are nonmetallic, the walls are maintained at a high temperature so that the coating metal does not condense on them; then an adequate supply of coating vapor would be maintained at the surface of the heated substrate and the diffusion rate would be greatly increased. This is essentially the coating techniques developed by General Telephone and Electronics Laboratories and by the Thompson Ramo Wooldridge Company (56). The same technique is described in another section of this chapter and consists of applying a slurry of aluminum, with or without tin, to a substrate and heating in a vacuum to 1900 to 2000°F which is well above the melting point of aluminum or tin. Diffusion into the substrate occurs readily at this temperature.

The Thompson Ramo Wooldridge work consisted of heating a columbium substrate in a pack of the coating metal to about 2000 to 2400°F at a pressure of 10^{-4} mm Hg. Diffusion into the substrate occurs simultaneously with volatilization and deposition of the coating metal. However, by this process the rate of deposition is rather slow. It has been modified to include a halide salt carrier and the operating pressure has been reduced to 1500 to 10^{-2} mm Hg. This is, in essence, pack cementation operated in a vacuum retort.

Titanium has been evaporated on a heated steel substrate with moderate success. With the substrated heated to 900 to 1200°F, titanium diffuses with it and forms an excellent corrosion-resistant coating. Titanium has been shown (66) to improve the oxidation resistance of columbium alloys substantially. Titanium may also be applied by evaporation onto a heated substrate; however, there is difficulty in coating the points of contact for holding and heating the substrate, hence at least two evaporations are necessary for complete coverage.

HOT DIPPING METHODS

There are at least three dipping techniques used to apply coatings for high-temperature use: simple dipping of substrates in molten metals, dissolution from molten metals, and dipping in fused salts.

The application of coatings by dipping the substrate in a molten metal is widely used throughout the coatings industry. Well-known examples are dipping steels in molten zinc or aluminum. The successful application of these types of coatings depends a great deal on the skill of the operator. Hot-dipped coating for protection of the refractory metals has received much attention in past years (48, 62, 64, 75—77).

Hot-dipped coatings are normally applied by placing the substrate in a molten bath of the coating material. Usually, a flux covers the molten metal to prevent it from oxidizing and to aid in preventing the substrate from oxidizing as it is inserted in the bath. The dipping temperature and time vary with the coating material and substrate. Aluminum bath compositions operated in the range of 1200 to 2100°F have received much attention. Molten halide fluxes are commonly used over these melts (75—77). One flux formulation (80) that works well consists of 47KCl, 35NaCl, $14Na_3AlF_3$ (cryolite), and $6AlF_3$. Zinc melts do not necessarily use a molten flux on their surfaces (74).

Applying coatings by diffusion in a molten coating material is characterized by high rates of solution of the substrate in the melt. Consequently, dipping times range from about 1/2 to 5 min. This short time allows little or no diffusion of the coating metal into the substrate. Subsequent diffusion treatments are required if a diffused coating is desired. Diffusion treatments of heating in an inert atmosphere or vacuum are commonly employed after dipping. With the aluminum systems, diffusion treatments of 1/2 to 2 hr at 1700 to 2100°F are normally used.

Applying coatings by the dip technique sometimes has the disadvantages of attaining a uniform coating on complex shapes, poor coverage on corners, difficulty in coating deep blind recesses, and inclusions in the coating that are obtained during dipping. This sometimes results in poor reliability of dipped coatings.

Although applying coatings by the dipping technique is used in many evaluation and screening studies, at present no major coatings system for high temperature use is based on this technique except for the Naval Research Laboratory's zinc coating for columbium.

Flame-sprayed coatings are frequently given a dip treatment in molten aluminum or glass to seal the pores in the deposit. Dipped glass coatings have been used to protect the refractory metals during processing (77).

SELECTIVE FREEZING (DESOLUTIONIZING)

Dense, adherent, and ductile chromium coatings on molybdenum have been prepared by selectively freezing chromium solute from a supercooled melt of chromium and copper or tin (81). This process is referred to as selective freezing or desolutionizing. The most favorable conditions were the use of a tin-2 per cent chromium melt and slow cooling. Chromium coatings up to 4 mils thick were obtained that were non-porous, ductile, and adherent. This principle of deposition is applicable to any system in which the plating metal and base metal are isomorphous, form no intermetallics during the deposition process, and in which the coating metal is soluble in a low-melting metal solvent. Aluminum coatings applied from a molten calcium solvent have been reported using this type technique.

Fused Salts

Coatings of titanium and/or chromium have been applied to columbium alloys from fused salt melts of $TiCl_2$-NaCl, $CrCl_2$-NaCl, $TiCl_2$-$CrCl_2$-NaCl, and $TiCl_2$-NaCl in equilibrium with Ti-Cr alloys (66). Coating rates of 0.5 mil/hr have been observed on D-31 specimens treated at 1740°F. The advantages of the fused-salt dip coating technique are excellent uniformity of the coating, versatility of composition by salt concentration adjustment, and ease of scale-up (66). In addition, processing time to obtain an equivalent thickness as compared to pack cementation is much less. This is an achievement, since change in ductile to brittle transition temperature and the probability of recrystallization is lessened.

Applying titanium and/or chromium coatings by the dip fused salt technique consists of preparing a melt of NaCl-20 mole per cent $TiCl_2$ or $CrCl_2$. Metal chips are used in the melt to replenish the metal deposited out and to maintain the metal salt in a divalent state. Chromium and titanium go into solution in a halide melt in the divalent state. An argon atmosphere is maintained over the melt to prevent oxidation of the divalent metal to a higher valence state and of the substrates being coated. The melt is operated at 1652 to 1750°F; the parts to be coated are suspended in the salt solution by tantalum wires. If argon is bubbled through the melt to provide agitation, the cooling rate is 0.5 mil/hr. With a melt composition of NaCl-20 mole per cent titanium dichloride with 50 Ti-50 Cr metal chips in the melt, a composition of 40 Cr-60 Ti is deposited on columbium alloys.

The deposition mechanism is a disproportionation reaction of the general type $MCl_2 \longrightarrow M + MCl_x$ where M represents the depositing metal and x a higher valence state. At the temperature of deposition, the deposited metal diffuses into the substrate. However, the rate of diffusion is slower than the rate of deposition, and a layer of coating builds up on the substrate as well as diffusing into it.

Slurry Method

The slurry method of applying coatings for high temperature is being used to complement the hot-dipped method. Most coatings applied by the slurry method are of the same type that have previously been applied by the hot-dipped method (*64, 75*). Applying coatings by the slurry method consists of blending the coating composition in powder form, suspending the powders in a liquid carrier to make a slurry, and painting, dipping, or spraying the coating slurry on the substrate. After the suspension has air-dried, it is diffused into the substrate by heating in an inert atmosphere or vacuum. The liquid carrier or suspending agent can be any liquid that satisfactorily holds the coating particles in suspension and does not decompose and form undesirable compounds in the coating or with the substrate. Organic liquids are commonly used which decompose on heating or burn off without forming carbides. Organics that have been used are acetone, acetone-xylene (*64*), collodion-butylacetate, and nitrocellulose lacquers. A mixture of 2 parts collodion and 1 part butyl acetate suspends aluminum compositions satisfactorily. The collodion butyl acetate carrier liquid has a relatively high viscosity which is good for holding the coating powder in suspension, but the viscosity is low enough to allow the coating suspension to be applied by painting, dipping, or spraying.

Aluminum composition coatings are most frequently applied by the slurry method. However, other coating compositions can be applied by this technique. Klopp (*55*) silicided tantalum by suspending silicon powder and sodium fluoride in a carrier and heating to 2200°F to promote diffusion. Complex silicides can also be applied to molybdenum by this technique, but the depth of diffusion of the silicide into molybdenum is only about one-half that achieved by pack sedimentation in an equivalent time.

Small particle sizes must be used when applying coatings by the slurry method to avoid roughness and agglomeration in the diffused coating. Aluminum particles smaller than 325 mesh should be used when applying aluminide coatings by the slurry technique followed by subsequent vacuum diffused at 2000°F.

It is difficult to visualize a method of applying coatings simpler than by dipping, painting, or spraying the coating composition on a substrate. This technique has long been used in the enameling and ceramics industry. Diffusion of the slurry coating in an inert atmosphere does not present a problem of scale-up and coating large complex parts; however, diffusion in a high vacuum does present a size limitation problem.

EXOTHERMIC REACTION (*81—82*)

This coating technique has received some attention and a limited number of coating compositions can be applied by this technique. The general reaction is $MO_x + A \longrightarrow AO_x + M$, where M represents a metal whose oxide has a free energy of formation less than that of the oxide AO_x. A is commonly aluminum and AO_x is Al_2O_3. Other possible coating reactions are:

$$(1) \ SiO_2 + MO_x + Al \longrightarrow Al_2O_3 + MSi_x + MO_x$$

$$(2) \ B_2O_3 + MO_x + Al \longrightarrow Al + Al_2O_3 + MB_x$$

$$(3) \ C + MO_x + Al \longrightarrow Al_2O_3 + MC_x$$

These reactions are referred to as thermite reactions. Coatings are produced via these reactions by mixing the starting powders in a slurry and applying to the substrate as it has been discussed. After the slurry is applied to the substrate, the reaction is initiated by heating to a temperature of about 2000°F. Heat is a by-product of the reaction and surface temperatures of 5000°F are not uncommon; hence, the name exothermic reactions.

It is possible to produce presently established coating systems by thermite exothermic reactions. Two examples are:

$$(1) \ 3SnO_2 + 2Al \longrightarrow Al_2O_3 + Sn \ -381 \ Kcal$$

$$(2) \ MoSi_2O_7 + B \longrightarrow MoSi_2 + B_2O_3$$

The first reaction produces the type of coating developed by Lawthers (*25*) for tantalum. The second would produce a modified silicide on molybdenum. On heating the coating in air, a silicate glass would be formed which is known to be beneficial in a silicide protective coating system.

The most promising aspects of this coating technique is its possible use in coating repair. The coating composition could be painted or sprayed on "in-the-field" and infrared lamps or a torch used to produce heat to initiate the reaction. Thus, a defective spot in a coating could be repaired without disassembly of the vehicle and/or recoating the entire part.

REFERENCES

1. Structures Research Division, NASA, Private Communication, Langley Field, Virginia, August, 1962.
2. Preliminary Results of a Comparative Study of Several Commercially Available Oxidation Resistant Coatings on Mo-0.5 Ti Alloy Sheet, Presented at the Sixth Meeting of The Refractory Composites Working Group, Dayton, Ohio, July, 1962.
3. Dave Roller, Materials Laboratory, Wright Air Development Field, Private Communication on Thin Film Indicators, July, 1956.
4. Hardwood, J. J., "The Protection of Molybdenum Against High Temperature Oxidation," 43rd Proceedings of Am. Electroplaters' Soc., 1956.
5. Brenner, A, and Associates, "Protection of Molybdenum From Oxidation at Elevated Temperatures," *J. Electrochem. Soc.*, 108, 450 (1958).
6. Safranek, W. H., and Schaer, G. R., "Properties of Electrodeposits at Elevated Temperatures," 43rd Proceedings of Am. Electroplaters' Soc., 1956.
7. Brenner, A., and Associates, "The Use of Nickel Aluminum Alloy Coatings for the Protection of Molybdenum From Oxidation," *J. Electrochem. Soc.*, 108, 485 (1958).
8. Reid, W. E., and Ogborn, F. J., "The Adhesion of Electrodeposited Nickel to Chromium at Elevated Temperatures," *J. Electrochem. Soc.*, 107, 91 (1960).
9. Goodman, E. G., Value Engineering Co., Personal Communication, August, 1962.
10. Faust, C. L., "The Surface Metallurgy of Protective Coatings," *Metal Progr.*, 71, 101 (1957).
11. Withers, J. C., "Electroplated Cermet Coatings for Oxidation Protection of Substrates in Excess of 2000°F," WADD-TR 60-718.
12. Withers, J. C., "Electrodepositing Cermets," *Products Finishing,* 62 (August, 1962).
13. Huminik, John, "Development of Oxidation and Erosion Resistant Coatings for Mo, Ta, and W," Contract DA 36-034-ORD-327ORD, March, 1961.
14. Hirakis, E. C., "Coatings for the Protection of Columbium at Elevated Temperatures," WADC TR 58-545.
15. Couch, D. E., and Connor, J. H., "Coatings of Nickel-Aluminum Alloys Prepared by Electrolysis," WADC TR 58-5.
16. Beck, W. J., "Use of Nickel-Aluminum Alloy Coatings for the Protection of Molybdenum," *J. Electrochem. Soc.*, 106, 783 (1959).
17. Withers, J. C., and Ritt, P. E., "Iridium Plating and Its High Temperature Oxidation Resistance," 44th Proceedings of Am. Electroplaters' Soc., 1957.
18. Rhoda, R. N., "Deposition of Several Platinum Metals From Molten Cyanide Electrolytes," *J. Am. Electroplaters' Soc.*, 49, 69 (1962).
19. Couch, D. E., "A Hydride Bath for the Electrodeposition of Aluminum," *J. Electrochem. Soc.*, 99, 234 (1952).
20. Brenner, A., "Electrodeposition of Metals From Organic Solutions, I. A General Survey," *J. Electrochem. Soc.*, 103, 652 (1956).
21. Conner, J. H. "Electrodeposition of Metals From Organic Solutions, II, Further Studies on the Electrodeposition of Aluminum From a Hydride Bath," *J. Electrochem. Soc.*, 103, 657 (1956).

22. Brenner, A., "Electrolysis of Organic Solvents with Reference to the Electro-deposition of Metals," *J. Electrochem. Soc.*, 106, 148 (1959).
23. Wood, G. B., "Electrodeposition of Metals From Organic Solutions, V, Electro-deposition of Magnesium and Magnesium Alloys," *J. Electrochem. Soc.*, 104, 27 (1957).
24. Paine, R. M., "An Investigation of Intermetallic Compounds for Very High Temperature Applications," WADC TR 59-29, Part I and II.
25. Sylvania Electric Products, Inc., Sylvania Division, "High Temperature Oxidation Resistant Coatings for Tantalum Base Alloys," Contract AF 33(657)7339 and ASA TR 61-233.
26. Campbell, T. T., and Abel, A., "Codeposition of Tin-Nickel Plate From Organic and Mixed Aqueous-Organic Solvents," Bureau of Mines Report of Investigations, 5482.
27. Audubert, Rene, and Mende, Serge De, "The Principles of Electrophoresis," New York, Macmillian Co., 1960.
28. Shyne, J. J., *et al.*, *Plating*, 42, 1255 (1955).
29. Werner, A. C., *et al.*, "Preparation of Protective Coatings for Electrophoresis," WADC TR 56-521 and WADC TR 58-11.
30. Brenner A, and Associates, *J. Electrochem. Soc.*, 101, 16 (1954); *Ibid*, 104, 21 (1957).
31. Lamb, V. A., and Reid, W. E., "Electrophoretic Deposition of Metals, Metal-lodis and Refractory Oxides," *Plating*, 47, 291 (1960).
32. Moore, D. G., *et al.*, "Basic Studies of Particle-Impact Processes of Applying Ceramic and Cermet Coatings," Natl. Bur. Standards, ARL 59, August, 1961.
33. Walton, J. D., *et al.*, Georgia Institute of Technology, Contract NOrd-15701.
34. Ault, N. N., and Wheildon, W. M., "Modern Flame-Sprayed Ceramic Coatings," Chapter in "Modern Materials," H. H. Hausner, Ed., New York, Academic Press, Inc., 1960.
35. Ingham, H. S., "Flame Sprayed Protective Coatings," *Materials Protection*, 1, 74 (1962).
36. "Properties and Applications of Flame Sprayed Refractory Coatings," *Metal Finishing J.*, 4, 313 (1958).
37. "Development and Possible Applications of Plasma and Related High Temperature Generating Devices," Materials Advisory Board Report 167-M, ASTIA Report No. 242334, August, 1960.
38. "Characteristics of Refractory Oxide Coatings Produced by Flame Spraying," *J. Am. Ceram. Soc.*, 40, 69 (1957).
39. "Contraction Stresses in Sprayed Deposits," *Metal Industry*, 93, 509 (1958).
40. Cunningham, D., "Flame Spraying of Metals," *Corrosion Technology*, 5, 71 (1958).
41. Leeds, D. H., "Summary Observations on the Interface Between Plasma-Sprayed Tungsten and 1020 Steel," Paper Presented at the Sixth Refractory Composites Working Group at Dayton, Ohio, June, 1962.
42. Galli, J. R., *et al.*, "Development and Evaluation of Rocket Blast and Rain Erosion Resistant Composite Coatings Produced by Flame Spray Techniques," WADC TR 58-493, ASTIA 209913.
43. Buffington, J. W., "Metal Spraying with Rockets," *Welding J.*, 35, 468 (1956).
44. Schoop, M. V., "A Modern Electric Arc Pistol," *Electroplating and Metal Spraying*, 6, 33 (1954).
45. Hall, W. B., "System 400 Coating for the Protection of Columbium," Report No. DM-60-97, Materials Information Memorandum, General Electric Co., April, 1960.
46. Wlodek, S. T., "Coatings for Columbium," *J. Electrochem. Soc.*, 108, 177 (1961).

47. Doane, D., "Oxidation Resistant Coatings for Molybdenum," WADC TR 54-492, Part III, April, 1957.
48. Blanchard, J. R., "Oxidation Resistant Coatings for Molybdenum," WADC TR 54-492, December, 1954, and June, 1955.
49. Herzig, A. J., "Protecting Molybdenum From Oxidation," *Metal Prog.,* **68,** 109 (1955).
50. Paprocki, S. J., *et al.,* "Gas Pressure Bonding," DMIC Report 159, Battelle Memorial Institute, Columbus, Ohio, 1962.
51. LaChace, M. H., *et al.,* "Fabrication and Evaluation of the Clad Sheets of Molybdenum," BMI-888, TID-4500, AD 24026.
52. Mond Nickel Co., Ltd. Personal Communication, September, 1962.
53. "Aluminum Coated Steel," *Metal Industry,* **100,** 187 (1962).
54. Krier, C. A., "Chemical Vapor Deposition," DMIC Report 170, Battelle Memorial Institute, Columbus, Ohio, 1962.
55. Klopp, W. D., *et al.,* "Development of Protective Coatings for Tantalum Base Alloys," ASD TR 61-676.
56. Gadd, J. D., "Advancement of High Temperature Protective Coatings for Columbium Alloys," Progress Reports on Contract AF 33(657)7396.
57. Sully, A. H., "Chromium," New York, Academic Press, Inc., 1954.
58. "Properties of Metallic Surfaces," The Institute of Metals, London, 1953.
59. Powell, C. F., "Vapor Plating," New York, John Wiley and Sons, Inc., 1955.
60. Beidler, E. A., *et al., J. Electrochem. Soc.,* **98,** 21 (1951).
61. Fansteel Metallurgy, Fansteel Metallurgical Corp., July, 1958.
62. Jefferys, R. A., and Gadd, J. D., "Development and Evaluation of High Temperature Protective Coatings for Columbium Alloys," ASD TR 61-66, Part I.
63. Lorenz, R. H., and Michael, A. B., Paper Presented at the 118th Meeting of the Electrochemical Society, Houston, Texas, October, 1960.
64. Krier, C. A., "Coatings for the Protection of Refractory Metals From Oxidation," DMIC Report 162, Battelle Memorial Institute, Columbus, Ohio, 1962.
65. Gadd, J. D., "Advancement of High Temperature Protective Coatings for Columbium Alloys," Second Interim Technical Report on Contract AF 33(657)7396.
66. Eaton, Russ, Paper Presented at the Refractory Composites Working Group, Dayton, Ohio, June, 1962.
67. "Glass Bonded Refractory Coatings," DMIC Memorandum 16, Battelle Memorial Institute, Columbus, Ohio, 1960.
68. Nelson, K. E., "Metal Protective Ceramic Coatings, Molecular Basis," WADC TR 56-136.
69. Bergeron, C. G., "Protective Coatings for Refractory Metals," WADC TR 59-526, Part II.
70. Mazdiyosni, K. S., "Synthesis and Pryolysis of Refractory Metal Alkoxides," ASD-TDR-62-90.
71. Ott, E., "Aluminum Phosphate Coatings," WADD TR 61-137.
72. Lewis, W. K., "Characteristics of Fluidized Particles," *Ind. Eng. Chem.,* **41,** 1105 (1949).
73. Othmer, D. F., "Fluidization," A Symposium at Brooklyn Poly Tech, New York, Reinhold Publishing Corp., 1956.
74. "Protection of Refractory Metals for High Temperature Service," U.S. Naval Research Reports 550, 5581, 5620, 5643.
75. Larothers, D. D., and Sana, L., "High Temperature Oxidation Resistant Coatings for Tantalum Base Alloys," ASD TR 61-233.
76. Bartlett, E. S., *et al.,* "Coatings for Protecting Molybdenum From Oxidation at Elevated Temperatures," DMIC Report 109, Battelle Memorial Institute. Columbus, Ohio, 1961.
77. Klopp, W. D., "Oxidation Behavior and Protective Coatings For Columbium

Base Alloys," DMIC Report 123, Battelle Memorial Institute. Columbus, Ohio, 1961.

78. Eubanks, A. G., and Moore, D. G., "Investigation of Aluminum Phosphate Coatings for Thermal Insulation of Airframes," NASA TN D-106.

79. Papers Presented at the Fifth Refractory Composites Working Group in Dallas, by Chance Vought and Marquardt Corp., August, 1961.

80. Klopp, W. D., "Development of Protective Coatings for Tantalum Base Alloys," First Quarterly Progress Report on AF 33(616)7884.

81. Wlodek, S. T., *Trans. Metallurgical Soc. of AIME,* **218,** 716 (1960).

82. Walton, J. D., and Poulos, N. E., "Cermets From Thermite Reactions," *J. Am. Ceramic Soc.,* **42,** No. 1 (January, 1959).

83. Goetzel, C. G., "Refractory Coatings for Tungsten," WADD TR 60-825, March 1961.

5

TESTING AND EVALUATION
OF COATINGS

ELLIOT GOODMAN

Chief, High Temperature Research Group
Value Engineering Company
Alexandria, Virginia

In addition to the many difficulties involved in developing new coatings for high-temperature environments, are the problems associated with selecting suitable, reliable and reproducible tests for evaluating them. The only truly reliable method of testing coatings is in the actual service environment. However, in most cases this is time-consuming and extremely costly. As a result, many screening tests and methods of simulating particular service conditions have been devised. The large number of tests being performed and the many variations used in any one test make the task of selecting a coating for a given application, very difficult. Comparison of results from different organizations is misleading and in many cases impossible, due to the lack of standardized tests. There are many parameters in most of the tests and each investigator chooses the ones that he believes will suit his particular needs.

This chapter outlines some of the more important tests used by investigators in the coating field. These include screening tests, nondestructive tests for coating inspection and proof tests used to evaluate coatings under simulated service conditions. By no means are all of the tests being performed by organizations engaged in coating development included. Only the more prevalent tests and the most widely used variations of these are presented. Specific details of particular tests have been omitted.

OXIDATION TESTING

The basic performance criterion of a coating is its ability to withstand the thermal conditions and oxidizing nature experienced during high temperature operation. The refractory metals would seem to be ideally suited for many high-temperature applications because of their high melting points and good mechanical properties. However, their poor oxidation resistance above 2000°F presents a major deterrent to their effective use in most high-temperature environments. Thus, the degree of oxidation protection afforded a substrate by a coating should be the first parameter studied in a coating evaluation program.

The temperatures usually employed in oxidation tests are in the 2000 to 3000°F range, although specimen temperatures in the arc plasma jet oxidation test may exceed 3500°F in some cases. The samples are tested at the expected service temperature for a specified period. Browning (1) established three temperature classes for which satisfactory reproducible coatings of minimum thickness appear feasible. Standard temperature-measuring devices such as Pt-Pt + 10% Rh thermocouples, various types of optical pyrometers, potentiometer pyrometers, and other measuring and recording equipment are used. A detailed discussion of high-temperature measuring techniques may be found in the literature (2, 3).

The lifetime of the coating is usually defined as the time until initial destruction of the surface due to melting, spalling or cracking of the coating, or melting or oxidation of the substrate occurs. Frequently the life is affected by a diffusion failure and not by a defect in the coating.

In addition, coated samples are observed for dark spots which may occur during cooling after thermal testing. The dark spots are caused by poor adherence of the coatings, which permits higher cooling rates for the coating in the damaged areas than for the remainder of the sample. Many coatings maintain their general shape so that visual inspection cannot reveal the location of poorly adhered areas. It is not until the part is heated that the defects become apparent.

Failures can usually be uncovered by gently probing the surface with a pointed instrument. In general, failures can usually be found at the dark spots observed during cooling. Failures occurring at the edges are usually apparent, and are concentrated only on the sharpest corners of a part. When evaluating coatings on tungsten, tantalum, columbium and molybdenum substrates, the evolution of the volatile oxide of these refractory metals is indicative of coating failure in most cases. However, some coatings will heal themselves if the heating continues, even though it appears that the part is failing.

Various methods are used to present oxidation data and many parameters are used in this type of evaluation. When samples are tested for a specified time, but not to failure, the appearance and integrity of the coating serve as performance criteria. In other tests, the time to failure is used as a measure of coating performance at the particular test temperature. The weight change of the coating substrate composite per unit area is widely used as a parameter for evaluating coating performance (*4, 5*). In general, coatings which exhibit the lowest weight change are superior. Other evaluating parameters used include volume of material lost during testing and depth of erosion.

For example, Koubek and Timmins (*6*) defined an index of performance, I.P. for an oxyacetylene test by the following:

$$I.P. = E.\ R. \times \frac{200°C}{T.\ T.\ 200°C}$$

where E. R. = erosion rate, mils/sec

T. T. 200°C = Time in seconds for the temperature on the back surface to reach 200°C.

Oxidation testing can be combined with other test procedures, such as tensile testing and bend testing, to determine the effect of these conditions on the oxidation resistance of the coating. These tests will be covered in some detail in a later section of this chapter.

Static Oxidation Tests

By far the easiest and most economical method of determining the oxidation resistance of a coating system is by static oxidation. The sample is placed in a furnace which is at the desired test temperature and is held at this temperature for a predetermined time, or until the coating fails. This test may be performed in stagnant air or stagnant oxygen (*7, 8, 9, 10, 11*).

In an evaluation program, it is desirable to test all specimens of one series at the same time and under identical test conditions so that directly comparable data are available. By performing oxidation tests in a furnace, a relatively large number of specimens can be tested at one time, thus assuring an identical test environment. Although this test is not representative of actual end-use conditions, coatings which cannot withstand these conditions will certainly not withstand more stringent environments. Thus, this is the best way of eliminating many coatings from the more expensive and sophisticated test methods.

Static oxidation tests can be performed in a continuous weighing apparatus. The sample is suspended in a furnace and attached to an analytical balance which permits weighing of the sample while it is at temperature. A series of samples may be tested at one time by suspending them in an annular furnace and rotating them. At certain intervals, the rotation is stopped and the sample that is under the balance at that time is weighed. The other samples are weighed in succession by stopping the rotation when they are under the balance. By using this method, the weight of the sample can be monitored throughout the test without introducing another variable by cooling the sample and then weighing it.

Dynamic Oxidation Tests

Many investigators (*12, 13, 14*) conduct furnace oxidation tests by introducing oxygen or air into the furnace during the testing period. There are many variations of this procedure. In its simplest form the specimens are introduced into the furnace which is at the test temperature and air or oxygen is metered into the furnace at rates up to about 5000 lbs/ft^2-hr.

In a more elaborate set-up, dried air is metered into a preheated furnace in order to raise the specimens to the test temperature, after which the specimens are placed in the test furnace. The flow rate of the air can be regulated to simulate, to some extent, the free stream mass velocity, Reynolds Number and temperatures encountered in various re-entry conditions.

Mason and Walton (*13*) described a piece of equipment in which the test piece is placed in a closed container filled with argon. An "Inconel" tube is held against the sample and oxygen is introduced into the tube after the sample has been raised to the test temperature. The argon pressure in the main body of the furnace prevents oxidation of the test piece except in that area surrounded by the "Inconel" tube.

Artificially Damaged Specimen Oxidation Test

Because of the increasing size, complexity of shape and nature of objects being coated today, the probability of applying coatings having defects is very high. Also, coatings used for leading edge components of re-entry vehicles may be damaged by meteroid impacts. Service operation in the presence of coating discontinuities, therefore, is a likely one and should be considered in the evaluation procedure.

To simulate these conditions, an artificial reproducible defect is made by drilling a small-diameter hole, or a hardness tester is used to make a standard indentation in the coated sample. The sample is then oxidation-tested to determine the self-healing properties of the coating and whether the coating still affords oxidation protection to the bulk of the substrate (*14, 15*). Artificially damaged specimens are also used in other evaluation tests, such as tensile testing (*16*).

One method being used for oxidation testing is electrical heating of the test specimen by direct resistance. The specimen, in many cases a coated wire, is held in water-cooled grips through which the current is supplied. Oxidation tests can be made either at one temperature or by thermal cycling to room temperature with an air blast.

Lawthers and Sama (*17*) used the direct resistance method, with a tensile-type sample. Current was fed through copper clamps. Tensile leads were applied to the samples during the test and an air blast was directed on the samples at predetermined intervals. This cycle was continued until the coating failed.

There are several disadvantages inherent in this resistance heating method of oxidation testing. The interior of the sample is hotter than the surface and any diffusion reactions that might occur may proceed more rapidly than with other heating methods. Samples tested in this manner are heated from the inside out, while in actual use components are heated from the outside and the heat transferred to the interior. Another disadvantage is due to the fact that if the cross-sectional area of the sample is decreased during the test, the resistance increases, causing a rise in temperature and an increase in the rate of oxidation.

Resistance heating oxidation testing does offer several advantages, however. It affords visual observation of the oxidation, thus enabling the investigator to determine more readily the mechanism of coating failure. Also, when using water-cooled grips, there is a temperature gradient along the wire which reveals coating performance over a wide range of temperatures at the same time. In addition, this test is economical and easy to perform and is generally considered a good screening test.

Another method used to screen various coatings is the oxyacetylene torch. This flame test exposes the samples to a more severe environment than do tests conducted in a furnace; nevertheless, the oxyacetylene test retains the advantage of being relatively economical and easy to perform.

In its simplest form this test consists of an oxyacetylene torch to which oxygen and acetylene are metered to produce a specified ratio of oxygen to acetylene which is kept constant throughout the test sequence. The coated specimen is mounted at a fixed distance from the torch tip and the flame is allowed to impinge on the specimen for a fixed time or until coating failure. Test coupons may be mounted at a 90° angle to the flame stream or at a 45° angle to approximate aerodynamic heating.

The torch and facility may be enclosed in an insulated compartment to avoid disturbing the flame with air flow in the test area. In addition, this shielding serves to keep the amount of air aspirated into the flame constant (*18*). This minimizes fluctuations from run to run and keeps conditions constant for all samples tested.

Powers *et al.* (*19*) used a small furnace heated by oxyacetylene torches. One torch was used to burn the oxygen and acetylene mixture while another torch was used to introduce only oxygen to ensure an oxidizing atmosphere. To maintain the same oxidizing conditions from day to day, a bare ATJ graphite specimen was inserted in the flame before starting the test run to determine if there was approximately the same weight loss.

Other gas-oxidizer combinations have also been used instead of acetylene and oxygen (*20*), such as oxygen with kerosene or hydrogen.

These torch tests may be conducted by keeping the oxidizer to fuel ratio constant and thereby subjecting samples to a constant heat flux or by testing at a particular specimen temperature. Keeping the heat flux constant is much more advantageous, since it does not depend on specimen emittance.

Another advantage with torches is that the flame chemistry can be made oxidizing, reducing or neutral. Flame temperatures for the oxygen-acetylene torch range from 4800 to 6300°F depending on the fuel-oxidizer ratio.

Thermal Cycling

All the oxidation tests described are frequently accompanied by some form of thermal cycling. The test piece is heated to the test temperature for a specified time and is then allowed to cool to room temperature or to some low temperature, usually in the 200°F to 300°F range. This cycle is repeated until coating failure. This procedure also subjects the sample to mild thermal shock. Removing the test specimen from the test environment and cooling it permits the investigator to examine the specimen for failure. Specimens may be weighed after each cycle and a plot made of weight change versus time. The time of coating breakdown corresponds to the point or area on the curve where there is a change of slope on the graph which indicates substrate oxidation (*21*).

Specimens may be subjected to cumulative oxidation by testing, for example, 8 hrs at 1800°F then raising the temperature to 2000°F and testing for 4 hr, followed by 4 hr at 2200°F and 4 at 2400°F; the test is stopped, of course, if failure occurs. Various combinations of temperature limits and times at each temperature are possible and many different test conditions are employed by investigators using thermal cycling (*17, 22, 23*). Figure 5.1 shows a coated panel undergoing thermal cycling using a plasma jet as the heat source.

THERMAL SHOCK RESISTANCE TESTING

Many coating evaluation programs include a test for determining the ability of the coating to withstand thermal shock. Test specimens which are flame-tested with an oxyacetylene torch can be thermal shocked by alternating an air blast of known velocity for a specified time with the flame impingements. This cycle is repeated for a specified amount of cycles or until failure.

Jefferys and Gadd (*22*) used a curved coupon in the alternating torch-air blast thermal shock tests. The curved shape imposes severe thermal stresses on the coating and substrate during heating and cooling. On heating, the coating on the front of the specimen is in tension and that on the back is in compression. During cooling the stresses reverse.

(Courtesy of University of Dayton)
Fig. 5.1. Thermal cycling of a coated panel using a plasma jet.

ENVIRONMENTAL SIMULATION

In general, there are four categories of high-temperature service to be simulated. First, are the applications characterized by short time thermal exposures at a very high heat flux and enthalpy. The second category includes applications requiring long time exposure to low heat flux and enthalpy levels. The third category is the very high enthalpy and low heat flux applications at long exposure times. Short time exposure at a high heat flux and low enthalpy is the fourth service category.

Arc Plasma Torches

Currently, many facilities are using an arc plasma jet for materials evaluation. A plasma jet is an arc-gas device capable of heating gas to extremely high temperatures. A simple plasma jet is shown in Figure 5.2. The gas temperatures attained are not limited by internal heats of reaction, since no combustion takes place. By adding electrical energy

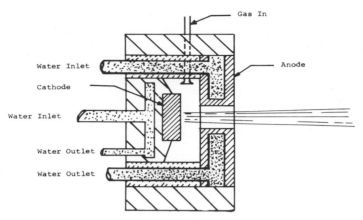

Fig. 5.2. A simple arc plasma jet.

continually, plasma jets can develop gas temperatures over 30,000°F. The ability to attain high heat fluxes and enthalpies, and the relative ease with which variables can be controlled make the arc plasma jet an attractive tool for materials evaluation.

At the first meeting of the Refractory Composites Working Group, a sub-working group was formed to investigate the various tests used to evaluate refractory coatings and to suggest the most suitable method of standardizing materials screening tests. A small arc plasma jet was chosen as the most feasible method of simulating high temperature environments. It was then necessary to standardize the plasma jet equipment, environmental parameters, instrumentation, specimen configuration and data collection methods. A standard method of calibrating the test facility had to be developed and adopted by all the participating organizations.

The standard test proposed by the sub-working group has been modified several times and this test as it is generally recommended is outlined in the following paragraphs. The equipment most widely used is a 40-60 KW plasma jet consisting of a conical water-cooled tungsten cathode, a hollow water-cooled copper anode, and parts for tangentially injecting the nitrogen stabilizing gas. The effluent then passes into a mixing chamber where oxygen is injected to produce simulated air of 79% nitrogen and 21% oxygen which then passes through a conveying nozzle having a 1/2 in. exit diameter. Using air as the stabilizing fluid causes severe oxidation of the tungsten cathode during operation. By using nitrogen as the stabilizing gas and injecting the oxygen so that it does not contact the electrical arc, longer operating times can be achieved.

In order to determine the energy added to the effluent gas and thereby calculate the gas enthalpy at the nozzle, the total energy to the arc must be calculated. The electrical power to the plasma head is measured with a voltmeter and ammeter and the total energy to the arc is therefore:

$$P = 3.413 \ EI$$

where

P = total energy (Btu/hr)
E = voltage drop across the arc (volts)
I = current through arc (amps)

the heat lost to the chamber walls can be calculated from the temperature increase of the cooling water:

$$q' = w \ C_p \ (T_{out} - T_{in})$$

where

q' = heat lost to chamber (Btu/hr)
w = water flow rate (lbs/hr)
C_p = specific heat of water (Btu/lb, °F)
T_{out} = outlet water temperature (°F)
T_{in} = inlet water temperature (°F)

The energy of the effluent gas streaming, q, is the total energy added to the arc minus the heat lost to the chamber walls:

$$q = P - q'$$

where q = energy added to the gas (Btu/hr)
The gas enthalpy is defined by:

$$H = \frac{q}{w}$$

where H = gas enthalpy (Btu/lb)
w = gas flow rate (lb/hr)

A blunt-faced type of water-cooled calorimeter is used to measure heat flux (Figure 5.3). The heat flux is determined by the rate of heating of the calorimeter coolant divided by the nominal heat transfer area of the blunt face.

$$q = \frac{w \ C_p \ T}{A}$$

where

q = heat flux (Btu/ft^2, hr.)
w = cooling water flow rate (lb/hr)
C_p = specific heat of cooling water (Btu/lb, °F)
T = temperature rise of cooling water (°F)
A = area of calorimeter (ft^2)

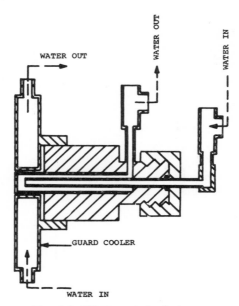

Fig. 5.3. Water-cooled calorimeter.

The calorimeter is provided with a water-cooled ring around the tube so that heating is confined to the calorimeter face. A gap between the ring and the calorimeter prevents heat transfer between the two components.

The test facility includes a sliding bar mount that permits the interchange of the calorimeter and test sample (Figure 5.4). Before testing, the calorimeter is placed in the plasma discharge and the power input to the torch is regulated to establish the desired heat flux, typically 100 to 500 Btu/ft^2/sec. A calorimeter of this sort can only be used as a relative standard for calibration of the flame. The surface emittance and the condition of the calorimeter surface exposed to the energy source influence the heat transfer rate; therefore, these rates cannot be applied directly to the test samples.

Investigation of nonoxidizing, nontarnishing surface coatings for the target areas has been carried out in an effort to obtain more uniform heat flux data.

A water cooled pitot tube (Figure 5.5) is inserted in the flame in order to measure the stagnation pressure of the stream and thus be able to calculate the velocity of the gas impinging on the sample.

$$P_i = P_s + \frac{\rho V^2}{2g_c}$$

(Courtesy of METCO, INC.)

Fig. 5.4. Plasma torch test set-up showing a coated test sample and water-cooled calorimeter.

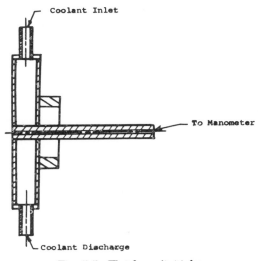

Fig. 5.5. Flat face pitot tube.

where

P_i = impact pressure (lb/ft^2)
P_s = static stream pressure (lb/ft^2)
ρ = gas density (lb/ft^3)
V = gas velocity (ft/sec)
g_c = gravitational constant (32.2 lb$_m$, ft/lb$_f$, sec^2)

By substituting

$$\rho = \frac{w}{AV}$$

where

w = gas flow rate (lb/sec)
A = area of discharge orifice (ft^2)

into the above equation the velocity can be determined.

$$V = \frac{2g_c \, A \, (p_i - p_s)}{w}$$

Once the plasma jet is calibrated, the test specimens are mounted in the holder and tested. It is important to maintain constant operating conditions and to periodically check the heat flux during a set of tests on various samples.

Various tests can be performed utilizing the arc plasma jet as the heat source. In one test, the sample is placed in the flame and tested to failure. If no failure occurs, the heat flux is increased and the sample retested to failure. In a variation of this procedure the specimen is thermal cycled. The specimen is heated for a specific time and then allowed to cool. This is repeated until failure. In a third test, or one that can be incorporated with any of the above two, temperature-time curves are obtained for the front and back faces of each test specimen. Samples are evaluated by determining the volume and depth of erosion and weight (*24, 25*).

Other types of plasma jet units are being used. Molella (*26, 27*) used a water-stabilized electric arc for evaluating coatings. The arc operates in the vortex formed by a rapidly swirling body of water. Temperatures over 30,000°F can be developed as a result of the increased current density arising from the restricted cross-sectional area of the vortex and the cooling of the outer arc regions, which forces most of the current to flow in the center. A schematic diagram of this apparatus is shown in Figure 5.6. The arc is struck in a vortex of water between the two electrodes. Figure 5.7 shows the water-stabilized electric arc before operation. Koubek and Timmins (*6*) used a water-stabilized arc and found the water vapor in the plasma exhaust a major drawback. This

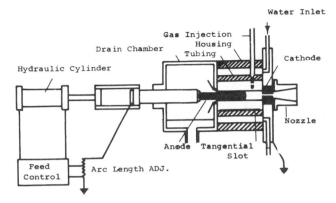

Fig. 5.6. Schematic diagram of water-stabilized electric arc.

(Courtesy of Picatinny Arsenal)
Fig. 5.7. Water-stabilized electric arc.

is based on the fact that many materials are attacked by water vapor at high temperatures. For example, the electrodes may be partially consumed by this vapor thus contaminating the plasma effluent.

Gaseous Oxygen-Hydrogen Rocket Motor

Various investigators are using a small rocket motor which uses gaseous oxygen and gaseous hydrogen as the propellant to obtain a high velocity and high temperature test stream. Oxygen and hydrogen are injected into a water-cooled combustion chamber using the necessary oxidizer to fuel ratio to obtain the desired flame temperature and exhaust velocity. The combustion gases are exhausted through the nozzle and allowed to impinge on the test sample.

Since the combustion chamber is water-cooled, the length of the firing is limited only by the number of compressed oxygen and hydrogen cylinders that are attached to the motor and by the life of the nozzle. In order to prevent nozzle failure while testing test specimens in the exhaust stream, a water-cooled copper nozzle can be used.

A typical water-cooled nozzle attached to an oxygen-hydrogen rocket motor is shown in Figure 5.8. The heat flux at the test sample can be regulated by changing the mass flow rate of the propellant or by changing the distance of the specimen from the rocket nozzle. Figure 5.9 shows how the heat flux at a test sample varies with respect to its distance from the nozzle.

Other fuel-oxidizer combinations are used to supply high-velocity, high-temperature gas environments for coating evaluation. One such facility is a ram jet described by Aves and Bourland (*21, 28*). The ram jet operates on JP-4 fuel and compressed air, with direct oxygen injection which produces an exhaust gas chemistry ranging from complete reducing to 22 per cent excess oxygen.

Low Pressure Testing

Perkins (*29, 30*) studied the oxidation behavior of silicide base coatings and concluded that the performance of these coatings were significantly reduced in static oxygen at pressures below 5 mm Hg and in moving air at pressures below 50 mm Hg. Work is being performed along these lines at the University of Dayton (*31*).

Oxidation behavior at low pressures is determined by Perkins (*32*) by using the vacuum apparatus shown in Figures 5.10 and 5.11. The sample is heated rapidly to the test temperature in vacuum and the oxidizing gas is admitted to the desired pressure. For dynamic tests, the gas is admitted through a choked orifice placed 1 inch from the surface of the specimen and pressure is adjusted by balancing the leak rate against the pumping rate. Static tests are conducted in pure oxygen in a sealed system and the pressure is maintained by adjusting the leak rate to equal the rate of oxygen consumption by the specimen.

(Courtesy of U.S. Naval Ord. Lab.)
Fig. 5.8. Water-cooled nozzle installed on O_2-H_2 rocket motor.

High-enthalpy, hypersonic wind tunnels are being used to subject materials to actual service conditions experienced during re-entry or high altitude flight. There are three classifications of re-entry vehicles. (1) Sub-orbital vehicles, such as the IRBM and ICBM which experience the highest peak heating rates of 1200 to 3000 Btu/ft^2 sec. However, this heat flux lasts for a relatively short time. (2) Orbital vehicles, characterized by satellites and boost-glide vehicles experiencing heat fluxes of of 200 to 500 Btu/ft^2 sec, but for a longer time than sub-orbital vehicles. Consequently, the total heat input is comparable to that of ballistic re-entry. (3) Super-orbital vehicles which must sustain heat fluxes of 200 to 1100 Btu/ft^2 sec for very long periods. The total heat input for this class of vehicles ranges from 50,000 to 300,000 Btu/ft^2. The heating rates encountered by the three classes of re-entry vehicles are summarized in Figure 5.12.

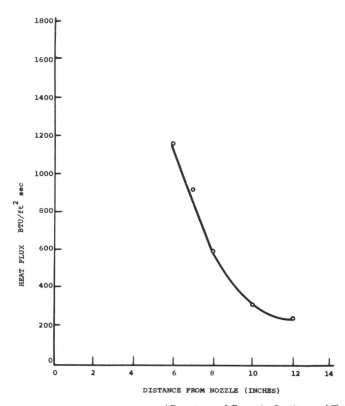

(Courtesy of Georgia Institute of Technology)
Fig. 5.9. Heat flux measurements in the exhaust stream of a gaseous O_2-H_2 rocket motor.

The hyperthermal wind tunnels now being used are capable of simulating the stream total enthalpies and heating rates encountered by the majority of ballistic missiles, satellites and super-orbital vehicles. The heat transfer simulation capability of one type of hyperthermal tunnel is shown in Figure 5.13. Larger models are available to duplicate conditions encountered by superorbital vehicles (*33*). These hyperthermal facilities consist of some means for heating the working fluid which is usually air. The heated gas is expanded through an axisymmetric nozzle into a free jet test section. After passing through the free jet test section, the gas passes through a diffuser and cooling section and is exhausted to the atmosphere. The test section is enclosed in a large plenum chamber as shown in Figure 5.14. The test specimens are

(Courtesy of Lockheed Missiles & Space Co.)
Fig. 5.10. Equipment used to measure oxidation rates at low pressures.

mounted on a rotatable hub so that a number of samples may be tested sequentially without interrupting the facility between samples.

The working fluid for the hypersonic facility may be heated by passing it through the bed of a pebble bed heater as reported by Milling (*34*). This type of bed utilizes refractory oxide pebbles such as zirconia. The bed is heated by the combustion products of a propane-air-oxygen burner which are passed down through the bed. Compressed air, or any other gas which might be used as the working fluid, is passed up through the pebble bed heater and allowed to expand through the nozzle.

One disadvantage associated with this type of equipment is the relatively long time necessary to heat the bed. Because of the poor thermal shock properties of zirconia, beds using this material must be heated very slowly to assure proper operation.

High temperature air for expansion through the test nozzle of a hyperthermal facility can be obtained by using an electric arc plasma generator. An example of such a tunnel is shown in Figure 5.15 which shows the plasma head, the test section and the plenum chamber containing the diffuser. This type of heating is very versatile and the test stream

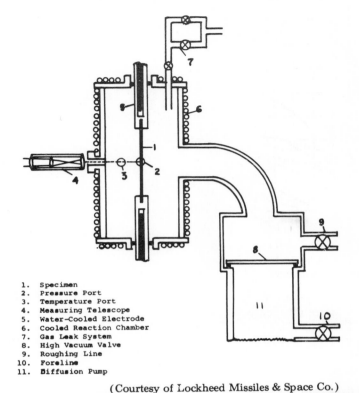

1.   Specimen
2.   Pressure Port
3.   Temperature Port
4.   Measuring Telescope
5.   Water-Cooled Electrode
6.   Cooled Reaction Chamber
7.   Gas Leak System
8.   High Vacuum Valve
9.   Roughing Line
10. Foreline
11. Diffusion Pump

(Courtesy of Lockheed Missiles & Space Co.)

Fig. 5.11. Schematic diagram of low pressure oxidation rate apparatus.

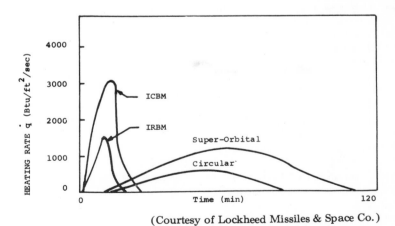

(Courtesy of Lockheed Missiles & Space Co.)

Fig. 5.12. Heating rates for different classes of re-entry vehicles.

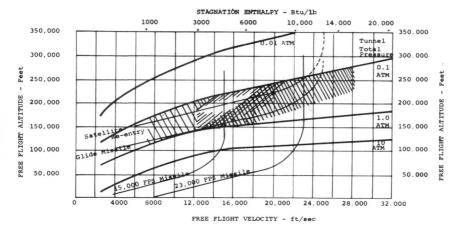

(Courtesy of Plasmadyne Corp.)

Fig. 5.13. A typical heat transfer simulation capability chart for a hypersonic, hyperthermal wind tunnel. Shaded area shows tunnel capability.

flow is essentially continuous. Heat transfer rates to the test sample can be controlled by controlling the total enthalpy of the gas, the total pressure of the test stream and the size of the test specimen. The Mach number of the test stream may be varied by changing the dimensions of the exhaust nozzle.

Solid Propellant Rocket Nozzle Testing

Currently, the only way to completely simulate service conditions when evaluating a nozzle coating is to test it in the actual propulsion

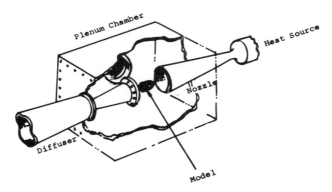

Fig. 5.14. Schematic diagram of a hypersonic, hyperthermal wind tunnel.

(Courtesy of Plasmadyne Corp.)
Fig. 5.15. A hypersonic, hyperthermal wind tunnel.

unit for which it is intended. Full-scale nozzle evaluation tests, however, are extremely costly in a development program. Instrumentation in these large scale firings is usually limited and relatively few such tests can be made.

An important tool being used in many nozzle development programs is the small-scale rocket motor for simulation of large propulsion engines. Exact simulation cannot be accomplished as yet, due to the complexity of the propellant exhaust products. Extensive high temperature kinetic data are still lacking so that the extent to which the combustion products approach equilibrium is not known. Furthermore, the equilibrium composition changes along the length of the nozzle as the pressure and temperature decrease; combustion reactions may still be taking place during expansion in the nozzle. Reaction of the exhaust products with the nozzle material further complicates the situation. Various investigators are working on procedures for characterizing the combustion products in solid propellant nozzles as well as determining the reactions occurring between exhaust products and nozzle materials (35).

Heat Transfer. An important factor to be considered when simulating full-scale engines is the heat flux. If the nozzle material used in the small motor is the same as that of the full scale engine, the heat flux depends on the enthalpy of the exhaust gases, chamber pressure, nozzle diameter and certain physical properties of the gas.

Many high-energy solid propellants contain metal additives such as aluminum. Therefore, the exhaust products will contain molten aluminum or aluminum oxide which, when contacting the cooler surface of the nozzle, will solidify and release energy to the surface. Work by Ungar (*36*) indicates that the nozzle surface temperature increases as the oxide layer decreases until a thin molten layer remains which is a relatively constant thickness. Consequently, any analysis of nozzle heat transfer must include the effects produced by this metal oxide layer.

In simulating conditions in a full scale engine, the weight fraction of oxide particles in the small motor exhaust should be the same as in the large motor. If the heat flux has been simulated by adjusting the chamber pressure, the effect of oxide particles on nozzle performance will be simulated.

Chemical Reactions. A major factor contributing to nozzle failure is the chemistry of the exhaust products. The chemistry of solid propellant combustion products is complex and the composition of the exhaust products may vary along the length of the nozzle due to dissociation reactions. A particular fuel may produce a flame that is either oxidizing or reducing depending on temperature conditions. It is evident that the chemical composition in the simulated nozzle must be the same as in the full scale nozzle.

Reactions of the exhaust products with the nozzle material are controlled either by the kinetics of the reaction or by the diffusion rate of the exhaust products into the surface of the nozzle. The rates of the chemical reactions can be duplicated by controlling the combustion products, free-stream temperature and nozzle surface temperature. If the solid propellant contains a metal additive, the oxide layer must be present since it, too, will affect the chemical reactions in the nozzle.

The shear stress on a nozzle surface is a function of the chamber pressure and the location in the nozzle. The shear stress removes weak or failed material from the surface and exposes unfailed material to the exhaust stream.

Other mechanical effects must also be simulated. The erosion caused by solid particles in the exhaust gas is a contributing factor to nozzle failures. Solid particles such as aluminum or aluminum oxide have been inserted in the fuel lines of test H_2-O_2 rocket motors.

Thermal shock is imposed on a nozzle structure due to the large temperature differences present in the material. This is especially significant during transient heating which occurs during initial motor start up.

There are three approaches to designing small-scale tests for simulation of large solid propellant motors. One is to use the same solid propellant but incorporate it in a smaller engine. Another is to use a combination of liquids, gases and powders to duplicate the exhaust products and temperature of the large motor. The third method is to use a simple combination of liquids or gases which will produce the same oxidizing or reducing effect as that of the solid propellants.

A small solid propellant motor has been developed which allows different operating parameters to be varied (*37*). The basic engine consists of a central cubical steel manifold to which are attached cylindrical steel tubes containing end-burning solid propellant charges. One face of the manifold contains the test nozzle through which the combustion products are discharged. The type of propellant, number of charges and length of each charge can be easily controlled and varied to allow various burning times and combustion pressures.

Simulating Solid Propellants With Liquid Propellants. The second method of simulation is the use of a combination of liquids, gases and powders in a static liquid motor. The composition of the combustion products of a solid propellant is determined by the temperature, pressure and atomic composition. Thus, the chemical composition of the exhaust products can be simulated by reproducing the atomic composition and the enthalpy of formation of the propellant. Work along this line has been done by Jablansky (*38*) by selecting a series of chemicals which among them, contain the desired elements. Further duplication of the various solid propellant compositions is accomplished by using the appropriate mass balance. The temperature, as well as the composition of the combustion products, can be simulated in this manner.

A liquid engine with a water-cooled thrust chamber having the same chamber pressure, propellant mass flow and nozzle geometry as the solid propellant motor being simulated is used. In addition to simulating the chemical species, the heat flux can be reproduced closely by adjusting the gas enthalpy, chamber pressure, internal characteristics of the nozzle and certain properties of the exhaust gas. The heat flux can be calculated from the effective film coefficient, wall temperature and adiabatic wall temperature. Colucci (*39*), Ungar (*40*), Bartz (*41*) and others have presented equations for deriving the convective film coefficient. Colucci and Ungar have made several temperature-time measurements in solid propellant nozzles to determine the heat flux.

Gaseous Propellant Rocket Motors

The basic design of the gaseous oxygen-gaseous hydrogen rocket motor being used for simulating solid propulsion is also used in simulating liquid motors. Figure 5.16 gives the salient features and Figure 5.17 is an exploded view. The motor contains an injector which has six oxygen jets impinging on a central hydrogen jet. This configuration allows for a large radial momentum which causes good mixing. The temperature and composition of the exhaust stream is uniform which is probably due to the turbulence generated by the injector and to the relatively large characteristic lengths which are normally used.

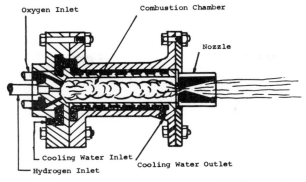

Fig. 5.16. Schematic diagram of a gaseous O_2-H_2 rocket motor.

A water-cooled nozzle is used to determine the heat flux to the nozzle surface and to check the performance of the motor before testing actual nozzle materials. The amount of coolant water to the combustion chamber and water-cooled nozzle, and the change in water temperature in each case permits the heat flux to be calculated. Figure 5.18 shows the effect of mass flow rate of fuel on the heat flux through the combustion chamber and through the nozzle. The fuel flow rate is represented here by the pressure of the fuel in the line. These data were obtained by Walton and Mason (*13*) and are indicative of heat fluxes obtained by other facilities under similar conditions.

The hydrogen and oxygen are regulated from a bank of cylinders through critical flow orifice meters to the injector of the combustion chamber. Solenoid valves are located before the injector so that rapid

(Courtesy of Value Engineering Co.)

Fig. 5.17. Exploded view of gaseous oxygen-hydrogen rocket motor.

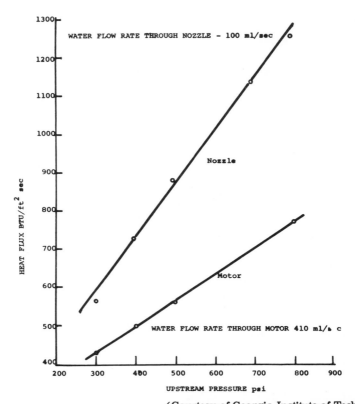

(Courtesy of Georgia Institute of Technology)
Fig. 5.18. Effect of fuel flow rate on the heat flux in the nozzle and motor chamber of an oxygen-hydrogen rocket motor.

starting and stopping of the firing can be accomplished. The ignition of the propellant is usually initiated by igniting a low flow of hydrogen which occurs outside of the nozzle. When the main propellant solenoids are opened, the flame is drawn back into the chamber.

Instrumentation is provided for measuring chamber pressure, oxygen and hydrogen upstream and downstream orifice line pressures, inlet and discharge cooling water temperatures, gas supply temperatures, and inlet and outlet motor coolant pressures.

Nozzle performance is usually determined by the time it takes for the chamber pressure to drop 5 per cent or by the area index, which is the area under the chamber pressure-burning time curve (13). Erosion rate and pressure decay, defined as the pressure loss divided by burning time, are used to a lesser degree. To minimize fluctuations from day to day operation, a standard nozzle such as ATJ graphite is fired.

The time to 5 per cent pressure drop or area index of the test nozzle can be divided by that of the standard nozzle fired the same day to give a performance index. A more detailed discussion of the oxygen-hydrogen motor and its operation may be found in the references (*13, 36, 42, 43*).

The hydrogen-oxygen rocket motor affords a rapid and inexpensive method of screening rocket nozzle materials under conditions of high shear stresses and severe thermal shock. By varying the ratio of oxidizer to fuel, the flame temperature and the characteristic exhaust velocity, *C*, can be controlled. Flame temperatures of most solid propellants in use today can be reproduced with this gaseous motor. In addition, the presence of a large quantity of water vapor in the exhaust products produces severe chemical erosion conditions for many nozzle materials. Lowrie (*35*) reported that water and carbon dioxide are the major chemical constituents in the exhaust which cause nozzle failure for many materials. This motor can be adjusted, however, to give varying degrees of oxidizing or reducing flames as the case may require. Ungar (*36*) has shown that this type of motor can produce the same mechanism of failure in a test nozzle and can also produce heat flux levels of the same magnitude as larger motors using different propellant combinations.

STRENGTH AND PHYSICAL PROPERTIES OF COATINGS

As high-temperature coatings are developed, their mechanical properties and the properties of the coating-base material combination must be determined. It is only in this manner that maximum utilization of the high-temperature materials can be accomplished. Of prime importance to the design engineeer is the knowledge of the effect, if any, a particular coating has on the engineering properties of the substrate being used. The effect of the coating on the ductility and strength of the substrate, as well as the characteristics of the coating must be determined. High-temperature mechanical properties are necessary for predicting coating performance under extreme thermal conditions.

The knowledge of high-temperature tensile strength, creep strength and stress rupture properties for any promising combination of materials is vital. Various programs for evaluating these are being carried out by a number of facilities (*15, 28, 44, 45*).

In describing the mechanical tests performed on coated specimens, only the features which are unique to high temperature testing are described. Detailed descriptions of the standard aspects of these tests can be found in the literature (*46, 47*).

Tensile Testing

In an elevated-temperature tensile test the specimen to be tested is loaded by standard testing machines. The specimens can be heated by their own resistance to the passage of an electric current, by induction, or in an infrared radiant heating furnace. Extensometers are used to measure the elongation of the rod or flat-shaped specimens. In an extensometer used at the Southern Research Institute (*45*), ceramic contact arms are used to translate the elongation within the gage length into flexture of the extensometer springs. Strain gages mounted on either side of the springs translate the strain to the proper recording devices. Figure 5.19 shows a bar-type tensile specimen in the loading fixture with the extensometer in place. A schematic drawing of this set-up is shown in Figure 5.20. In some tests, in order to protect the specimens from oxidation at elevated temperatures, a flowing curtain of argon gas is applied to the gage section of the specimen through a pair of fish-

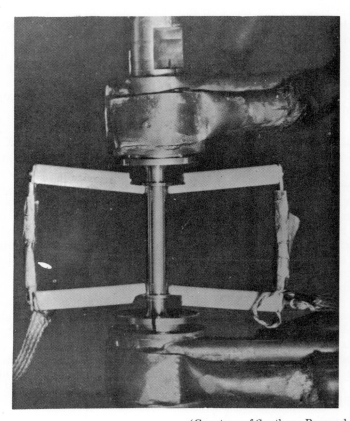

(Courtesy of Southern Research Institute)
Fig. 5.19. Tensile specimen in loading fixture with extensometer and water-cooled electrical connectors.

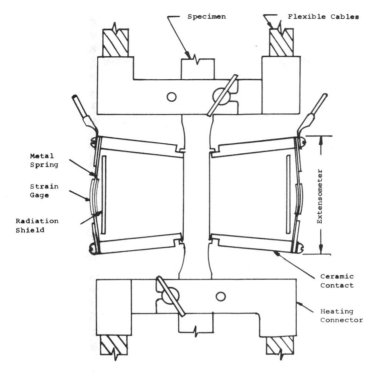

Fig. 5.20. Extensometer and heating connectors mounted on a tensile specimen.

tail nozzles as shown in Figure 5.21. A general view of a tensile test set-up is shown in Figures 5.22 and 5.23.

In one test, the effect of high-temperature oxidation under a creep-producing stress on the strength and ductility of the coating-substrate composite at room temperature is determined. In this test, the specimens are heated while a load is maintained equal to a fixed percentage of the yield strength of the base material. The effect of these prolonged conditions on the strength of the material can be determined by a tensile test at room temperature. The data obtained from this test are an indication of the protection afforded the substrate by the coating. The effect of the coating and subsequent coating treatment on the mechanical properties of the base metal can be determined by comparison to results obtained from uncoated samples.

Levinstein (16) describes a test which takes into account fluctuating mechanical loads and thermal cycling that will be expected by structural parts in service. The coated specimen is tested at a temperature near the

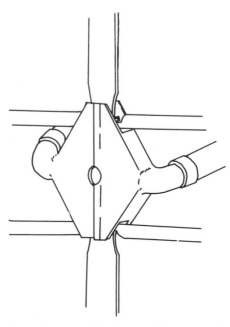

Fig. 5.21. Fish-tail nozzle assembly for applying a protective inert gas curtain around heated specimens.

maximum operating temperature to be encountered. A combination of a mean loading, usually 85 per cent of the rupture strength of the base material at the test temperature, and alternating loading is applied. The effect of thermal cycling can be determined by a test similar to one described by Aves (*21*). In the thermal cycling sustained load test, a tensile specimen is loaded to a load corresponding to approximately the load limit at the peak test temperature. The sample is then thermal cycled from room temperature to the peak temperature.

Creep and Rupture Testing

The creep test, in its simplest form, is performed by keeping the specimen at a constant temperature in a furnace or with heating by electrical resistance, and subjecting it to a sustained tensile load. This load causes the specimen to elongate, and a creep curve, which is the elongation versus test time, is obtained for evaluation. Several such creep tests are usually run with different applied stresses at a given temperature.

Kattus and Preston (*45*) measured creep with a bottom-loading creep machine employing dead-weight loading. The machine is shown set up for tensile creep in Figure 5.24 and a schematic diagram of the lever and fulcrum scheme used to attain the tensile loading is shown in Figure

(Courtesy of Southern Research Institute)
Fig. 5.22. Testing machine set-up for tensile determination in inert atmosphere.

5.25. In their procedure the creep specimens were heated to temperature and held at temperature for 8 minutes, after which the load was applied. The specimens were then held at constant temperature and at a constant load for 10 hrs or until 5 per cent creep strain had occurred in the coated creep specimen.

The rupture test is the same as the creep test except that the loads and creep rates are higher and the test is carried out until the material fails. The equipment for the stress rupture test is essentially the same as for the creep test.

Bend Test

Bend tests are used in materials evaluation programs to determine the extent of coating ductility and the effect of the coating and coating

Fig. 5.23. General arrangement of tensile testing equipment.

process on the ductility of the substrate. Many different types of bend tests are in use. In the test being performed at The Pfaudler Company (*48*), coated sheet samples are bent around a die having a known nose radius. A series of dies of successively smaller radii are used. The largest die has a 1.5-in. radius and the smallest has a knife edge. The test setup is shown in Figure 5.26.

A variation of this test has been proposed by the Refractory Metal Sheet Rolling Panel of the Materials Advisory Board (*49*) and is being used by a number of organizations. This bend test utilizes a fixture in which the test specimen is supported freely on two rollers and loaded through another spool of specified radius as shown in Figure 5.27. The distance between supports is adjustable to allow a constant ratio of span to sheet thickness of 15. The specimens are loaded at a constant crosshead speed of 10 in./min. Jefferys and Gadd (*15, 22*), following this procedure used a bend radius of $4T$, a specimen thickness of $12T$ and a beam support distance of $15T$, where T is the thickness of the sample. The cross-head speed was 10 in./min. The maximum angle to

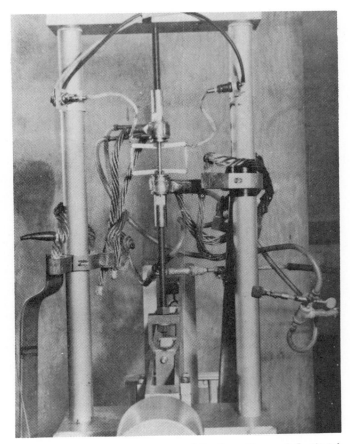

(Courtesy of Southern Research Institute)
Fig. 5.24. Creep machine set-up for tensile-creep determination.

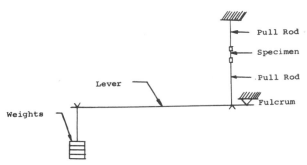

Fig. 5.25. Schematic diagram of lever system used to attain tensile loading during a creep test.

(Courtesy of The Pfaudler Co.)
Fig. 5.26. Bend test apparatus.

which the sample can be bent without failure was determined. A ductile coating composite was considered, one that could be bent 90° without failure. The temperature range at which the specimen changed from ductile to brittle, called the brittle-to-ductile bend transition temperature range, was determined for the coated samples. The lower the transition temperature, the more ductile the coating.

Bend tests can be performed on an uncoated specimen and on an as-coated piece to determine whether the bend transition temperature is raised, which would indicate that the coating caused embrittlement.

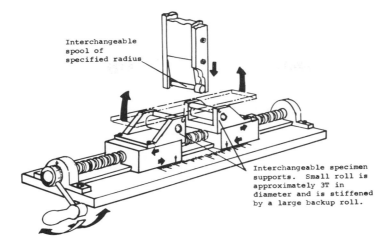

Interchangeable
spool of
specified radius

Interchangeable specimen
supports. Small roll is
approximately 3T in
diameter and is stiffened
by a large backup roll.

(Courtesy of The National Academy of Sciences)

Fig. 5.27. Bend test fixture showing interchangeable specimen supports and loading spool.

Bond Strength

A very significant problem for people engaged in coating development is the lack of adhesion between coating and substrate. A great deal of work has been performed to determine the best way of preparing the substrate surface to insure adequate bonding of coating and metal. Consequently, a method of measuring the bond strength must be available. In general, the bond strength of coatings are measured in shear and in tension.

One of the most widely used methods of measuring the shear strength of coating bonds was proposed by Ingham and Shepard (50). The arrangement shown in Figure 5.28 is used. After assembling and blast-

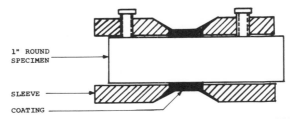

1" ROUND
SPECIMEN

SLEEVE

COATING

(Courtesy of METCO, INC.)

Fig. 5.28. Apparatus for determining the shear strength of a coating to substrate bond.

ing the test section of the specimen, the sleeve is removed so that any abrasive which worked under the sleeves can be removed. The equipment is reassembled, the specimen preheated and the coating applied. After coating, the set screws are removed and the shear strength is measured using a press equipped to measure the applied load.

Leeds (*51, 52*) modified this method by using a water-cooled shear specimen. It was felt that this would minimize any effect that preheating had on the bond strength.

Moore and his co-workers (*53*) used an arrangement shown in Figure 5.29 to measure shear bond strength. The test specimen is placed between two knife edges with 0.050 in. protruding. The protruding section is coated and the force necessary to shear the metal from the coating shell is determined. This is done by attaching a bucket to the specimen and feeding small lead shot into it at a constant rate until the coating layer is sheared from the metal. The weight of the lead shot and the bucket at failure, divided by the coated surface area is the shear strength of the bond.

Ingham and Shepard (*50*) and Bliton and Rechter (*54, 55*) as well as other investigators (*53*) use methods for measuring the coating-to-substrate tensile bond strength which are basically the same. The coating is applied to the flat face of a cylindrical specimen, usually one in. in diameter. The coating is then ground flat and the coated cylinder is bonded to a similar uncoated cylinder by using a suitable adhesive.

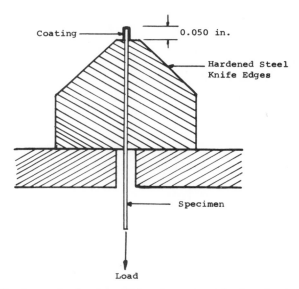

Fig. 5.29. Apparatus for determining shear strength of coating bond (*53*).

The cylinders, which are tapped at the outer ends are attached to the heads of a tensile tester and the joint tested until failure. If the failure occurs within the coating rather than at the metal-coating interface, the test is not considered valid.

Porosity

The majority of porosity tests consist of applying a pressurized gas to a coating and determining the flow rate through the coating. Ingham (56) used a cylindrical or flat coupon type sample and used the porosity apparatus shown in Figure 5.30. The fixture with the sample is immersed in a container of water and nitrogen or helium is let into the apparatus until the desired test pressure is obtained. The gas flow rate through the coating is determined with a flow meter. In another variation, this test may be used to determine a relative permeability by determining the maximum gas pressure for which there is no gas flow through the coating.

As gas penetrates a coating into an evacuated chamber, the pressure difference on either side of the coating may be measured. A quantity

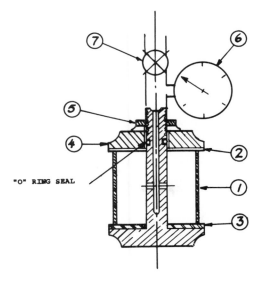

```
    1.  Coated Sample
  2.&3.  Gaskets
    4.  Pressure Plate
    5.  Clamp
    6.  Pressure Gage
    7.  Shut-Off Valve
```

(Courtesy of METCO, INC.)

Fig. 5.30. Apparatus for determining porosity in coatings.

of gas is defined by its pressure, volume and temperature. Since the volume and temperature of the evacuated chamber is fixed, the change in pressure across the coating is a direct measurement of the rate of permeation of the gas through the coating. The permeation rate, M, is

$$M = \frac{PA\ (p_1 - p_0)}{d}$$

where A is the area of the coating, $(p_1 - p_0)$ is the difference in pressure on the two sides of the coating, d is the coating thickness, and P is a constant of proportionality called the permeability. Bliton and Rechter (54) described a procedure which uses the permeability, P, which is the cm^3 of air passing through one cm^2 of coating one cm thick per min. per cm of mercury pressure differential, as the parameter for reporting permeability data. The air permeability data resulting from this test are reproducible and valuable for determining the homogeneity of a coating.

The porosity of deposits may be measured by making a contact print of a coating which has been stripped from the base metal as reported by Withers (8). The negative is made into an enlarged glossy print which is studied with a magnifying glass. The porosity is reported as the number of pores per square inch. This method is not considered accurate since the number of pores per square inch of coating at the coating-substrate interface may not be representative of the porosity throughout the remainder of the coating.

Ballistic Impact Test

Various investigators (20, 57) use a ballistic impact test to simulate conditions which occur when foreign matter entrained in a combustion gas stream strike a rotating hot engine component.

Figure 5.31 shows the furnace setup used by Climax Molybdenum Company (57) for ballistic impact testing. The coated specimen is mounted in the furnace with one edge protruding through a slot in the front of the furnace. The furnace is heated to the test temperature with a gas-compressed air blast burner. An air rifle is used to propel a steel pellet which strikes the leading edge of the specimen. After impacting, the specimen can be removed from the furnace and subjected to an oxidation test to determine the effect of the impact on the coating integrity.

NONDESTRUCTIVE INSPECTION TECHNIQUES

Nondestructive testing becomes an important consideration when coatings move from the research stage to a point where they can be applied commercially. Before a coated structure is put into service, it should be inspected to insure that the coating is adherent and is free of cracks,

(Courtesy of Climax Molybdenum Co.)

Fig. 5.31a. Ballistic impact test furnace with air rifle in position for impacting coated specimen.

Fig. 5.31b. Plasma arc sprayed aluminum piston heads show the results of an impact test to determine coating adherence.

discontinuities, voids or other flaws which might cause failure of the substrate. The possibility of coating flaws is greatly increased by the complexity of the structures being coated. The following are some of the nondestructive methods that are being used or are being investigated to determine the quality of coatings.

Visual Inspection

The simplest quality test is visual observation of the coated piece. Although this is relatively easy to perform, it does not have a great deal of reliability unless performed in good light with the aid of a magnifying glass. In general, the visual inspection should be made by experienced personnel and should be supplemented by other tests.

Red Dye Penetrant

The dye penetrant system is used to detect surface cracks and pits in the coating. The surface to be tested is sprayed with a penetrating dye, which is allowed to soak in. The surface is wiped clean and an indicator is dusted or sprayed onto the coating. After a one-minute waiting period, the dye is drawn out of any surface crack or other shallow blemish and stains the indicator coating, thus revealing the outline of the crack.

Fluorescent Particle Inspection

This method is similar to the dye penetrant method. The test piece is immersed in a solution containing a fluorescent dye, allowing the dye to enter any cracks which may be present. After the surface has been cleaned, the specimen is coated with a developer solution. If there are any flaws in the coating, the fluorescent dye will seep through the developer in these areas and can be seen when an ultraviolet light is held over the sample.

Both dye penetrant techniques are used to detect surface cracks only. Subsurface defects cannot be detected with these methods. Shallow defects are difficult to detect since when the surface is wiped clean before spraying the developer and any penetrant which might have been in a shallow defect would be washed away in this step.

Radiography

Radiographic examination can be used to detect porosity, cracks and voids in the interior of a coating. X-rays or gamma rays are passed through the test material and onto a film plate so that a permanent record of the defects are obtained. The intensity of the x-ray and gamma penetrating radiation is modified as it passes through the material that is being tested. Any porosity, cracks or differences in thickness will show up differently on the film and the location of any internal defects can be ascertained by proper interpretation of the film.

Radiographic methods are slow and relatively expensive to set up. Health precautions must be taken to protect the operator against radiation. Complex shapes are difficult to analyze and defects must be more than 2 per cent of the total coating thickness in order to be detected. The radiographic technique, therefore, is not suited for detecting small flaws in large, complex structures, although it gives good results for less complicated units.

Eddy Current

Surface and subsurface flaws can be measured by using eddy currents, induced in the part to be inspected by joining it with the electromagnetic field of a primary AC coil. The part may pass through the primary coil, or a probe coil can be moved over the part surface. The induced eddy currents react on the primary coil and change its impedance. The induced currents in the test piece are influenced by the defects in the piece, the conductivity of the piece and by its hardness and size. By using the proper coils and frequencies any one or two of these variables or defects may be measured or detected. Eddy current inspection is not practical when highly configurated and complex structures must be tested. Aves (*21*) has found that this type of inspection is not suitable for detecting edge or corner defects, and in some cases, surface roughness will produce signals similar to those produced by a defect.

Ultrasonic Testing

Ultrasonic testing consists of introducing ultrasonic energy into a test material and measuring the modifications of the sound field caused by defects present in the material. The energy which is reflected back by the defects in the sample is picked up by a transducer, transformed into an electrical impulse and displayed on a cathode-ray oscilloscope.

Longitudinal waves, shear waves or surface waves may be used for ultrasonic testing depending on the size and shape of the test piece and the size, shape and orientation of the defect. Longitudinal waves enter the test material in a straight line until they strike a boundary or a discontinuity. The first boundary encountered by the entering wave is the one between the transducer and the test piece. A portion of the incident energy is reflected by the boundary and an initial pulse or "blip" is registered on the oscilloscope screen. The rest of the incident energy travels through the material until it strikes a defect or the back surface. The location of the defect can be found by measuring the distance of the blip caused by the defect from the blips caused by the front and back surfaces of the test piece (Figure 5.32).

Discontinuities may be oriented in such a way that straight-beam techniques cannot be used to detect them. In such instances the sound beams are introduced at an angle to the surface of the test material in order to produce shear waves as shown in Figure 5.33. If the angle at which the beam is introduced is increased sufficiently, surface waves will be formed. These waves follow the contour of the test piece and are extremely valuable in detecting flaws near the surface. Figure 5.34 is a sketch of a surface wave test and shows how a defect in the sample is registered on the oscilloscope screen.

There are two basic types of ultrasonic testing systems. In resonance testing a variable frequency is used. When the natural frequency of the material thickness is reached, the amplitude of the vibration increases a

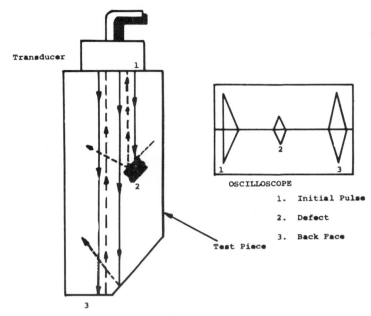

Fig. 5.32. Schematic diagram showing the path of longitudinal ultrasonic waves.

great deal and can be produced on an oscilloscope. Resonance techniques are used mainly for measuring thicknesses. In the pulse-echo technique a constant frequency is used to introduce the waves into the test material for a fraction of a second. The sound travels through the material and the energy reflected from a flaw or the back surface is picked up by the transducer. The transducer then sends out another pulse of sound energy and waits for the reflected energy.

Whymark and Lawrie (*58, 59*) utilized the transmission technique for detecting defects in coatings and to determine the bond strength between coating and substrate. They found that, for the coating and sub-

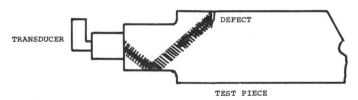

Fig. 5.33. Path of shear waves used to detect defects which are difficult to locate with longitudinal waves.

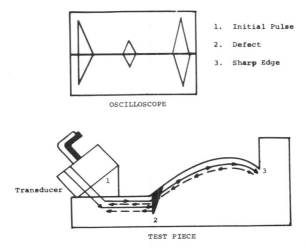

Fig. 5.34. Surface waves used to detect defects close to the surface.

strate they were investigating, measuring the amount of energy reflected by a flaw was not adequate in detecting the defect. This was caused by the fact that the coating-substrate bond had such a high reflection coefficient that any defect would not change the total reflection coefficient appreciably.

There are several limitations to the use of ultrasonic testing, as illustrated by the following examples. If the surface of the material being tested is rough, the entering sound beam will be scattered to such an extent that the test is useless. Very complex pieces are difficult to test without contoured transducers and irregular surfaces will cause blips on the oscilloscope screen which make detection of defects difficult. Grain boundaries within the material will act like defects and scatter the entering sound waves. Defects which are at an angle to the incident beam are difficult to spot because they reflect the energy at an angle rather then in a straight line to the transducer. It is often difficult to distinguish between discontinuities that occur close together. In addition, defects are detectable only if the size is an appreciable portion of a sound wavelength.

Evaporograph

Another nondestructive inspection technique is the evaporograph, described by Aves (21). It consists of a thin membrane whose front face is coated with a material which absorbs radiation and changes temperature from point to point depending on the amount of radiation received. If white light illuminates the membrane, the variation in the oil thickness on the membrane changes the interference colors of the reflected white light, thus providing a visible colored image of the field of view. Voids or cracks in a coating will radiate heat differently from the rest of the sample and a picture of this defective area can be obtained by this technique.

The nondestructive testing methods which have been described are only some of the techniques available to the engineer for evaluating coatings before subjecting coated components to actual service con-

TABLE 5.1. SCREENING TESTS USED TO EVALUATE
HIGH TEMPERATURE COATINGS

Test	Factors Evaluated
Thermal cycling static oxidation	Oxidation resistance Thermal shock resistance
Thermal cycling sustained load test in air	Effect of coating on ductility of base Effect of specimen creep on the coating Integrity Thermal shock resistance Oxidation resistance
Plasma-arc or oxyacetylene torch test	Coating emissivity Thermal shock resistance Oxidation resistance Melting point
Bend tests	Coating adhesion Ductility
Tensile tests	Effect of coating or processing on base material strength Ductility Elongation
Metallographic observation	Substrate structure Coating structure Coating thickness Bond characteristics Detection of inclusions

Microhardness traverse	Cross-sectional hardness of coating and
	   substrate
	Effect of processing on substrate
	   ductility

Electron microscope inspection	Detection of injurious inclusions in substrate or coating
Fatigue tests	Effect of coating or coating process on substrate Fatigue properties Fatigue strength of coated metal system

X-ray diffraction	Determine the results of processing on
	   coating composition. The composition
	   of the coating at various depths within
	   the coating can be determined by con-
	   trolled polishing followed by x-ray

ditions. These methods represent the more common nondestructive techniques used for coating evaluation. Other nondestructive tests as well as more detailed descriptions of the tests outlined here, are presented by McMaster (*60*).

CONCLUSION

Screening tests are performed during the initial phase of coating development. Since the number of samples that are coated during this optimization phase is large, a combination of screening tests should be used to eliminate the samples which do not perform satisfactorily. A screening program usually consists of some type of oxidation test, metallographic examination, flame test and tensile test. The coatings which look promising in the screening tests are tested under conditions which simulate the intended service environment.

Once a particular coating system is found to withstand service conditions, it may be used to protect the full-scale structure. Techniques must be developed for nondestructive testing of the final structure before it is put into service. Nondestructive techniques can be used to detect surface and subsurface holes, cracks and discontinuities as well as poor coating to substrate bonding. Tables 5.1, 5.2 and 5.3 are a compilation of many of the screening, proof and nondestructive tests being used for high-temperature coating evaluation.

Before selecting test methods for coating evaluation, the service requirements and the environments to be simulated should be defined.

TABLE 5.2. PROOF TESTS USED TO EVALUATE COATED
STRUCTURES UNDER SIMULATED
OPERATIONAL CONDITIONS

Test	Factors Evaluated
Ram jet	Thermal shock resistance, Vibration resistance, Erosion resistance, Oxidation resistance, Structural integrity Evaluated simultaneously over a representative time-temperature profile (i.e., glide re-entry profile)
Quartz lamps test	Simulates the effects of aerodynamic heating on a desired configuration
Plasma arc test	Can be programmed to follow a desired time-temperature profile determining variations of the factors evaluated in the ram jet test, vibrations and erosion excluded
Rocket blast tests	To evaluate coating under exceptionally severe thermal shock conditions

TABLE 5.3. NONDESTRUCTIVE TEST TECHNIQUES FOR USE IN TESTING COATING INTEGRITY BEFORE SERVICE

Test	Purpose of Test
High temperature controlled oxidation followed by magnified visual observation	To determine coating flaws by observation of thorough coating oxidation To determine weakness existant in bond strength due to thermal shock
Evaporgraph	To indicate coating discontinuities on flat panel surfaces Unsuited for determining edge or corner defects
Electromagnetic inspection	To detect porosity, cracks, pits; unsuitable for determining corner or edge flaws
Ultrasonic inspection	To detect surface and subsurface flaws; unsuitable for use on thin skins or in determining corner or edge defects
Fluorescent particle inspection	To detect surface cracks, pits and similar coating defects
Red dye penetrant	To detect surface flaws in coatings
Radiographic inspection	Sensitivity difficult to control for detecting small coating flaws in assembled structures
Visual magnifying glass	Not as suitable or reliable as when performed after an exposure test

Once these service conditions are determined, tests which simulate conditions experienced by the end-item coating can be selected.

REFERENCES

1. Browning, M. E., "Developmental Work in High Temperature Protective Coatings for Refractory Metals at General Dynamics/Fort Worth," Presented at the Fifth Meeting of the Refractory Composites Working Group, General Dynamics/Fort Worth, August 1961.
2. Anon., "Temperature: Its Measurement and Control in Science and Industry," (Am. Inst. Phys.), New York, Reinhold Publishing Corp., 1941.
3. Bockris, J. O'M., et al., Eds., "Physico-Chemical Measurements at High Temperatures," London, Butterworths' Scientic Publications, 1959.
4. Klopp, W. D., et al., "Development of Protective Coatings for Tantalum-Base Alloys," ASD TR-61-676, Battelle Memorial Institute, March, 1962.
5. Chao, P. J., et al., "Research in Protective Coatings for Refractory Metals," Report No. PF 62-7, Presented at the Sixth Meeting of the Refractory Composites Working Group, The Pfaudler Co., June, 1962.
6. Koubek, F. J., and Timmins, A. R., "High Temperature Materials Test Facilities at the Naval Ordnance Laboratory," NAVWEPS Report 7315, U.S. Navy Ordnance Laboratory, January, 1961.
7. Holtz, F. C., et al., "High-Temperature Oxidation Protective Coatings for Vanadium-Base Alloys," ARF 2227-2, Armour Research Foundation, November, 1961.

8. Withers, J. C., "Electroplated Cermet Coatings for Oxidation Protection of Substrates in Excess of 2000°F," WADD Technical Report 60-718, October, 1960.
9. Brown, B. F., et al., "Protection of Refractory Metals for High Temperature Service," NRL Report 5550, November, 1960.
10. Cox, J. W., *et al.,* "Oxidation Protection of Columbium Base Alloys," UCRL-6187, University of California, October, 1960.
11. Klopp, W. D., *et al.,* "Development of Protective Coatings for Tantalum-Base Alloys," Presented at the Refractory Composites Working Group Meeting, Battelle Memorial Institute, August, 1961.
12. Jefferys, R. A., and Gadd, J. D., "Development and Evaluation of High Temperature Protective Coatings for Columbium Alloys," ASD Technical Report 61-66, Part I, Thompson Ramo Wooldridge, Inc., May, 1961.
13. Mason, C. R., and Walton, J. D., "Investigation of High Temperature Resistant Materials," Summary Report No. 2, Georgia Institute of Technology, 1958.
14. Chao, P. J., *et al.,* "Recent Development of Oxidation Resistant Coatings at Pfaudler," Presented at the Fifth Meeting of the Refractory Composites Working Group, The Pfaudler Co., July 1961.
15. Gadd, J. D., "Design Data Study for Coated Columbium Alloys," TM-3362-67, Thompson Ramo Wooldridge, Inc., March, 1962.
16. Levinstein, M. A., "Coating Evaluation Procedures," Presented at the Refractory Composites Working Group Meeting, General Electric Co., June, 1962.
17. Lawthers, D. D., and Sama, L., "High Temperature Oxidation Resistant Coatings for Tantalum Base Alloys," ASD Technical Report 61-233, Sylvania Electric Products, Inc., 1961.
18. Chao, P. J., *et al.,* "Development of a Cementation Coating Process for High-Temperature Protection of Molybdenum," ASD Technical Report 61-241, The Pfaudler Co., June, 1961.
19. Powers, D. J., *et al.,* "Investigation of Feasibility of Utilizing Available Heat Resistant Materials for Hypersonic Leading Edge Applications," WADC Technical Report 59-744, Vol. VII, Bell Aerosystems Co., December, 1960.
20. Graham, J. W., and Hall, W. B., "Protective Coatings for Molybdenum Alloys," Report No. R60FPD307, General Electric Co., March, 1960.
21. Aves, W. L., Jr., "Evaluation and Testing of High Temperature Oxidation Resistant Coatings on Refractory Metal Substrates," Presented at the Second Annual Symposium on Nondestructive Testing of Aircraft and Missile Components, Chance Vought Aircraft, Inc., February, 1961.
22. Jefferys, R. A., and Gadd, J. D., "Development and Evaluation of High Temperature Protective Coatings for Columbium Alloys," ASD Technical Report 61-66, Part II, Thompson Ramo Wooldridge, Inc., September, 1961.
23. Weissman, M., "Investigation of Protective Coatings for Refractory Metals," Report No. NA-61-807, North American Aviation, Inc., July, 1961.
24. Rosenbery, J. W., *et al.,* "Evaluation of Materials Systems for Use in Extreme Thermal Environments Utilizing an Arc-Plasma-Jet," WADD Technical Report 60-926, University of Dayton, June, 1961.
25. Wurst, J. C., "The Development of a Standardized Screening Test for High Temperature Materials," Presented at the Sixth Meeting of the Refractory Composites Working Group, University of Dayton, June, 1962.
26. Molella, D. J., "Investigation and Evaluation of Available Hypersonic Probe Materials and Oxidation-Resistant Coatings for Possible Use at 4000°F for 60 Seconds," Technical Memorandum No. ME-5-59, Picatinny Arsenal, December, 1959.
27. Molella, D. J., "Evaluation of Oxidation-Resistant Coatings in a Water-Stabilized Electric Arc at Temperatures to 2325°C (4215°F)," Technical Memorandum No. ME-1-62, Picatinny Arsenal, May 1962.

28. Aves, W. L., Jr., and Bourland, G., Jr., "Coating and Testing a Columbium Alloy Edge Assembly at Vought," Presented at the Sixth Meeting of the Refractory Composites Working Group, Chance Vought Corp., June, 1962.
29. Perkins, R. A., "Oxidation Protection of Structures for Hypersonic Re-entry," Presented at the Sixth Meeting of the Refractory Composites Working Group, Lockheed Missiles and Space Co., June, 1962.
30. Perkins, R. A., et al., "Problems in the Oxidation Protection of Refractory Metals in Aerospace Applications," Presented to the Seventh Symposium on Ballistic Missile and Space Technology, Lockheed Missiles and Space Co., August, 1962.
31. Cherry, J. A., et al., "Progress Report on the Evaluation of High Temperature Materials," Contract No. AF 33(616)-7838, University of Dayton, July, 1962.
32. Perkins, R. A., Personal Communication, August 28, 1962.
33. Stevens, R. A., and Burroughs, J. E., "Hyperthermal Research Facility," Progress Report No. 2, Presented at the Sixth Meeting of the Refractory Composites Working Group, General Dynamics/Fort Worth, June, 1962.
34. Milling, R. W., "The High Temperature Hypersonic Gasdynamics Facility," ASD Technical Note 61-107, Aeronautical Systems Division, September, 1961.
35. Lowrie, R., "Research on Physical and Chemical Principles Affecting High Temperature Materials for Rocket Nozzles," Semiannual Progress Report, Union Carbide Research Institute, December, 1961.
36. Ungar, E. W., "Rocket-Nozzle Testing and Evaluation," DMIC Memorandum 77, Battelle Memorial Institute, December, 1960.
37. Levitt, A. P., "The Variable Parameter Rocket Engine - A New Tool for Rocket Nozzle Materials Evaluation," Technical Report No. WAL TR 766.1/2, Watertown Arsenal, October, 1960.
38. Jablansky, L., "Investigation of the Effects of Simulation and Scale Up on Performance of Rocket Nozzle Materials," Presented at the DOD Rocket Nozzle Materials Development Meeting, Picatinny Arsenal, June 1962.
39. Colucci, S. E., "Experimental Determination of Solid Rocket Nozzle Heat Transfer Coefficient in Ballistic Missile and Space Technology," Vol. II, New York, Academic Press, 1960.
40. Ungar, E. W., "Heat Transfer to a Solid Propellant Rocket Motor Nozzle," Presented at the American Rocket Society Solid Propellant Rocket Conference, Battelle Memorial Institute, January, 1962.
41. Bartz, D. R., "A Simple Equation for Rapid Estimation of Rocket Nozzle Convective Heat Transfer Coefficients," Jet Propulsion, 27, No. 1, 49 (1957).
42. Goodman, E., et al., "Electrodeposition of Erosion and Oxidation Resistant Coatings for Graphite," Final Summary Report, Value Engineering Co., March, 1962.
43. Robbins, D. L., "Study of Thermal Erosion of Ablative Materials," Report No. 0274-01-3, Aerojet-General Corp., July, 1960.
44. Preston, J. B., and Kattus, J. R., "Determination of the Mechanical Properties of Aircraft-Structural Materials at Very High Temperatures After Rapid Heating," WADC Technical Report 57-649, Part II, Southern Research Institute, December, 1959.
45. Kattus, J. R., et al., "Investigation of Feasibility of Utilizing Available Heat-Resistant Materials for Hypersonic Leading-Edge Applications," WADC Technical Report 59-744, Vol. V, Southern Research Institute, November, 1960.
46. Lyman, T., Ed., "Metals Handbook," Cleveland, Am. Soc. Metals, 1948.
47. Anon., ASTM Standards, Philadelphia, Am. Soc. Testing Materials, 1958.
48. Payne, B. S., Personal Communication, August 15, 1962.
49. Raring, L. M., Chairman, "Evaluation Test Methods for Refractory Metal Sheet Materials," Report No. MAB-176-M, National Academy of Sciences-National Research Council, September, 1961.

50. Anon., "Flame Spraying Processes," Bull. No. 141, Metco, Inc., June, 1959.
51. Leeds, D. H., Personal Communication to the Editor, June 22, 1962.
52. Leeds, D. J., "High Mach Phase III, Arc Plasma Spray Investigations," Report No. TDR-930(2240-30)TR-1, Aerospace Corp., January, 1962.
53. Moore, D. G., *et al.,* "Studies of the Particle-Impact Process for Applying Ceramic and Cermet Coatings," ARL Report No. 59, Natl. Bur. Standards, August, 1961.
54. Bliton, J. L., and Rechter, H. L., "Determination of Physical Properties of Flame-Sprayed Ceramic Coatings." *Am. Ceram. Soc. Bull.,* 40, No. 11, 683-688 (1961).
55. Bliton, J. L., "Refractory Composites and Coatings," Presented at the Sixth Meeting of the Refractory Composites Working Group, Armour Research Foundation, June, 1962.
56. Ingham, H. S., Jr., "Evaluation Methods for Flame Spray Coatings," Presented at the Sixth Meeting of the Refractory Composites Working Group, Metco, Inc., June, 1962.
57. Blanchard, J. R., "Oxidation-Resistant Coatings for Molybdenum," WADC Technical Report 55-205, Climax Molybdenum Co., June, 1955.
58. Whymark, R. R., and Lawrie, W. E., "Ultrasonics and Ceramic Coatings," WADD Technical Report 60-157, Armour Research Foundation, May, 1960.
59. Lawrie, W. E., "Ultrasonic Methods for Nondestructive Evaluation of Ceramic Coatings," WADD Technical Report 61-91, Part I, Armour Research Foundation, April, 1961.
60. McMaster, R. C., Ed., "Nondestructive Testing Handbook," New York, The Ronald Press Co., 1959.

6

DESIGNING WITH COATINGS

JOHN HUMINIK, JR.

Vice President and Senior Scientist
Value Engineering
Alexandria, Virginia

Throughout industry, a host of far-reaching high-temperature problems exist which can utilize coatings to advantage—hot slag and metal resistance, hot chemical resistance and hot gas resistance are required of all manner and variety of equipment. The high-temperature materials industry is offering an ever-increasing selection of structural materials for the designer in this field. It is his responsibility, however, to scan these materials in an effort to select what he considers the optimum for his particular application.

Design Teams

The complex problems associated with the creation and building of high-temperature equipment or systems requires that people with specialized education and experience be coordinated into a functional team. Frequently, this is done by having a mechanical design section integrate the entire project until it is ready for production. This design section utilizes materials engineers, thermodynamics specialists, process engineers, stress analysts and the quality control department as consultants from which they obtain the information that is needed to complete the project.

In general, most design activities have materials engineers to advise the product designer on his choice of construction materials. Frequently, this materials engineering group has a testing laboratory to prove the compatibility of materials with a particular design. Therefore, the wise designer makes it a practice to work closely with the metallurgists, ceramists and plastic specialists when he begins his design. The process engineers who specialize in welding, heat treating, riveting, coating, forming and machining should also be consulted early in the program to ensure that the design chosen can be put into practice with the desired materials.

The designer of equipment that must operate at high temperatures is faced with the requirement that he familiarize himself with the properties, prices and problems of the available coating systems. He must know how each system is stipulated on drawings and how each is actually applied. He not only must select the structural base material for its mechanical and physical properties but he must select a coating system that will not cause detrimental effect on the properties of the base material, during application or operation.

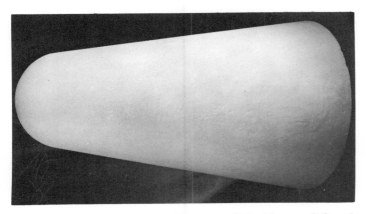

(Courtesy of The Marquardt Corp.)
Fig. 6.1. Nose cone coated with a protective ceramic material.

If the company is not large enough to justify the employment of the various specialists needed for a good high temperature design team, the employment of independent consultants must be considered. Justification for hiring outside firms or individual consultants will vary with each company and with each problem, some of the more common reasons appear below:

1. Short team programs do not demand an increase in permanent staff.

2. By utilizing the equipment available at an independent organization, capital equipment need not be purchased for problems not of a continuing nature.

3. Use of an independent organization permits complete control over both design and cost.

4. Troubleshooting and checking conclusions are advantageously done outside. If laboratory results do not work in practice, an independent group may be able to detect the fault more easily.

5. Independent evaluation of your product can usually be used legitimately in advertising.

THE SERVICE ENVIRONMENT

Before a designer can intelligently select the base materials and necessary coatings, he must understand the service environment. This is a necessity if reliable and economical end items are to result. The most important factor is, of course, the high temperature. However, the temperature is of no importance at all if some other environmental factor destroys the coating before fulfilling its intended function.

Since laboratory testing cannot simulate service conditions exactly, it is usually necessary to submit the final product to its most severe test—actual operation, before the designer can say "it works." This situation exists because materials have weaknesses, flaws or defects and man has an inability to predict these shortcomings, even with the help of all manner of statistical analysis, test equipment and inspection techniques.

The service environment can be considered to be all of the phenomena and occurrences that will influence the operation of a particular piece of high temperature hardware. An example would be a space craft that heats up on launch and then operates in a space environment where it must contend with both particulate and electromagnetic radiation and the impact of micrometeorites or meteorites, after which it attains even higher temperatures then when it was launched, as it enters the earth's atmosphere again.

Chemical Environments

Coatings for chemical processing equipment are usually required to be highly reproducible and reliable because of the length of time this equipment will operate. Parts operating in flue gases or inside furnace combustion chambers are required to withstand cyclic heating and hot spots without failure.

Materials used in high temperature chemical plant applications are usually subjected to conditions much different from those the designer had expected. Every unit must be shut down periodically, bringing with it some additional and unpredictable situations. Before it is shut down, the unit is usually purged, by either steam or some other gas or liquid. Then various parts of the unit are opened for inspection or cleaning. This exposure to moisture and fumes from neighboring processes can cause material damage not previously expected. Therefore, the designer must know how the material will tolerate inoperative periods at ambient temperatures as well as the more routine and predictable conditions of service at higher temperature.

Liquid metal corrosion is a problem in the operation of nuclear energy heat exchangers. The problem also exists in liquid metal cooling of rocket nozzles and re-entry structures.

The mechanism of this corrosive effect is different from ordinary corrosion which takes place in aqueous chemical or electrochemical environments or gaseous environments. According to Dvorak (1), ordinary corrosion is characterized by electron transfer while liquid metal corrosion can proceed by any of the following means:

1. Uniform corrosion as a result of simple melting.
2. Formation of low melting alloys between the hot and solid metal.
3. Intercrystalline penetration by the corrosive media.
4. Special types of corrosion caused by impurities in the hot metals.

Uniform corrosion by simple melting is, for example, the corrosion of titanium in molten lead or the corrosion of an austenitic stainless steel by sodium.

As an example of intercrystalline high temperature destruction, one can mention the corrosion of ferritic and austenitic stainless steels by sodium sharply contaminated with oxygen if the temperature is over 1250°F. A Soviet scientist (V. S. Lyasenko) attributes this destruction to the formation of alloys between sodium oxide and intercrystalline matter (1). The latter is found in most steels; it is composed of oxides (SiO_2, CaO, MgO, Al_2O_3) that readily form low-melting alloys with sodium oxide and enable the hot sodium to penetrate along the grain boundaries. This statement by Lyasenko is based on a spectral analysis of a corroded piece of steel which found sodium at considerable depth. A suitable high-temperature coating would prevent this.

Another type of high-temperature corrosive attack is the so-called extraction corrosion. An example is "extraction" of nickel from austenitic stainless steel by Pb-Bi alloys, mercury or lithium. The reaction starts on the surface, causing austenite eventually to transform to ferrite. The ferrite may then be unsatisfactory for the structural requirements and fail catastrophically.

When molten metals contain impurities such as nitrogen, carbon or hydrogen, the impurities may increase the ability of the liquid metal to penetrate the structural metal. Carbon in either sodium or lithium can carbonize stainless steels at 1470°F. Hydrogen in sodium causes an attack of zirconium, resulting in the formation of zirconium hydride which precipitates in the grain boundaries during cooling, creating a brittleness.

Still another possibility is the destruction of zirconium by oxygen-contaminated sodium. In this case ZrO_2 is formed on the surface of the zirconium. Stress cracks develop in the oxide layer and extend into the base material.

Other hot chemical environments have been known to attack high-temperature metals. Notably, sulfur has been credited with many failures in chemical processing equipment. The author has seen cracks occur in pressure vessels in the areas where a soap solution was used to detect pressure leaks. In that case the soap was rich in sulfur. The damage did not occur until the pressure vessel was operated for considerable time at high temperature, thus allowing the sulfur residue to penetrate the metal. In this case a coating was not needed— only more care in checking for leaks. Another consideration when operating dissimilar coated or uncoated parts in a large or complex chemical system is the possibility of one material being carried to another which is intolerant of it. The chemical media then can become aggressive toward a small part of the system until failure occurs. Weld joints are examples of areas that usually possess slightly different corrosion resistance from that of the unheated metal.

The design factors affecting high-temperature systems utilizing hot chemicals or liquid metals which must be considered are listed below:

1. Maximum operating temperature.
2. Cyclic fluctuations in temperature.
3. Temperature drop of the entire system.
4. Purity of hot metal or chemical.
5. Rate of flow of the hot media.
6. Number and variety of material which come into contact with the hot media.
7. Mechanical stresses on the structure.

The technical advantages of using hot metals for coolants or higher temperatures for certain chemical processing equipment can be more easily attained if coatings are considered in the design stages. The disadvantages in using coatings for such systems are based on the difficulty of coating intricate piping and the lack of knowledge in coating joints and valves. Figure 6.2 reveals a vitreous coated duct system which is typical of the parts used in chemical industry. These parts were fired at 1000°F before being placed in service.

The possibility of having a coating actually attack the material it is supposed to be protecting always exists. A good example of this is the work at the National Bureau of Standards by Richmond (2) showing a frit composed of silicon oxide, barium oxide, beryllium oxide and cerium oxide that actually attacked type 310 austenitic stainless steel at high temperature instead of protecting it. Further tests indicated that the cerium oxide was detrimental above a certain percentage.

Low-Pressure Environments

Whenever extremely low environmental pressures are encountered, such as in high-temperature vacuum apparatus or in outer space, direct evaporation of the coating must be considered. Under these conditions the surface stability of coatings depends only on the surface temperature

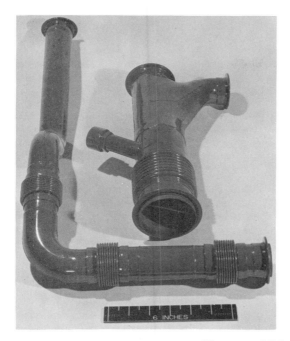

(Courtesy of Solar Aircraft Co.)

Fig. 6.2. High pressure duct system coated to protect the low alloy steel from corrosion and oxidation.

and corresponding vapor pressure. Direct evaporation of a coating is significant not only as a loss in thickness, but because it may affect the optical properties of the surface. The emittance and reflectivity characteristics are related to surface conditions and would no doubt change as the surface evaporates.

Since coatings are usually made up of several materials, each of which may have a different vapor pressure at a given temperature, non-uniform loss of surface usually occurs. This could account for severe reflectivity or emittance changes. In general, the emittance of a pure metal is very low, usually below 0.04, whereas oxidized surfaces of that same metal may exceed 0.8. Some of the newer high-temperature coatings are deposited as a pure metal and then oxidized before going into service. Should these thin oxide layers be removed by evaporation where there is insufficent oxygen to form a new oxide, the metal surface, with its different and undesirable optical properties, is left as the working surface. (The oxide is usually more stable than the metal; molybdenum, tungsten and the other refractory metals are the exceptions.)

Fortunately, these particular material involvements can be simulated in the laboratory so that the designer can be familiar with the problems that his coated parts will encounter at low pressure. Also, since an increasing amount of vacuum research and testing is being funded by the Defense Department and NASA, more specific data for design use can be expected in the near future.

Radiation Environments

Structural shapes and other hardware used within nuclear power reactors or in space applications can be subjected to both particulate and electromagnetic radiations of sufficient energy to alter or destroy the properties of the materials used for their construction. It is known, for example, that the solar cells of Earth satellites such as Bell Telephone's Telstar are deteriorating because of irradiation. Therefore, it is necessary to research the mechanism of radiation failure in the coating systems being considered for interplanetary space ships. The radiation damage problems are of greatest interest to the solid state physicist who is still searching for the most compatible theoretical explanation of these phenomena. It has been well established that radiation damage is due to ionization effects *or* to dislocation or displacement of atoms in a material by charged particles passing through it. The number and magnitude of these displacements are functions of the intensity and duration of irradiation and the type and structure of the material.

In general, the following effects of irradiation on materials have been observed in nuclear reactor experiments (3):

1. Decrease in density
2. Change in dimensions
3. Increase in hardness
4. Increase in tensile strength
5. Increase in yield strength
6. Decrease in electrical resistivity
7. Decrease in ductility
8. Change in magnetic susceptibility

The type of radiation damage which can occur also depends on the kind of material. For example, it is generally agreed that plastic materials are disturbed drastically by ionization effects, while metals are not as readily ionized. In metals, which are good electrical conductors, most of the damage is attributable to displacement. Some ceramic materials which might be used in coatings are known to be affected quite drastically and similarly to plastics by ionization.

Ionization damage is not always possible in ceramic coating materials because some of them can be considered to be electrically conductive. It is felt that the ability to conduct electricity also allows the material to dissipate ionization effects, as is evident by the conductive materials heating up during irradiation. On the other hand, the coating systems that are insulative will retain the electrons liberated by ionization, and this will result in permanent changes, manifested by a decrease in Young's modulus. However, at the higher temperatures this will be less likely to occur since the ceramic coatings behave plastically like metals. Therefore, their ability to deform possibly allows them to tolerate radiation damage more easily.

The energy intensity of cosmic rays is sufficient to produce secondary particles, including electrons and mesons, when they strike the Earth's atmosphere. Although cosmic rays can produce atomic dislocation in materials, their effects are considered negligible at the present time (4).

The electromagnetic radiation from the sun in the visible and near visible wavelengths varies inversely with the square of the distance. Thus, the total solar radiation at Earth is 440 Btu/(hr) (ft^2); at Mars it would be 195 Btu/(hr) (ft^2); and at Venus, 840 Btu/(hr) (ft^2) (5). The retention of this heat in any coating depends on its surface characteristics. Since the earth and its atmosphere absorb only two-thirds of this solar radiation, any satellite or space vehicle near the sunny side of the earth would also receive this reflected radiation as well as the direct rays. The earth also radiates heat directly; the amount depends on the surface temperature and is consistent with the assumption that the earth is essentially at thermal equilibrium, receiving the same heat input from the sun as it re-radiates to space. The earth radiates at the longer wavelength, while the sun radiates mostly at the shorter wavelengths. Therefore, the heat received by a coated or bare surface of an aerospace object will depend on the absorptivity of the surface for both the longer earth wavelengths of radiation and the shorter wavelengths received from the sun. The heat-balancing system must be well designed to handle this combination effectively.

Hostile Gaseous Environments

Gaseous environments as encountered in chemical processing equipment, high-temperature metallurgical furnaces or as by-product fumes from neighboring processes pose problems that are principally chemical in nature. They attempt to react with coatings in a manner that will break down their protective characteristics by forming low-melting eutectics or brittle compounds, corroding them, or penetrating them to attack the structural base material. Hot coatings can be expected to absorb the normal gaseous elements found in the earth's atmosphere. If oxygen or hydrogen is able to penetrate the coatings through defects or because of diffusion phenomena, embrittlement of some of the structural refractory metals presently being used by designers is likely to occur.

Entrance into the atmospheres of other planets will cause material problems that are different from those found on earth. For example, the atmosphere surrounding Jupiter is believed to be mostly hydrogen and helium though some methane and ammonia may be present. Severe buffeting of the space craft also may occur to a suspected turbulent atmosphere on that planet. Most of the other large planets (beyond Mars) also have reducing atmospheres. Coatings that must withstand high-speed entry into both oxidizing and reducing atmospheres will need special qualities not always found in today's coatings. Venus has an atmosphere which is rich in carbon dioxide resulting in a lower heat transfer than for the earth's atmosphere. Mars is said to have an atmosphere rich in nitrogen, resulting in entry heating problems very similar to those of the earth's.

Water vapor can also attack metals simply for reasons of chemical equilibrium. In these instances, the dissociation pressure of the metal oxide is higher than the partial pressure of oyxgen in the water vapor (6). Carbon monoxide and carbon dioxide are also known to have attacked metals at high temperatures.

Sulfur is known to attack many materials if present in a gaseous stage at high temperature. Hydrogen sulfide and sulfur dioxide and elemental sulfur gases can form sulfide scales on materials by fundamentally the same mechanism as oxygen forms oxide scales. The evaluation of the reaction mechanism is, however, more complicated because the number of stable sulfides, in particular for the transition metals, is much greater than that of the oxides. In addition, sulfates may be formed when oxygen is present with sulfur.

Chlorine and hydrogen chloride will attack molybdenum disilicide coatings by forming silicon and molybdenum chlorides, which volatilize readily.

As nearly all gases can affect coatings in some way, the designer should have tests carefully conducted to evaluate any unfamiliar coating-base material combinations in the presence of a gas.

Abrasive Environments

Particles of matter carried in a gas or liquid impinging upon a surface at high temperature constitute one of the most destructive environments that can be encountered. This is especially true in solid propellant rocket nozzle applications where high-pressure gases carrying particles at several times the speed of sound tend to wear away the coatings. Temperatures in this type of environment will range from 4500 to 7000°F; however, these temperatures occur in the flame, and the coatings do not necessarily attain these temperatures.

Beyond the earth's atmosphere, the environment encountered by a vehicle would not be entirely free from matter which could inflict damage on its surface; for example, there exists a large cloud of particles generally found in the plane of the planets. The source of these clouds of ceramic-like dust is believed to be comets, although a portion presumably comes from the asteroids. This cloud of particles is believed to extend from the region of the sun to beyond the orbit of earth. The layer has been observed by reflected light in the outer solar corona and from the zodiacal light near the earth. They presumably range in size from one to fifty microns. At the present time there is not sufficient knowledge of how these particles will affect coatings. Work has been done by NASA to learn more about the collision and penetration characteristics of micro-meteorites dust (7). Relatively little data are available on the resistance of specific coatings to this environment.

OPERATIONAL TIME PERIOD

In addition to knowing the environment that a coating system will encounter, the time and conditions of operation must be considered. The longer operating systems can fail from diffusion phenomena or propagation of defects. Cyclic heating can develop stresses that cause coatings to shear off at the base material because of thermal expansion mismatch.

Coatings are used to protect structural metals while under a mechanical load. If this load is applied for an extended period of time, the creep behavior of the coated material must be known. The majority of coated components used in such service conditions under which creep characteristics of the material are an important factor in determining the life of the part are fabricated from high-temperature alloy or superalloy sheet stock.

Work conducted by Cuthill and co-workers (8) on stainless steels and "Nichrome" alloys has shown that a ceramic coating with a total cross section of less than 1/5 of that of the specimen can decrease the creep rate as much as 50%. The degree of improvement obtained in these tests is a function of the coating and base material composition in combination with the test temperature and the stress. This degree of improvement was shown to be greatly affected by relatively minor constituents in the base material. Some of the coatings failed during high stress at relatively low temperatures. Apparently the coating was not sufficiently plastic to deform with the specimen, and cracking of the coating occurred.

Internal-combustion engine valves have been coated with cobalt-chromium-tungsten in an attempt to improve the creep resistance, hot hardness and the general corrosion resistance. Aircraft engine exhaust valves operate up to 1600°F and durability is of utmost importance. The corrosion products include sulfur, lead, bromine, and chlorine. The efficient operational life of valves normally approaches 1000 hours, and longer life is attained in some cases. For example, a lifetime of 1200 hours is obtained when the valves are coated with a 67 Co-28 Cr-4 W-1C alloy. Aluminum-coated valves also have shown increased life.

Heat exchangers, exhaust manifolds and other high production parts are often aluminum dip-coated, followed by a diffusion heat treatment. High-temperature tests under cyclic thermal shock conditions such as rapid heating to 1600°F followed by air-blast cooling have conclusively indicated the usefulness of aluminum coatings on low carbon steel. Normally, aluminum-coated steel operates at temperatures well below 1000°F and is used more for its corrosion resistance than as a heat barrier. It does, however, prevent oxygen from reaching the steel because of its impervious nature.

Furnace parts that may operate for 10,000 to 20,000 hours require reliable materials that also must resist thermal cycling over a large temperature range. Furnaces routinely operate from ambient temperatures to 2300°F. Some furnaces operate up to 4000°F and a very few will reach 5000°F. In general, the furnace industry has a well developed knowledge and extensive experience from years of applied research. Competition has required that low-cost solutions be obtained in all designs; this is possible because of the relatively high quantities of parts produced. The military and space acitivites are usually not so fortunate, since their environments are not as well defined and the tolerances are more rigid. An exception is the coating of nozzle diaphragms and turbine blades for jet engines where the production rates are high. Chromalloy Corporation has reportedly coated one million such items in recent years.

Sometimes the operational time period for a coating may be very short. An example of such a requirement is a coating used to protect a part that is being brazed in air (Figure 6.3). The time a coating must be protective and the type of mechanical loads and chemical environment it must withstand must be ascertained before any selection of a final coating system is made.

THERMAL PROTECTIVE SYSTEMS

Once the service environment is understood and the time of operation is known, the designer must determine which thermal protective system will perform the task at the lowest cost. He may choose a system that utilizes only a minimum number of coated parts or he may require that the entire system function solely on coated parts and assemblies.

Assuming that a decision has been made to use a coating system to protect a particular structure, such as a re-entry vehicle or a rocket nozzle, someone on the design team must report on the existence and availability of a satisfactory design. He may know of an almost identical application where a particular design performed well, or he may face an entirely new problem where no engineering history can be directly applied.

(Courtesy of Solar Aircraft Co.)
Fig. 6.3. Stainless steel manifold parts being brazed in air with a high nickel brazing alloy. Special coating allows brazing in air.

The following 7 thermal protection concepts are available to the designer:

(1) *Heat Storage:* Retention of heat by the material, resulting in an increase in its temperature.

(2) *Liquid Film:* The liquid film that forms on the surface increases its own temperature, rather than transferring heat to the substrate.

(3) *Transpiration Cooling:* A liquid is ejected from the interior of a body and absorbs heat at the hot surface; it then leaves the system carrying heat with it.

(4) *Ablation:* Ablation is similar to liquid film cooling; it differs however, in that it melts, volatilizes or decomposes and blows away, carrying heat with it. The next layer is then heated until it is removed and the process continues similarly until the flight is finished.

(5) *Magnetohydrodynamics:* The effect of a magnetic field upon an ionized fluid stream adjacent to a material. The magnetic field deflects the fluid from its normal path, reducing the heat transfer by thickening the boundary layer and consequently reducing the velocity and temperature gradient adjacent to the surface.

(6) *Thermoelectricity:* Heat is transferred between two materials by means of an electric current through a junction of dissimilar metals or

coatings. The phenomenon is known as the Peltier effect, and can be used with an external power source to construct a refrigeration unit without moving parts.

(7) *Heat Transfer:* Heat is transferred through a material or a coated material to a circulating coolant which in turn transfers it to the atmosphere or to a heat storage area. If it uses the heat storage technique, the system will have a saturation point beyond which the surface material begins to raise its temperature.

DESIGN INNOVATIONS

Since it is known that no single coating or coating system is a cure-all and because some coatings for a particular structural material do not work in certain environments, the designer must use ingenious combinations of coatings in an attempt to obtain acceptable part life. An example of this approach was described by William L. Aves of Chance Vought Aircraft Company, during the first meeting of the AF-NASA Refractory Composites Working Group in 1958. He discussed inorganic refractory coating efforts, particularly the development of multi-layer flame sprayed metal-ceramic coatings. A problem existed with regard to aircraft safety in that an inadvertent rocket motor ignition might cause serious damage to the aircraft. To protect the aircraft it was essential to contain the entire rocket motor blast under full burnout conditions using a breech in the rocket exhaust. Initial tests of 0.125 inch 17-7 PH stainless steel, heat-treated to 190 KSI and coated on the blast side of the breech with a flame sprayed 20-mil alumina failed with complete burn-through in 0.7 second. The alumina completely eroded away. To develop a suitable breech material, tests were run in a rocket motor facility with tied down rockets for the full burning time.

Test specimens were exposed to the exhaust blast from 2.75 inch FFAR solid propellant rockets with an actual thrust time of two seconds, the excess fuel continuing to burn for about a minute more at a greatly reduced temperature. Six tests were made using coatings of: electroplated chromium (30 mils thick), two coatings of high melting silicates with organic binders (1/8 inch thick), a 40 mil molybdenum sheet electroplated with 50 mils of chromium and 1 mil of nickel, a 1/8 inch asbestos-impregnated silicone liner, all bolted or bonded to a 71 mil 17-7 PH steel-domed breech. None of the above coatings lasted the full two minutes. However, it was noted that molybdenum was highly erosion-resistant and had excellent bonding properties, while the alumina seemed to have good thermal shock resistance and heat-insulating properties.

To capitalize on these properties Chance Vought made a series of test specimens consisting of flame-sprayed alternating multilayers of molybdenum and alumina. For example, six layers of molybdenum with an average thickness of 2 mils per layer were applied alternately with five layers of alumina with a thickness of about 7 mils per layer onto the 71 mil 17-7 PH steel-domed breech. The resulting specimen endured the entire test with no spalling of the coating and only slight erosion of the top layer of molybdenum. In two other tests the 17-7 PH steel plate was coated with about an 18-mil multilayer of molybdenum and alumina as before and on top of this was bonded: a chromium-nickel electroplated 40-mil molybdenum sheet and, in the other test, a 1/8 inch glass-impregnated phenolic compound. On testing, the molybdenum and glass-impregnated phenolic liners shattered and disintegrated but the multi-layered coating on 17-7 PH backup plate did not burn through. A 32-mil titanium sheet bolted to the 17-7 PH steel back-up plate in a similar fashion without the multilayered coating burned completely through in 1 second.

To evaluate the reliability of such multilayered coatings several more were tested. The specimens were prepared conventionally by thoroughly cleaning and grit blasting with clean alumina or 20 to 40 mesh crushed quartz grit. Using either a Metco or Mogul oxyacetylene flame spray gun (interchangeably), the molybdenum was applied by metallizing with a 1/8-inch wire and the alumina was applied either in powder or rod form with equally good results for this application. The specimens withstood the test easily with no burn-out, and one was reused and ex-posed to a second full test with only negligible change. Other tests where-in multilayered molybdenum alumina coatings have protected 60 mils of aluminum for two seconds of thrust burning from a rocket blast temperature of 4500°F without damage have been made. This coating consisted of 4 layers of Mo with a total thickness of 12 mils, alternated with three layers of Al_2O_3 with a total coating thickness of 39 mils. In this particular test the aluminum substrate reached a maximum temperature of about 500°F 50 seconds after the test began. The same type of multilayered Mo-Al_2O_3 coating with a total thickness of 51 mils completely protected a titanium alloy substrate under identical test conditions, the substrate reaching a maximum temperature of about 600°F 50 seconds after the test began.

Similar tests were performed using other multilayer combinations applied to different substrates. Poor performance results have been ob-tained with zirconia regardless of what other laminating metal was used with it, complete burn-out usually occurring in the rocket motor test. One impressive test was made wherein a 40-mil fiber glass substrate with a 50-mil alternating multilayer coating of Mo-Al_2O_3 survived the rocket test without any serious effect. Such a composite system might find application as a good thermal and erosion-resistant coating perhaps for the protection of aircraft leading edges. It has been found that the Mo coating should be applied as the first coating since it forms a better bond than "Nichrome" or a ceramic.

Another test was made of a multilayer Mo-Al$_2$O$_3$ coating wherein 9 layers of Mo were alternated with 8 layers of Al$_2$O$_3$ on a "Hastelloy X" afterburner rake. The rake was exposed three times for a total of 18 minutes to severe vibration and a temperature of 3000°F. The coating lost about three layers during each exposure but completely protected the rake.

Another technique is to flame-spray strips of Mo and Al$_2$O$_3$ alternately, using a barrier or masking screen, and changing the direction of spray so as to build up a complex weave or grid type of coating of alternating rows and perpendicular columns of Mo and Al$_2$O$_3$. This technique apparently gives a more resistant, better bonded coating. The weaker plane in a multilayer Mo-Al$_2$O$_3$ coating exists in the alumina and not at the Mo-Al$_2$O$_3$ interface. A multilayer coating of Mo and Al$_2$O$_3$, when tested in tension, parted within the Al$_2$O$_3$ layer and not at the Mo-Al$_2$O$_3$ interface. The multilayered Mo-Al$_2$O$_3$ coating has been put on graphite and the resulting body was tested for 10 minutes at 4500°F in air without failure of the coating.

Other important attributes of multilayered coatings include good compressive strength. By varying the metal layers, either considerable distortion or no distortion of the coating can be attained prior to cracking of the coating. The harder, more brittle metals allow but little distortion before cracking. Additional burst strength and adhesion have been obtained in simple internal or external tubular parts by adjusting and synchronizing two flame spray guns to deposit suitably thick coatings, one to follow the other. By rotating the tube at the desired rate, two continuous laminated coatings suitable for certain parts of rocket motors can be obtained.

Solar Aircraft Company has frequently used sprayed ceramic coatings applied in layers as seen in Figure 6.4. Solar has also developed a series of ceramic, cermet and metallic coating mixtures during the 15 years it has been performing research in this field. It has identified some 29 coatings for use in specific environments when applied to a wide range of structural metals.

Marquardt used a woven metal mesh or perforated metal sheet in a chemically bonded, self-supporting refractory coating (Figures 6.5 and 6.6). The largest job using this technique was a heat exchanger, 4 feet in length and 2 feet in diameter with a 1 5/8-inch coating. The reinforcing wire had 25,000 spot welds made on it and one ton of coating ingredients were used. The melting point of the Marquardt composites ranges from 3500 to 4200°F.

In some cases, it may be possible to use the "coating" as the entire high temperature part. Electroforming, which utilizes thick plating on a shaped mandrel to give the part, or flame spraying onto a shaped mandrel also can develop suitable parts. In both processes the mandrel is subsequently removed from the deposits.

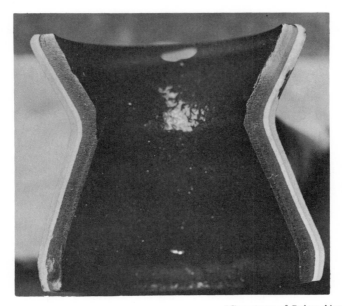

(Courtesy of Solar Aircraft Co.)
Fig. 6.4. Rocket nozzle built up in layers by plasma-flame spraying. Wall composition varier from 100% tungsten (inside) to 100% zirconium oxide (outside).

Only metals that can be plated well can be electroformed. Thus, the process is unsuitable at the present time for Be, Ti, Mo, W, Ta, and Cb. Electroforming is actually occurring if thick electroplates are used to protect a part; this is because the coating itself will have structural load-bearing properties. The properties of composites arising from this kind of processing should be carefully evaluated before production quantities are attempted.

Vapor deposition has also been used to form thick coatings; however, success has been uncommon except with the pyrographite coatings.

Figure 6.7 shows the use of refractory bonded graphite on a tungsten part in an attempt to conquer a severe rocket motor problem.

A similar tungsten-graphite bonding problem has been undergoing research at Narmco. This work utilizes carbide coating on the graphite followed by hot pressing to the tungsten. In this work, the graphite substrates were slurry-coated with a composition consisting of $60Ta\text{-}10ZrH_2\text{-}30W$ powder blend and fired at 5500°F to fuse the coating and to convert the metals to their respective carbides.

A high melting point alone is not always needed to protect structural materials. An interesting innovation has been made by Sama and Campbell of General Telephone and Electronics Laboratories (*9*), who showed

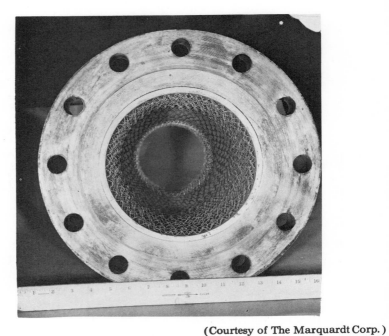

Fig. 6.5. Exit nozzle with wire reinforcement in place before refractory coating is applied.

that a tin-aluminum coating could operate in a high velocity environment and not be "blown" away even though it is in a liquid state. The system actually forms a molten layer on the surface during high-temperature operation. Table 6.1 reviews the coatings being developed

TABLE 6.1.

Alloys	Sylcor-GT&E Labs Coating Designation	Type	Method	Approx mp, °F	Max Protection Temp, °F
Ni, Co	NC101	Aluminide	Pack	2800	2200
Cb	R 503	Aluminide	Hot dip	3000	2300
Cb	R 504	Ti-Al	Pack dip	2700	2500
Cb	R 506	Ti-Si	Pack	2800	2600
Cb	R 505	Sn-Al	Slurry	*	2400
Ta	R 501, 505A	Sn-Al	Slurry	*	3300
Ta	R 506	Ti-Si	Pack	3200	2800
Mo	R 507A, B	Mod. Silicide	Pack	3450	3200
W	R 507A, B	Mod. Silicide	Pack	3750	3450

*Liquid phase exists at 1200°F and above

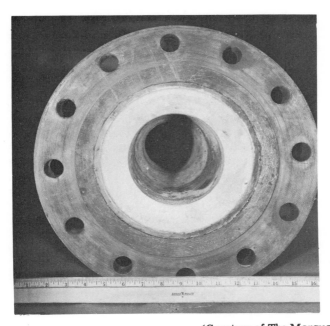

(Courtesy of The Marquardt Corp.)

Fig. 6.6. Exit nozzle with refractory coating (Thermarq ZSF101) applied to form a structurally sound coating.

by Sama and Campbell. Note that the two slurry coatings of tin-aluminum are functioning at a temperature well above their melting point.

Ablative plastic coatings can be sprayed by plasma torches over laminated ceramics, cermets or metals to form unusual and effective high-temperature re-entry bodies.

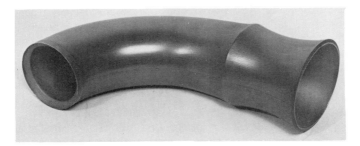

(Courtesy of Super-Temp Corp.)

Fig. 6.7. A combination tungsten and high density graphite nozzle bonded with a refractory cement.

Diffusion coatings or electroplates have been spray-coated and slurry-coated with ceramics for high-temperature abrasive environments. In these cases the diffusion or electroplated coating furnishes the oxidation protection while the ceramic furnishes the abrasion resistance.

Other investigators have experimented with vapor-deposited coatings over sprayed or electrodeposited coatings. Success has been slight in those cases because of thermal expansion differences causing cracking of the coating while cooling in the retort.

The designer must use initiative and careful planning to select a multi-composed system that will have a reasonable chance for success.

Frequently, it will be desirable to apply different coatings to different areas of a part. This is required, for example, when one end of a part is subjected to wear and the other end subjected to impact blows or perhaps chemical attack.

Reinforced plastics have been gaining increased attention for use in structural applications in the past few years mainly due to high strength, low density, low thermal conductivity, excellent resistance to chemical attack and good electrical properties.

Structural plastics, as a general category of design materials, is as broad a generalization as metals. The most common structural plastics utilize a fibrous material which provides good tensile properties and an organic resin binding material which supports the fibers and provides good compressive properties. This composite material is generally referred to as a fiber reinforced plastic, or simply as a structural plastic. The reinforcing fiber may be any one of a variety of glasses, inorganic fibers, organic fibers or metals. The binding materials can be polyester, silicon, phenolic epoxy or melamine resins whose properties can be altered tremendously by modification of their molecular arrangement. The reinforcement and binding materials selected determine the overall characteristics of the composite material.

One of the most severe deterrents to expanded use of plastics, until recently, has been their severe deterioration in performance after exposure to temperatures over 400°F. Recently, however, several heat-resisting resins have been developed which have extended the temperature capability of these materials up to 1000°F for certain short time applications. These materials have been used experimently in temperature environments higher than 5000°F for very short periods. Various coatings applied by plasma spraying or electrodeposition have enabled these materials to operate for longer time periods above 500°F.

The thickness of coating required to protect a structural plastic is determined by the time of exposure and the tolerance of the material combination to thermal shock as cooling thickness increases. In one case an insulator (bubbled zirconia or the foamed silicates) was used over the structural plastic followed by a suitable erosion resistant top coat.

Experimental heat shields have been made by using honey-combed metals which have been partially embedded in the plastic and sprayed with a cermet until the protruding honeycomb is completely covered.

FABRICABILITY

Coatings which can be formed, welded, machined and repaired without detriment will always be desired. However, today's products tend to lack, at least in part, some of these characteristics which means that one must design around these limitations.

Riveting or bolting is presently the preferred method for joining, especially for metals that recrystallize from the welding heat. Because many of the refractory metals depend on cold work to produce a fibrous structure that is strong and ductile, any heating such as welding anneals the metal and causes loss in strength and ductility. Standard procedure is to form the parts and then pre-assemble them so that all holes can be drilled properly. The rivets or bolts are then coated separately and applied to the coated parts. The entire assembly is then recoated. Close inspection of the parts is required during the entire fabrication to insure cracks or laminations do not go unnoticed. Figure 6.8 shows a riveted part which was coated after assembly. The appearance of such parts are not usually outstanding since complete cleaning cycles cannot be used. This is because chemical cleaners may be entrapped under rivet or bolt heads causing destructive corrosion.

Most parts are welded before coating when this is required. In general, no welding should be performed on coated parts since brittle alloys and compounds could form in the weld zone or weld deposit as a result of base metal-coating reactions. Frequently a weld is difficult to coat because of the various oxides which have formed during the actual welding operation. Thorough cleaning will insure a minimum of difficulty in this respect. The tin-aluminum coatings developed by General Telephone and Electronics Laboratories have been actually repair welded with little difficulty. Recoating is required however, to re-establish complete high temperature protection.

Surface Finish

The as-deposited surface finish of coatings will vary with the type of coating and the process used to apply it. The rougher coatings will require some kind of machining operation to make them smoother for certain applications. Usually grinding is used as the machining method since it does not apply as much stress on the brittle coating materials as do the other methods.

Generally, most coatings will be in the 75 to 300 RMS finish range as-deposited. The exception is electrodeposited coatings which will essentially develop the same surface finish as the base material. The silicide coatings have a finish which is nearly as smooth as the starting base

(Courtesy of The Pfaudler Co.)
Fig. 6.8. A pack-cementation coated 12" x 12" molybdenum alloy skin panel. Part required coating without cleaning due to lap joints.

material. After grinding a finish ranging from 1 to 32 RMS can be attained on nearly all of the coating materials. All grinding operations should be undertaken with care, since heat checking can occur on the coating surface from local overheating by the grinding wheel. A chemical penetrant inspection would probably reveal heat checks (a type of craze cracking) and should be used as final inspection tool.

Coating Thickness

Coating thickness tolerances that can be maintained also vary with the coating process and the shape of the part being coated. In general, the control of thickness in electroplating is the most easily attained with accuracy to 1 mil. The pack cementation and vapor deposition processes can be controlled fairly well. The sprayed coatings can rarely hold tolerances better than 2 mils; usually they range from 3 to 4 mils in tolerance as deposited.

Complex shapes can have wide variation in coating thickness, especially in the recessed areas where coating is difficult. Holes, thin slots, and fasteners all tend to suffer from insufficient coating thickness. Designers must therefore be very careful in specifying a minimum thickness for these hard-to-coat areas, otherwise failures in these sensitive areas can be expected.

Control of the thickness of production or semi-production high temperature parts is an important quality control function. It is also important from the weight standpoint. After all, coatings do weigh something and must be considered, just as the weight of the other components of the system are considered.

Calculation of these factors is usually by weight and can involve a considerable amount of time when a large number of types or alternate solutions are being appraised at one time. To simplify the task and reduce the chance of error, Richard L. Giovanoni of The Westinghouse Electric Corporation has devised alignment charts for round shapes, similar charts can be made for other shapes. A sample of one of the charts prepared by Giovanoni appears in Figure 6.9. This chart is used in the following manner. Line 1 is drawn from A to C. Intersection on Scale B is marked. Intersection point on B is connected to value of density on Scale D and extended to Scale E where the answer is obtained.

Example Problem: Find weight of 0.005 in. tin coating
applied to a 0.050 in. base wire.
$$D_1 + D_2 = 0.050 + 0.060 = 0.120$$
$$T = 0.005$$
Density = 0.264
Answer: 0.265 x 10^{-3} lbs per linear inch of coated wire.

This chart can be expanded for use with any coating as long as the user knows the density of the particular coating material of interest.

The reader may wish to study the derivation of this chart more closely. Therefore, the mathematics from Giovanoni's notebook are presented below:

"In preparing such a chart, it simplifies construction to get rid of the square terms and reduce the basic formula to a linear function by expanding the squares. In our specific case, we came down to a 1st power equation of the form.

$$\text{Wgt} = \frac{\pi dL}{2} T (D_2 + D_1) \tag{1}$$

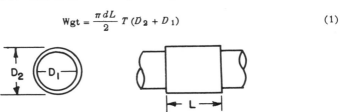

d = density of coating material
T = thickness of the coating
L = length of coating
D_1 = OD of base material
D_2 = Coated OD of final combination

This brings it down to terms read directly from the normal specifications. We arrived at the above Eq. 1 by the following steps:

$$Wgt = d\,(\pi R_2{}^2 L - \pi R_1{}^2 L). \tag{2}$$

We can put common terms together and get:

$$Wgt = \pi dL\,(R_2{}^2 - R_1{}^2). \tag{3}$$

Expanding R^2 terms we then have:

$$Wgt = \pi dL\,[(R_2 + R_1)(R_2 - R_1)]. \tag{4}$$

Since specifications are usually written in terms of diameter, we can substitute $D/2$ for R. We also note that $R_2 - R_1$ is actually coating thickness, therefore we get:

$$Wgt = \pi dL \left(\frac{D_2}{2} + \frac{D_1}{2}\right) T. \tag{5}$$

Then finally, factoring the 1/2 term we get Eq. 1.

In making the chart we have used a unit length of 1 inch and a density in terms of lb/in^3. Diameter and thickness are in terms of inches.

In some cases, where a standard density is employed, then a further simplification can be made where $\frac{\pi d}{2}$ is a simple constant."

HANDLING PRECAUTIONS

A certain amount of damage might occur to a coating before it is actually used because of the following factors:

1. Mechanical wear and tear during handling.
2. Oxidation in air causing changes in the emittance characteristics.
3. Corrosive atmospheres causing material deterioration.
4. Contamination from dirt and dust or oils.
5. Fingerprinting of thermal control coating materials by workers.

These preventable problems can be related to the way the coated item is handled, stored, or adjusted into position in the assembly. The quality control inspectors must be extremely sensitive to the problems occurring from rough handling techniques or accidental droppage. Improper packing causing undue stress on a part has been known to fracture an otherwise acceptable item.

The designer must carefully consider how his parts are to be handled from the time they are manufactured up until their actual usage.

This is an often neglected phase of a design job because people tend to unconsciously assume that the handlers, packers, inspectors, etc., are all familiar with the material. This has proved to be the exact opposite on many occasions, much to the dismay of all concerned.

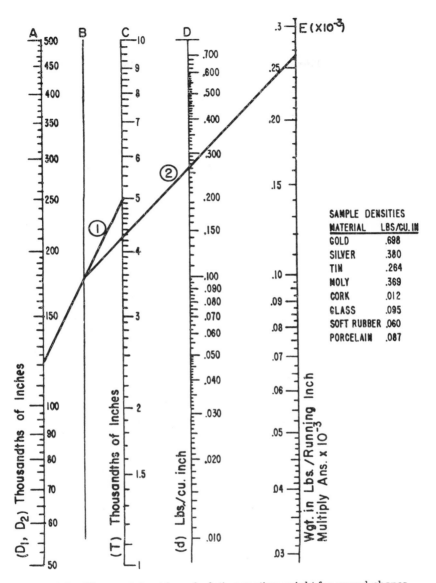

Fig. 6.9. Alignment chart for calculating coating weight for round shapes.

Generally, it is not known that today's high temperature coatings are sensitive, requiring rather careful treatment. This careful treatment extends back to the raw material, which should be of uniform quality both in surface condition and chemical composition. Surface defects such as inclusions, deep nicks, or burrs should be prevented whenever possible because experience has shown that these are the points where many failures occur. Nonmetallic materials such as graphite or plastics should always be kept oil-free; otherwise, adherence will be poor. Non-uniform chemical composition of the base materials can cause improper coatings to form when a metallurgical bond is desired, such as in a diffusion type process. Heavily scaled materials are difficult to clean before coating, therefore all handling operations such as heat treating should be controlled to reduce the possibility of developing surfaces which are undesirable for coating applications.

During production coating operations all parts must be suspended and racked in such a manner that no damage will occur during the actual coating or in removing the parts from the toolings. Good racking is shown in Figures 6.10 and 6.11.

Fig. 6.10. Solar aluminized Rene' 41 turbojet partitions suitably racked to avoid damage and to insure uniform coating.

Fig. 6.11. Forced air heaters after coating with aluminum-ceramic ALCERMET* mixture at day and night div. of Carrier Corporation.
*Trademark

Procurement Cautions

To prevent a bad experience with an unfamiliar coating process or material it is necessary to ask the following questions:

(1) Is the supplier reputable and sufficiently experienced with this product?

(2) Does he have satisfactory quality control of his product?

(3) Is he likely to have labor problems which might affect delivery dates?

(4) Can he respond to change in your needs rapidly?

(5) Is he close enough for economical delivery?

(6) Can he prove successful applications of a similar nature?

(7) Do other customers of the supplier speak well of him?

(8) Will he help work out any problems that may arise in your particular application?

(9) Does he have other commitments which may affect your order?

(10) Will he help you cut acquisition costs such as qualifying visits, telephone calls, incoming inspection, etc.?

The designer should be aware of the multitude of problems which have been reported by the suppliers during the course of their product development. The same problems again manifest themselves during attempts to use the coatings in production.

The following listing highlights the most obvious of these problems:

Poor adherence, due to improper cleaning or surface preparation.

Pin holes in the coating that allow oxygen to reach the base material.

Poor edge coverage is frequently reported as cause of premature failure.

Excessive diffusion between coating and base material is usually the cause of failure in the systems that operate for a considerable time.

Thermal shock failures caused by thermal expansion mismatch and poor thermal conductivity.

Brittleness, preventing anything but the most cautious handling, especially at low temperatures.

Lack of self-healing ability causes pinholes or cracks to remain open causing attack of the base material.

Poor erosion resistance caused by slight changes in the coating composition.

REFERENCES

1. Dvorak, A., "Problems of Corroding Structural Materials by Liquid Metals," *Jaderna Energie* (*Czech.*) **6**, No. 5, 155 (1960).
2. Richmond, J. C., *et al.*, "Ceramic Coatings for Nuclear Reactors," *J. Am. Ceram. Soc.,* **38**, No. 2 (February, 1955).
3. Housner, H. H., and Roboff, S. B., "Materials for Nuclear Power Reactors," pp. 74-87, Reinhold Publishing Corp., 1955.
4. Allen, J. M., "Environmental Factors Influencing Metals Applications in Space Vehicles," DMIC Report 142, OTS PB 151101, December, 1960.
5. Mitchell, M. W., "Thermal Environments in Space," General Electric Co., Light Military Electronics Department, Utica, New York (From p. 21 ref. above).
6. Kubaschewski, O., and Evans, E. L., "Metallurgical Thermochemistry," London, Pergamon Press, 1958.
7. Summers, J. L., "Investigation of High Speed Impact," NASA TN D-94, October, 1959.
8. Cuthill, J. R., *et al.,* "Effect of a Ceramic Coating on the Creep Behavior of Some High-Temperature Alloys" *Am. Ceram. Soc. Bull.,* **38**, No. 1 (January, 1959).
9. Seigle, L. L., *General Telephone and Electronics Laboratories,* Private Communication to Editor, June 26, 1962.

7

MECHANISMS OPERATING IN COATINGS

MILTON R. SEILER

Battelle Memorial Institute
Columbus, Ohio

AND

JOHN HUMINIK, JR.

Vice President and Senior Scientist
Value Engineering
Alexandria, Virginia

Phenomena occurring within or on a coating operating at high temperatures constitute the most important factor in the useful life of a coating. These phenomena can cause a premature failure if they are not controlled.

Radiation damage, diffusion, oxidation, emittance characteristics, vaporization, chemical reactions, thermal shock susceptibility, and thermal fatigue must all be considered individually and together if coatings are to become more predictable in behavior and more widely accepted as a solution for high-temperature problems. Most of these factors have been covered throughout the book, and it is not necessary to duplicate the material here. This chapter will cover some of the specialized facets of the mechanisms operating within or against a coated part.

THERMAL PHENOMENA

The concept of heat exchange (heat transfer) covers a whole series of phenomena involving the transfer of heat from one set of bodies to another, or from parts of one body to other parts of the same body, as a result of a difference in temperature.

Thermal fatigue and thermal shock are terms used to denote the effects of temperature changes or alternating exposures at higher and lower temperatures on the life of a material. The differences between thermal fatigue and thermal shock are primarily related to the rate of change of temperature and to the severity of the temperature gradient. Thus, when the service life is primarily determined by the number of thermal cycles, failure is generally ascribed to thermal fatigue. However, when the severity of the temperature gradient or the rate of change in temperature is the primary cause of failure, the failure should be ascribed to thermal shock.

When it is important to minimize the effects of thermal fatigue and shock, care should be taken to produce structures essentially free from microcracks and notches. The high stresses which may cause thermal fatigue or shock failures may be due to one or a combination of factors. These factors are: (1) stresses caused by differential thermal expansion, (2) operational stresses, (3) residual stresses from the coating application process, and (4) stresses resulting from differences in thermal conductivities which may be encountered in structures whose elements are constructed from dissimilar metals. Sometimes in joints that are riveted or clamped together, so-called fretting corrosion or friction oxidation may cause fatigue cracks in the coating surfaces which only are in "friction" contact with each other.

The relatively few published articles on actual cases emphasize the many variables usually involved in thermal fatigue or shock situations. Often the failures are attributed to some other cause and are never actually evaluated in their true light. Most failures involve either tri-axial stresses (notch effects) or some kind of material deterioration in addition to the application of the thermal fatigue or shock aspects.

Thermal Fatigue

Thermal fatigue is a term used to denote the effects of temperature changes or alternating exposure at higher and lower temperatures on the life of a material. The changes in temperature may be a part of the operating cycle or they may occur as a result of shut-down of a process which ordinarily would operate at high temperatures. Coatings as well as the structural base materials will suffer from thermal fatigue.

Mechanical fatigue is associated with alternating or varying stresses above or below the elastic limit. Ordinarily it occurs below the elastic limit. Since thermal fatigue involves changes in temperature (which in turn causes changes in the elastic limit), it is often very difficult to ascertain whether or not the failure occurred above or below the elastic limit. For these reasons, it should not be implied that thermal fatigue involves only plastic deformation. However, since an analysis of most thermal fatigue failures indicates that plastic deformation occurred before failure, it is felt that, if in a heating or cooling cycle the stresses do not exceed the elastic limit of the material and that plastic flow does not actually result, thermal fatigue failures will not generally occur. We should bear in mind the fact that at the lower temperatures most coatings do not have much elasticity and are generally considered to be brittle. However, in some cases, the cycles of operation will be so numerous that a fatigue failure might occur from propagation of the smallest coating or base material defect, even if the elastic limit is never exceeded.

In materials that are coated, failures may occur due to large thermal gradients. Generally, the higher conductivity materials have a much better chance for survival since they distribute the heat much more evenly in a relatively short time.

A factor to consider when coating on an insulator is that the gradient in the coating may be less than if the same coating were applied to a conductive base material. However, in a practical sense, the coating must take the full heat load and not depend on the insulative back-up for anything but structural strength.

Thermal Shock

Thermal shock is generally used to describe one or more violent applications of stress caused by a rapid temperature change which produces a severe temperature gradient in the material. Thus, thermal shock is associated with the fact that the resulting stresses exceed the tensile strength of the coating. It is also conceivable that a coating on the opposite side of a panel which is being heated could fail from rapid application of compressive stresses. Sometimes a coating will be cracked on the first heating and flake off as soon as it is cooled. In those cases comparatively long operation can be maintained as long as the temperature is not varied.

The rate of heating has a great effect on whether or not failure will result from thermal shock. Frequently, the designer can reduce or change his heating rate in an effort to prevent thermal overload on a particular coated part, thus preventing premature failures.

Some success in understanding fracture due to thermal shock has been obtained by using the concept of a critical or breaking stress (*1*), which is the maximum permissible value of the algebraic sum of residual and thermal stress. Residual stresses in a coating are simply those arising from a finite difference in the thermal expansion coefficient between base metal and coating. Lauchner and Bennett (*1*) have derived an expression for this residual stress. Extending their results to the case of thermal expansion coefficients being independent of temperature, we obtain

$$S_r = \frac{(a_2 - a_1)(T_e - T_0)}{\dfrac{2}{E_2}\dfrac{t_1}{t_2} + \dfrac{1}{E_1}}\frac{1}{1 - u}$$

where

S_r = residual stress
E_2 = modulus of elasticity of metal
E_1 = modulus of elasticity of coating
t_2, t_1 = metal and coating thickness
a_2, a_1 = metal and coating coefficient of thermal expansion
T_e = equilibrium (zero-stress) temperature
T_o = ambient temperature
μ = Poisson's ratio

In order to predict thermal shock resistance under transient heat flow conditions it is necessary to know the heat transfer coefficient h. If a body initially at temperature T_o is suddenly quenched into a bath at temperature T_q, the heat transfer coefficient at the surface is defined by the relation

$$\text{surface heat flux} = h(T_q - T_s) = -\left.\frac{k \partial T}{\partial x}\right|_{x=0}$$

where k = thermal conductivity and T_s = instantaneous surface temperature.

Kingery (2) has discussed shock resistance and its dependence upon h. For a finite value of h, the temperature change required to fracture, ΔT_f, after exposure of the surface of a solid to a sudden change in temperature, is given by

$$\Delta T_f = k S_b (1 - u) S / h E a$$

where S_b is the breaking stress and S is a shape factor.

The degree to which coatings are resistant to shock is thus seen to depend upon the factor $k S_b (1 - u)/E h a$. The greater this factor, the more resistant is the coating. Thermal conductivity should be high so that thermal gradients are minimized. The thermal expansion coefficient a and the heat transfer coefficient h should be small. Prestressing can also influence shock resistance. Residual compressive stress can improve resistance to the shock of sudden cooling in thin coatings (1). Coatings greater than 30 mils in thickness seem relatively unaffected by prestressing (1).

THE EMITTANCE OF HIGH-TEMPERATURE COATINGS*

Coatings find use as a temperature-control medium in outer space where the only means of heat transfer is by radiation. In the discussion to follow, we will consider the emittance of coatings intended for use at temperatures of 1500°F and above. In recent years there has been

---

*Milton R. Seiler, Battelle Memorial Institute.

increased attention to coatings of this type to dissipate the heat of re-entry and to control operating temperatures of combustion walls and nozzles in rocket propulsion systems.

The definitions of Worthing (3) have become accepted terminology in the field of radiant heat transfer. The term "emittance" refers to a characteristic of a given specimen; its magnitude depends upon the manner of fabrication, surface finish, and thickness of the specimen. *It is the ratio of a specimen's rate of emission of radiant energy to that of a black body radiator at the same temperature and under the same viewing conditions.* "Emissivity" is a special case of emittance and is a fundamental material property. It is defined as *the emittance of a specimen with an optically polished surface and with a sufficient thickness to be opaque at all wave lengths.* The terms "spectral" and "total" refer, respectively, to radiation in a narrow wave length interval and to the weighted average spectral emittance over all wave lengths. "Hemispherical" refers to emission at all possible angles into a hemisphere, while "normal" refers to emission in the direction perpendicular to a surface. In space applications it is obvious that the hemispherical spectral emittance and the hemispherical total emittance of coatings are the most important.

Most coatings for radiation control are applied in thicknesses not exceeding a few mils. Metals are sufficiently opaque in this thickness range so that a base-metal, metallic coating system will possess the emittance of the coating. This is not in general true for ceramic and plastic coatings, which have a transparency that is strongly dependent upon temperature. The result is that emittance in these latter systems is a bulk as well as a surface phenomenon, being dependent upon coating thickness and base-metal emittance in a very complicated manner. Gardon (4) has demonstrated from first principles that emittance is indeed strongly dependent upon thickness in transparent glasses. It was also demonstrated that in thin, transparent sheets (by "thin" we mean that the thickness is less than the reciprocal of the absorption constant), the hemispherical spectral emittance is definitely greater than the normal spectral emittance. For most other materials, the hemispherical and normal values are nearly identical.

It is of interest to consider briefly the methods used in emittance measurements. They may be divided into *absolute* and *comparative* methods. Absolute measurements involve measurement of the power input of a specimen and the resulting absolute surface temperature. The determination of the input power can be quite bothersome unless losses to the power leads, thermocouples, or sample supports are known accurately. Comparative techniques involve a comparison of specimen radiation with that of an artificial black body at the same temperature. The usefulness of this method is that absolute temperature is not critical; instead, the sample temperature is matched differentially with that of the black body. In general, this differential measurement may be performed with greater precision than an absolute temperature measurement. Even if the absolute black body temperature is known to only a few per cent, this does not significantly affect the precision of the measurement since the emittance of most materials is a slowly changing function of temperature. However, the emittance of any material is a difficult property to measure precisely, and there is considerable variation in the data reported by various workers for the same or similar material. Since this is true at moderate temperatures, it will undoubtedly become even more apparent at the higher temperatures. Recently, there has appeared a compilation of many excellent approaches toward emittance measurements (5).

The measurement of sample temperature, whether absolutely or differentially, is usually one of the major sources of error in emittance measurements. No generally satisfactory techniques have been perfected for the determination of the surface temperature of ceramics, metals, and plastics without some perturbation of the sample heat balance. In one of the few attempts, Thomas (6) has treated analytically and experimentally the errors associated with imbedded thermocouples. He found that a 3-mil Pt, Pt-10% Rh thermocouple with a 5-mil bead, used to determine temperature in an 8-mil-thick platinum strip, was in error by 3.2 per cent at 1400°C because of conduction losses to the thermocouple. The use of an optical pyrometer does not completely avoid this problem since the spectral emittance at 0.65 micron must be determined in a separate measurement with reliable temperature data so that the pyrometer reading can be corrected. These are areas requiring more research if reliable emittance data are to be obtained. Furthermore, it must be admitted that the measured emittance of partially transparent materials is sensitive to the method of heating; those methods which lead to high temperature gradients normal to the specimen surface will also lead to erroneously high emittance values because of the influence of bulk emission from volume elements at significantly higher temperatures than the surface temperature.

With all of these problems in mind, it would be proper to review the available data on the emittance of high-temperature coatings. Most measurements have been performed in an air or inert environment; however, to supply information for space applications, measurements in vacuum are also desirable. The hard vacuum of space can cause sublimation, with consequent alteration of surface texture and emittance. The results of hemispherical total emittance measurements in air can also be significantly different from those in vacuum if the specimen's spectral emittance shows considerable structure in the regions of atmospheric absorption bands. Organic coatings would be particularly troublesome in this regard.

Figure 7.1 is a plan view of an apparatus used by the author for the measurement of normal total emittance in vacuum. A thermopile detector is positioned equidistant from an artificial black body and a sample. The axis of the thermopile bisects the angle formed by the normal drawn from the sample surface and the axis of the cylindrical black body. In this way, the thermopile may be allowed to view alternately the black body and the sample with identical detection geometry. To accomplish these measurements, electrically controlled shutters on water-cooled, 1/8-inch apertures are operated from outside the vacuum cham-

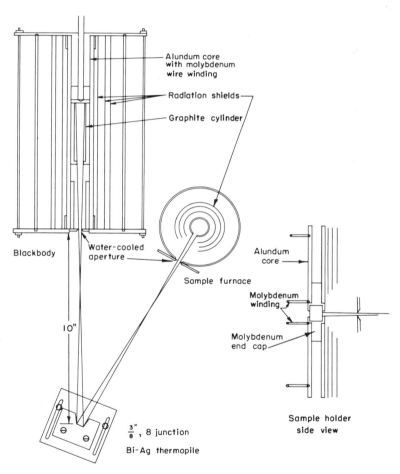

Fig. 7.1. Schematic drawing of emittance apparatus.

ber. A differential thermocouple is used to match sample and black body temperature. The method provides for a relatively compact system with provision for control over an ambient atmosphere. Figure 7.2 is a photograph of the complete system. No great precision is possible since the ever-present temperature measurement problem still exists; however, the results shown in Figure 7.3 for graphite in vacuum (10^{-5} mm Hg) compare favorably with the work of Olson and Morris (7) on graphite in a nitrogen atmosphere and the work of Fieldhouse, *et al.,* (8) on graphite in an argon-hydrogen atmosphere.

In Table 7.1 there is compiled the total emittance of coatings at 1500° F and above. The data are reported in arbitrary increments of 500°F. It should not be assumed that the original workers performed measurements at these exact temperatures; in most cases the data had to be interpolated from curves or tables. It is noted that there is an extreme shortage of data above 1500°F on useful coatings for the refractory metals; furthermore, no data were found for coatings at 3000°F or above. There is also a need for more analysis of the effect of time-at-

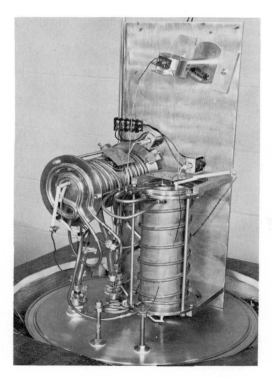

Fig. 7.2. Apparatus for normal total emittance measurement.

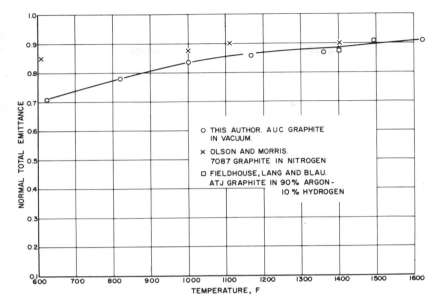

Fig. 7.3. Emittance of graphite.

temperature and the resulting alteration of emittance. Reaction with gases, diffusion of the coating into the base metal, and sublimation can all be important mechanisms at elevated temperature.

With regard to sublimation in vacuum, the maximum possible rate of loss at temperature T (°K) can be predicted from the relation (*16*)

$$\dot{m} = \left(\frac{M}{T}\right)^{\frac{1}{2}} \frac{P}{17.4},$$

where $\dot{m}$ is the loss rate in gm per sec per cm^2 of surface, M is the molecular weight of the material, and P is the vapor pressure in mm Hg at temperature T. A calculation of the loss rate for the refractory metals is shown in Table 7.2.

It can be concluded that coatings are becoming increasingly important as means for temperature control by radiation. There are a variety of methods suitable for determining emittance, but all methods depend ultimately upon precise determination of either the sample's absolute temperature, uniformity of sample temperature, or the difference between sample and reference cavity temperature. This is perhaps one of the most critical problems awaiting solution in this field of high-temperature measurements.

TABLE 7.1. HEMISPHERICAL TOTAL EMITTANCE e_{ht} AND NORMAL TOTAL EMITTANCE e_{nt} OF COATINGS AT TEMPERATURES OF 1500° F AND ABOVE

Coatings	Coating Thickness, mils	Emittance 1500°F	Emittance 2000°F	Emittance 2500°F	Remarks	Reference
Coatings on "Inconel"						
Flame-sprayed alumina	30	0.45 to 0.50			e_{ht}	9
N-143 enamel (boron-free barium beryllium silicate frit with cerium oxide additive)	2	0.73			e_{ht}	10
A-418 enamel (NBS frit No. 332 – 70%, Cr_2O_3 – 30%)	5.4	0.68			e_{nt} in air	11
A-418 enamel		0.75			e_{ht}	10
B-1 enamel (NBS frit No. 332 – 60% black stain – 25% Cr_2O_3 – 15%)	6	0.68			e_{nt} in air	11
B-4 enamel (NBS frit No. 332 – 60% Cr_2O_3 – 5% CoO – 15% Fe_2O_3 – 20%)	3.8	0.77			e_{nt} in air	11
B-12 enamel (NBS frit No. 332 – 60% $CoO \cdot Mn_2O_3$ Spinel – 40%)	2	0.85			e_{nt} in air	11
B-12 enamel	6.9	0.81			e_{nt} in air	11
W-3 enamel (NBS frit No. 332 – 60% CeO_2 – 20% SnO_2 – 20%)	2	0.70			e_{nt} in air	11

Coating						Ref.
W-3 enamel	6	0.60			e_{nt} in air	11
Flame-sprayed alumina	not given	0.55	0.45		e_{nt} in air	12
Flame-sprayed zirconia	not given	0.52	0.45		e_{nt} in air	12
Zirconium oxide	not given	0.70	0.64		e_{nt} in air	13
Coatings on Stainless Steel						
Rokide A on 430 SS	30	0.45	0.45		e_{ht} in vacuum (10^{-5} mm Hg)	9
Rokide Z on 430 SS	30	0.40			e_{ht} in vacuum	9
Rokide Z on 430 SS	10	0.50 to 0.60			e_{ht} in vacuum	9
Rokide on 446 SS	not given	0.62	0.55		e_{nt} in air	13
A-418 enamel on 321 SS	not given	0.74			e_{ht} in vacuum (10^{-5} mm Hg)	10
N-143 enamel on 430 SS	not given	0.6–0.7			e_{ht} in vacuum	10
Coatings on Iron						
Flame-sprayed alumina	not given	0.89			e_{ht} in vacuum	10
Coatings on Molybdenum						
N.R.C. Al-Si	5	0.35	0.33	0.33	e_{nt} in helium atm.	14
N.R.C. Al-Si (pre-oxided)	5	0.42	0.35	0.30	e_{nt} in helium atm.	14
Durak-MG	1.5	0.39	0.35	0.37	e_{nt} in helium atm.	14
Durak-MG (pre-oxidized)	1.5	0.47	0.41	0.36	e_{nt} in helium atm.	14
Coatings on Tungsten						
Modified W-2	1.5	0.31	0.36		e_{nt} in helium atm.	14
Modified W-2	2.5	0.36	0.38			

(*Continued*)

TABLE 7.1. (*Continued*)

Coatings	Coating Thickness, mils	Emittance			Remarks	Reference
		1500°F	2000°F	2500°F		
Coatings on 80 Columbium-10 Titanium-10 Molybdenum Alloy						
Modified W-2	1.5 to 2.5	0.35	0.43	0.49	e_{nt} in helium atm	14
Coatings on Graphite						
SiC	not given	0.79	0.71	0.62	e_{nt} in helium atm	14
Coatings on Titanium						
Rinshed-Mason J-15934 paint (silicone paint with aluminum pigment)	1	0.66			e_{ht} in air	15
Rinshed-Mason Q-36K802 (silicone paint with carbon black pigment)	0.9	0.75			e_{ht} in air	15
Vita Var PV 100 (white paint with silicone vehicle and titanium dioxide pigment)	0.7	0.71			e_{ht} in air	15
Pratt and Lambert 91-1524 paint	0.5	0.7			e_{ht} in air	15
Coatings on Molybdenum — 0.5% Titanium						
Durak MG	not given	0.63	0.63	0.63	e_{nt} in 90 Argon – 10 H_2	8
Durak MG	not given	0.60	0.59	0.55	e_{nt}	8

TABLE 7.2. MAXIMUM LOSS RATE IN VACUUM OF UNCOATED
REFRACTORY METALS AT 4000°F

Element	Vapor Pressure,[a] mm Hg	$\dot{m}$, g/cm^2-sec	In./hr[b]
Molybdenum	10^{-4}	1.1×10^{-6}	2×10^{-4}
Tantalum	5×10^{-7}	7.8×10^{-9}	6×10^{-7}
Rhenium	10^{-6}	1.6×10^{-8}	10^{-6}
Tungsten	8×10^{-8}	1.2×10^{-9}	9×10^{-8}
Zirconium (molten)	10^{-3}	1.1×10^{-5}	2×10^{-3}

[a]"Vapor Pressure Curves for the More Common Elements," Compiled by R. E. Honig, RCA Laboratories, Princeton, N. J.
[b]Estimated using room-temperature density.

There are yet insufficient data on emittance above 1500°F. Variables such as coating thickness, roughness, composition of the environment, oxidation, sublimation, diffusion of the coating, and even the method of sample heating need to receive close attention.

CHEMICAL REACTION

The nature and severity of the reactions which might occur between coatings and their substrates is a difficult and complex subject. Experimental data and studies of solid-solid chemical reactions have been extensively reported in the literature, but relatively few studies have been made on the reactions that occur at high temperatures between the coating and the metal it supposedly protects.

Reaction studies made at high temperatures usually consist of compatability evaluations in which various reactants are heated together for short times prior to microscopic examination for any evidence of harmful reactions such as the formation of volatile or molten phases. Table 7.3 reviews some of the experimental results of these compatability tests (*17*).

The foremost conclusions one can make about high temperature reactions are that these reactions take place in a very short time period at the temperatures which we are discussing (1500 to 7000°F) depending on the materials involved. Even in those cases in which the product of a reaction is solid, the temperature dependence of diffusion processes is such that they will occur relatively rapidly and thus not offer a wide barrier to the progress of the reaction. Because of this ability to approach equilibrium at a finite rate at high temperatures, it is generally concluded that thermodynamic factors will be the major criterion determining whether or not a reaction will occur and that the indefinite circumvention of a harmful, but thermodynamically favored, reaction by means of a diffusion barrier is not possible (*17*). It appears, from the present state of the art, that the most that can be expected is that the extent of the

TABLE 7.3. SUMMARY OF THE REPORTED REACTIONS
BETWEEN REFRACTORY METALS AND OXIDES

System	Temp, °F	Time, min	Remarks	Reference
$W + ThO_2$	5072	1	Particles sintered in foil; no other reaction	18
$W + ThO_2$	5432	1	Same as above	18
$W + ThO_2$	5432	3	Same as above	18
$W + ThO_2$	3992	4	Reaction occurs	19
$W + Al_2O_3$	3992	1	Al_2O_3 molten; no reaction; oxide did not adhere to the foil	18
$W + Al_2O_3$	4532	5	Al_2O_3 molten; wet and adhered to foil; interface is very sharp; no reaction	18
$W + Al_2O_3$	5432	1	Same as above; Al_2O_3 vaporizing fairly rapidly	18
$W + ZrO_2$	4532	1	Particles sintered to foil; no other reaction	18
$W + ZrO_2$	5072	1	ZrO_2 partially molten; adhered to the foil; no evidence of other reaction	18
$W + ZrO_2$	5432	1	ZrO_2 completely molten; adhered well to the foil; no indication of other reaction	18
$W + ZrO_2$	2912	4	Reaction occurs	19
$W + MgO$	3992	1	Some slight sintering; interface slightly irregular	18
$W + MgO$	4532	5	Interface severely eroded; all of the MgO reacted	18
$W + MgO$	5432	1	Same as above	18
$W + MgO$	3632	2	Reaction occurs	19
$W + HfO_2$	5252	2	HfO_2 molten, wets tungsten; slight reaction in the form of interdiffusion; no new phases distinguishable; same as above	18
$W + HfO_2$	5432	1	Same as above	18
$W + Y_2O_3$	3992	2	Particles sintered to foil	18
$W + Y_2O_3$	4532	1	No other reaction	18
$W + Y_2O_3$	5432		Y_2O_3 molten; no other reaction	
$W + BeO$	3632	2	Reaction occurs	19
$Mo + Al_2O_3$	3272		No physical alteration of interface	
$Mo + BeO$	3272		No physical alteration of interface	
$Mo + BeO$	3452	4	Reaction occurs	19
$Mo + MgO$	3272	4	No physical alteration of interface	
$Mo + MgO$	2912	4	Reaction occurs	19
$Mo + ThO_2$	3272		No physical alteration of interface	
$Mo + ThO_2$	3992	4	Reaction occurs	19

(Continued)

TABLE 7.3. (*Continued*)

System	Temp, °F	Time, min	Remarks	Reference
Mo + TiO$_2$	3272		No physical alteration of interface	
Mo + ZrO$_2$	3272		No physical alteration of interface	
Mo + ZrO$_2$	3992	4	Reaction occurs	19
Nb + Al$_2$O$_3$	3272		No physical alteration of interface	
Nb + BeO	3272		Penetration along grain boundaries and alteration of oxide; corrosion of oxide observed; new phase formed at interface	20
Nb + MgO	3272		No physical alteration of interface; penetration along grain boundaries and alteration of oxide	20
Nb + ThO$_2$	3272		No physical alteration of interface; corrosion of oxide observed; penetration along grain boundaries and alteration of oxide	20
Nb + TiO$_2$	3272		No physical alteration of interface; corrosion of oxide observed	20
Nb + ZrO$_2$	3272		No physical alteration of interface; penetration along grain boundaries and alteration of oxide	20

reaction can be kept within tolerable limits for a finite time. Since the thermodynamic factors appear to be so important, it is worthwhile considering to what extent successful predictions about the probability of harmful reactions occurring can be made on the basis of published thermodynamic data. However, much of the data is not presently available, and only an empirical approach can be used in those cases.

The uncertainties associated with the developing of reaction equations for systems in which all the possible products are not known present a formidable barrier to the theoretical solving of these problems. The literature contains many reports of the existence of new, complex compounds and it is reasonable to assume that many more will be identified as the technology advances. Even if the compounds which may be formed are known, it is also of vital practical importance to know whether they are present at the operating temperature as a gas, liquid, or solid. Thus, not only is the compound identification important, but some of the basic physical properties of the compound must be known before the significance of possible reactions can be evaluated.

Even when some confidence is felt about the state of knowledge of the possible reaction products, thermodynamic calculations can still lead to erroneous conclusions through the assumption that the reactants are truly of stoichiometric proportions, since a deviation from stoichiometry can have profound effects on the thermodynamic stability of the desired compound. In practice, this will be difficult since research programs to develop coatings do not normally have perfect stoichiometry in the compounds they purchase from commercial sources. In fact, production quality control of coatings would be extremely difficult if stoichiometic standards were required.

Chemical reactions are closely related to the diffusion processes but are not limited to diffusion. Chemical reactions can cause the formation of a new, more stable compound or cause the distruction of one or both reacting materials. The experimental evaluation of every system of interest is presently the only means to acquire this knowledge.

RADIATION EFFECTS ON MATERIALS IN SPACE*

The radiation encountered by space vehicles consists of electromagnetic radiation and particle flux. Each has its characteristic effects on materials. The sun is the dominant source of electromagnetic radiation; however, there is still controversy over the origin of particulate matter.

Solar Electromagnetic Radiation

The solar spectrum ranges from the short wave length x-rays to the long wave lengths of the far infrared. However, nearly 99 per cent of the total energy is contained within a wave length interval of 3,000 to 40,000 angstroms. The spectral distribution throughout the visible spectrum may be approximated by a 6,000°K black body. Beginning in the ultraviolet region below a wave length of 1400 angstroms, there is considerable structure in the solar spectral distribution due to various emission lines of excited atoms. At very short wave lengths (below 200 angstroms), sunspot activity greatly affects the radiation intensity. Summed over all wave lengths, the total solar irradiance at satellite altitudes is about 0.14 watt per sq. cm of area.

On the earth, ultraviolet radiation is effectively screened by the highly absorbing atmosphere. However, in space applications, it is the ultraviolet portion of the solar spectrum which can cause varying degrees of damage to materials. Metals are essentially unaffected, but plastics and some ceramics are susceptible to damage. In the case of plastics, there may occur liberation of gaseous products (hydrogen or hydrocarbons),

*Milton R. Seiler, Battelle Memorial Institute.

rupture of atomic bonds, and formation of free radicals. Glasses tend to lose their transparency and may discolor. There is little information of use to the design engineer; however, it is known that transparent materials may also undergo some increase in brittleness.

Particle Flux

Radiation due to particulate matter includes primarily the electron and proton flux within the Van Allen radiation belt, the solar-flare radiation, and cosmic radiation.

Van Allen Radiation. Present understanding of the Van Allen radiation belt shows that there are largely two components: a proton belt (*21, 22*) centered at a distance of about 1.5 earth radii and an electron component (*22, 23, 24*) centered at 3.5 earth radii. Although the nature of these belts is not yet completely understood, it is found that the proton flux may be as high as 10^4 protons/cm^2-sec with energies above 40 Mev. The electron flux may approach 10^8 electrons/cm^2-sec with energies above 20,000 ev.

Solar Flares. Solar flares inject electrons and protons with energies of a few hundred Mev. The radiation decays with a lifetime of a few days. Information does not appear to be available on the electron flux, although the proton flux (*25*) can be in the range of 10^2 to 10^4 protons/cm^2-sec. In addition, there is an occasional burst of protons with energies of a few Bev.

Cosmic Radiation. Cosmic radiation consists of high-velocity atomic nuclei; in order of decreasing relative abundance they are: hydrogen, helium, lithium, beryllium, boron, carbon, nitrogen, oxygen, and others in lesser amounts (*26*). Protons (the hydrogen nuclei) and alpha particles (the helium nuclei) are by far the most abundant. When these primary nuclei strike nitrogen or oxygen nuclei in the atmosphere, neutrons are produced with a flux of approximately 1 neutron/cm^2-sec. The primary proton flux is about 2 protons/cm^2-sec.

The above discussion indicates the general particulate radiation environment to which materials and coatings are exposed. From information obtained to date, there is no apparent damage to materials by cosmic radiation. This is because of the low flux level. There is yet insufficient data on the damage to engineering materials and coatings exposed to the Van Allen radiation; although it is known that Van Allen radiation could cause damage if a vehicle were exposed to the belt for several years. Based upon present knowledge, the greatest concern has been the damage to semiconductor devices (*27, 28, 29*).

As the activity of man in space becomes greater, the problems with materials due to radiation damage become extremely important. Coatings may serve as shields for people within space crafts to protect them from radiation, meteorite penetration, and re-entry heating.

OXIDATION

Coatings designed to prevent oxidation of refractory metals accomplish this objective only in a limited way. The coating is not a complete diffusion barrier to foreign gases. Furthermore, metallic coatings and the metal component of cermet coatings are themselves subject to attack by oxygen.

There are numerous growth rate laws for the oxidation of metals. If the surface oxide layer is porous and offers no barrier to the flow of the reacting gas, then the time rate of oxide growth is constant and independent of oxide thickness:

$$\frac{dx}{dt} = K_1 = \text{rate constant} \tag{1}$$

or

$$x = K_1 t + K_2 \tag{2}$$

where K_1 and K_2 are constants. Thus, the oxide thickness x bears a linear relation to the exposure time t. On the other hand, if the growth rate depends inversely on the first power of oxide thickness (diffusion limited), then we have a parabolic growth law:

$$\frac{dx}{dt} = C_1/x \tag{3}$$

and

$$x^2 = 2C_1 t + C_2. \tag{4}$$

This parabolic relation is obeyed only if the diffusion coefficient of oxygen through the oxide layer is constant and equilibrium is maintained on both sides of the layer. The constants K_2 and C_2 are not necessarily the initial thickness of the film. Gulbransen (30) has used these constants to account for decrease in surface roughness as reaction proceeds, effects of the heat of reaction, the effect of the metal taking oxygen into solution, the change in oxide composition, and other effects. If the oxide density ρ is constant, the thickness x is simply related to the mass per unit area, M. We have $M = \rho x$. In many cases, however, the oxide is progressively changing and no unique value of density can be obtained.

Other relationships between oxide thickness and time have been observed. Two of these are the cubic relationship, $X^3 = K_c t$, and the logarithmic relationship, $X = K_e \log (bt + 1)$, where K_c, K_e, and b are constants.

Regardless of the rate equation found to hold for the oxidation of a particular metal, it is well established by kinetic theory that the rate constant of most systems should depend upon temperature T in the manner:

$$k = Ae^{-Q/RT} \tag{5}$$

where Q is the activation energy, A is a constant, and R is the universal gas content. This is the Arrhenius equation as first applied to the oxidation of tungsten by Dunn (*31*).

The rate constant also varies with gas pressure. Wagner and Grunewald (*32*) found the rate constant to vary as the seventh root of the oxygen pressure for the oxidation of copper at 1832°F. Entirely different results were noted by Lustman and Mehl (*33*) who found that the oxidation rate near 1830°F decreased with increasing oxygen pressure above about 0.025 atmosphere. The condition of the copper surface as well as the thickness of the film should influence the interpretation of these resutts.

We discuss the available information on the oxidation of metals with emphasis on temperatures above 1500°F. In general, it is found that most studies of oxidation have been conducted at relatively low temperatures, usually not exceeding 1300°F.

Oxidation of Molybdenum

Molybdenum will maintain a bright polished surface up to about 400°F, tarnishing sets in about 550°F, and the adherent oxide layer is stable up to about 1100°F. The oxidation is parabolic (*34*) between 480 and 660°F; the predominant oxides being MoO_2 and MoO_3. The rate is more nearly linear from 840 to 1110°F (*34, 35*). Above 1460°F, where the oxide MoO_3 melts, a weight loss proportional to time has been observed (*35, 36*). Coatings must obviously be used for the surface of molybdenum if operation is required at 1000°F and above.

Oxidation of Tantalum

Above 600°F, the oxidation rate of tantalum is known to be parabolic (*37*). At about 2300°F, the rate is similar to that of nickei but greater than for chromium and niobium which are nearly identical in their rates. An alloy of 60 to 70 per cent Ta—40 to 30 per cent Cr was found to be the most oxidation resistant at 1250°C.

Oxidation of Chromium

A parabolic rate law of the form

$$(\Delta m)^2 = Kt + \text{Constant} \ (\mu g/cm^2)^2$$

has been observed (*38*) over the range of 1292 to 1652°F. At 1292°F, $K = 2.38 \times 10^{-14} \ (\mu g/cm^2)^2/sec$. The activation energy for K is 66,300 cal/mole (Eq. 5). At 2282°F the rate is nonparabolic (*37*), possibly because of the reaction of carbon contained in the chromium with oxygen and subsequent loss of carbon monoxide.

Oxidation of Tungsten

A complete understanding of the oxidation of tungsten is not yet available. Tungsten is resistant to oxidation up to about 600°F, where it begins to tarnish. Above 600°F, the oxide changes progressively from WO to WO_3. Up to 1300°F the oxidation is diffusion limited and, therefore, is parabolic. Defects which are not self-heating set in above 1300°F with the result that the oxidation rate becomes more nearly linear and much more rapid. Below 2200°F, tungsten is less oxidation resistant than tantalum or columbium but it is more resistant than molybdenum. Above 2200°F, the oxide WO_3 becomes quite volatile in air. Melting of the oxide begins at about 2500°F, and the oxidation of tungsten becomes catastrophic.

An excellent review of the oxidation of tungsten, including all of the observed rate laws, has been compiled by Barth and Rengstorff (39). A review of high temperature coatings for the refractory metals molybdenum, columbium, tantalum, tungsten, and vanadium has been made by Krier (40).

Samsonov et al. (41) have studied the reaction of the oxides BeO, MgO, and ZrO_2, and the carbides of zirconium, hafnium, columbium, and tantalum when in contact with the refractory metals columbium, molybdenum, and tungsten up to 3812°F. An oxide or carbide ring was pressed onto the metal sample and heated under vacuum for 0.5 to 5 hours from 1832 to 3812°F. It was found that columbium begins to react with BeO at 3092°F. A new phase, presumably columbium beryllide, formed at 3272°F. When BeO was in contact with molybdenum, a molybdenum beryllide formed at 3092°F. Tungsten did not form a beryllide with BeO; instead, at 3272°F the highly volatile tungsten oxides began to rapidly leave the tungsten surface.

MgO in contact with columbium (41) was stable up to 3452°F. No reaction of MgO with tungsten or molybdenum was found until 3632°F was reached.

Zirconium dioxide reacted slightly with columbium and molybdenum at 3632°F and with tungsten at 3452°F.

Molybdenum usually began to react with the carbides of hafnium, zirconium, and columbium at 3272 to 3632°F and formed a new phase. At the boundary of the new phase, a solid solution of carbon in molybdenum was usually found. Tantalum carbide did not react with molybdenum until 3812°F.

Oxidation of Columbium

Some of the early work on the oxidation of columbium was performed by Bridges and Fassell (42) who found cusps in the oxidation rate vs temperature. The cusps as seen in Figure 7.4 were largely in the range of 550 to 600°C, varying slightly in temperature when oxygen pressure was changed from 14.7 to 400 psi. Gulbransen and Andrew (43) did not notice cusps. Brady and Ong (44) were able to describe the oxidation rate, as observed by various workers, by an equation of the

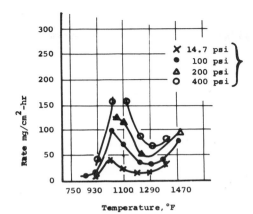

Fig. 7.4. Reveals cusps in oxidation rate of columbium. (Data of Bridges and Fassel.)

form

$$\text{Rate} = A' \exp\left\{\frac{-\Delta H}{RT}\right\}\theta^i$$

where $A' = 1.26.10^{16}$ mg/cm^{2}hr, $\Delta H = 52,000$ cal/mole, and θ^i is the fraction of available interstitial sites occupied by oxygen atoms. θ^i is related to the oxygen pressure p by the relation $p(\theta) = [\theta^i/(1 - \theta^i)]^2$ exp $\{(2\theta^i - 1)2E^{ii}/kT\}$. D exp $\{2(E^i + E^{ii} + 1/2E^d)/kT\}$. The values $D = 2.5.10^{24}$ psi, $E^{ii} = -4,600$ cal/mole, and $E_T = E^i + E^{ii} + 1/2E^d = -42,950$ cal/mole, were determined. The results describe oxidation of columbium over the range of 400 to 1200°C and pressure range of 1.47 to 605 psi.

Inouye (45) studied the oxidation of columbium in oxygen at pressures between 3×10^{-5} and 5×10^{-3} mm Hg and at temperatures of 850, 1000, and 1200°C. The rate controlling reactions were absorption of oxygen, diffusion through a CbO$_2$ layer, and the reaction of oxygen and CbO$_2$ forming Cb$_2$O$_5$.

In contrast to the behavior of molybdenum, the oxide of columbium, Cb$_2$O$_5$, is relatively stable. However, the diffusion of oxygen leads to scaling and progressive attack and embrittlement. Protective coatings are required above 1790°F, but fortunately failure of the coating would not be expected to lead to catastrophic failure.

Some alloying elements that tend to reduce the oxidation rate are Ti, Cr, Zr, V, Mo, and Ta, producing alloys with improved scaling resistance by an approximate factor of 25 and in resistance to internal oxidation by a factor greater than this. Such improvement, however, is probably still inadequate for the service environment, and such alloys have been found to be unfabricable in some cases. A general idea of the oxidation improvement in columbium alloys (46) is presented in Table 7.4.

Oxidation of Zirconium

Zirconium in powder form absorbs oxygen rapidly at 350 and 850°F, as found by Hukagawa and Nambo (47). Bulk zirconium begins to absorb oxygen at 1290°F (48) and more rapidly at 1560°F (49), although oxidation apparently begins at 390°F (50). Over the range of 390 to 795°F, a modified parabolic growth rate law seems applicable (50). The energy of activation for the rate constant is 18,200 calories/mole. Over a period of two hours, a 1000 A film will form at 525°F. In the same time the film is about 5000 A thick at 795°F. The oxide growth rate is still parabolic over the range of 600 to 1652°F (51). The activation energy is 32,000 cal/mole.

Zirconium will absorb about one atomic per cent oxygen at room temperature. Near the melting point, the solubility of oxygen in zirconium is about 55 atomic per cent (52). Apparently, it is impossible to remove this oxygen by vacuum heating, even at 2690°F (48).

Hayes and Roberson (53) have compared the weight gain of zirconium in air, oxygen, and nitrogen. Figure 7.5 reveals the results.

From metallographic examination, it was learned that oxygen did not significantly diffuse into zirconium below a temperature of 1470°F. Samples ignite spontaneously in oxygen at 1830°F.

Hickman and Gulbransen (54) have made an electron diffraction study of the oxide formed between 570 and 1100°F. The monoclinic form of ZrO_2 was found.

Additional studies are needed to learn the oxidation characteristics of all the materials proposed for use at elevated temperature. The few examples given above only serve to illustrate the complexity of the problem. In order to understand the mechanics of oxidation, one must therefore study, and where possible anticipate, the characteristics of the oxidation layers for every metal-gas combination.

TABLE 7.4. OXIDATION DATA

Material	Weight Increase (mg/cm^2) After 100 hours in Pure Oxygen		
	1472°F	1832°F	2192°F
Pure columbium	3600	6000	24,000
Single phase Cb alloys	20–50	70–100	200
Two phase Cb alloys	8	12	16
304 stainless steel	9	10	800
Haynes "Stellite" 31	0.5	10	30
Tungsten	600	6000	60,000

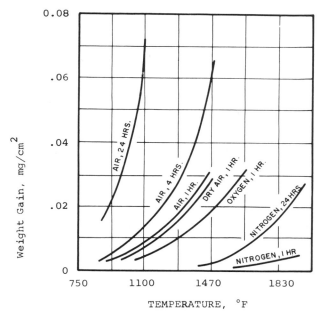

Fig. 7.5. Zirconium oxidation data.

One must be aware of the composition and structure of the stable compounds this combination is able to form. Since the energy states at an interface or surface differ from those in the bulk material, metallic compounds that are normally unstable in bulk may be formed on suitable surfaces.

It emerges from the above remarks that information on the chemistry of the surface compounds is essential for the understanding of oxidation, but a knowledge of the purely geometric relationship is not adequate. Since ionic diffusion is usually involved, more information on diffusion mechanisms and the electrical properties of the compounds is needed to view the entire problem. Accurate phase diagrams of the ceramics and metals are needed to a much greater extent than are presently available.

The theory of oxidation as developed by Wanger, Mott, and others is based on the diffusion of metal or oxygen atoms and ions through interstitial sites or through cation and anion defects in the oxide layer. The oxide layer is assumed to be uniform while the metal underlying the oxide is assumed to be structureless over a particular grain. Recent developments in metal physics have shown that crystal orientation, dislocations, and other defects determine the mechanical properties of the metal. These factors, also, may determine the nature of chemical reactions on metal surfaces.

DIFFUSION*

If coatings are to act as oxidation resistant layers for refractory metals, they must act as diffusion barriers for the inward diffusion of oxygen and the outward diffusion of the base metal. Furthermore, the coating itself must not significantly diffuse into the base metal; coatings applied by diffusion processes can be particularly troublesome in this regard. If the oxygen and metal concentrations remain constant on each side of an oxide layer and if diffusion across the oxide layer is the dominant rate-limiting process, then it can be predicted that the thickness of the oxide, x, should depend upon time, t, as

$$x^2 = Kt,$$

where K is a rate constant. This is the so-called parabolic rate law which is valid in some systems. There are also numerous other growth rate laws which have been observed on metals at high temperature.

Diffusion theory is based on the work of Fick (55) who first formulated the relation which later became known as Fick's first law:

$$J = -D(\nabla C), \tag{1}$$

where J represents the diffusion flux (cm^{-2} sec^{-1}), D is the diffusivity or diffusion constant (cm^2/sec), and C is the concentration of the diffusing material (cm^{-3}). Simply stated, Fick's first law states that the diffusion flux is directly proportional to the concentration gradient. As Eq. (1) is written, J and C can be functions of three arbitrary space coordinates as well as time. However, as considered by Fick, there are a large number of problems of interest where the flow is essentially one-dimensional; under these conditions, Eq. (1) becomes

$$J(x, t) = -D \frac{\partial}{\partial x} C(x, t). \tag{2}$$

Fick considered the constant of proportionality D to be independent of concentration and concentration gradient. These assumptions are usually valid only for very low concentrations. Furthermore, D turns out to be strongly dependent upon temperature.

Fick's second law may be obtained by taking the divergence of Eq. (1). The justification for this procedure is that, in any volume element,

---

*Milton R. Seiler, Battelle Memorial Institute.

the net rate of increase of diffusing material is just the algebraic dif ference between the incoming and outward flux. Thus,

$$\text{div } J = -\frac{\partial C}{\partial t} = -\text{div}(D\nabla C). \tag{3}$$

In the case of one-dimensional flow, Eq. (3) becomes

$$\frac{\partial C}{\partial t} = \frac{\partial}{\partial x}\left(D\frac{\partial C}{\partial x}\right) \tag{4}$$

Tsang (56) has recently treated the problem represented by Eq. (4), assuming that D is a linear function of the concentration. If D is invariant with concentration, Eq. (4) becomes Fick's second law:

$$\frac{\partial C}{\partial t} = D\frac{\partial^2 C}{\partial x^2} \tag{5}$$

There are a number of important diffusion problems which can be treated approximately by Eq. (5). The approximations assume that the diffusivity D is independent of concentration. The results of the calculations are therefore to be taken only as a guide in interpreting diffusion phenomena. More will be said later of the temperature and concentration dependence of D.

Table 7.5 compiles a few boundary-value problems which are of interest in predicting the concentration of a diffusing substance (solute) in a base metal. In all cases the diffusivity D is assumed independent of concentration. Case (a) deals with an impurity maintained at concentration C_0 in a gas phase at the surface of a base metal of "infinite" thickness. This is one of the more simple problems to treat. The second case (b) is slightly more realistic in that the effects of the termination of the base metal at a depth L are included. Cases (a) and (b) yield similar results if the diffusion is carried on for a sufficiently short time, that is, if the diffusion time is much less than L^2/D. Case (c) treats diffusion through a coating into an infinite base, while case (d) takes account of a finite base. In these two cases, the latter of which is derived in the Appendix, a coefficient K is introduced to account for the possibility that the concentration of the solute may not be identical on both sides of the coating-base interface. Case (e) treats the diffusion of the coating into the base metal. Note that the surface concentration depends inversely on the square root of the time. Finally, the case of outward diffusion into a vacuum is considered in case (f). Since the error function, erf (u); the complementary error function, erfc (u); and exponential functions may be found in tabulated form, the calculation of solute diffusion with constant diffusivity is relatively straightforward. The Appendix treats a problem which is representative of the complexities encountered in obtaining solutions. The Laplace transform method is

TABLE 7.5. SOLUTIONS OF SOME ONE-DIMENSIONAL DIFFUSION PROBLEMS

Case	Description	Solution
(a)	Solid of "infinite" thickness. Solute maintained at concentration C_0 at boundary $x = 0$ for $t > 0$. Initial concentration C_i. Figure 7.6-a. Ref. 58.	$C(x, t) = C_i + (C_0 - C_i) \operatorname{erfc} \dfrac{x}{2\sqrt{Dt}}$
(b)	Solid of finite thickness, L. Solute maintained at concentration C_0 at $x = 0$ for $t > 0$. Initial concentration C_i. Impermeable boundary at L. Figure 7.6-b. Ref. 59.	$C(x, t) = C_i + (C_0 - C_i) \displaystyle\sum_{n=0}^{\infty} (-1)^n \left(\operatorname{erfc} \dfrac{(2n+2)L - x}{2\sqrt{Dt}} + \operatorname{erfc} \dfrac{2nL + x}{2\sqrt{Dt}} \right)$
(c)	Solid of "infinite" thickness with coating of thickness w. Solute maintained at concentration C_0 at $x = w$ for $t > 0$. Initial concentration C_i. Figure 7.6-c. Ref. 60.	$C_2(x, t) = C_i + \dfrac{2(C_0 - C_i)}{K(R+1)} \displaystyle\sum_{n=0}^{\infty} \left(\dfrac{R-1}{R+1} \right)^n \operatorname{erfc} \dfrac{(2n+1) \dfrac{w}{\sqrt{D_1}} + \dfrac{x}{\sqrt{D_2}}}{2\sqrt{t}}$ $R = \dfrac{1}{K} \left(\dfrac{D_2}{D_1} \right)^{1/2}$ $K = \dfrac{C_1(0, t) - C_i}{C_2(0, t) - C_i}$
(d)	Solid of thickness L and coating of thickness w. Solute maintained at concentration C_0 at $x = w$ for $t > 0$. Initial concentration C_i. Figure 7.6-d. Solution outlined in Appendix.	$C_2(x, t) = C_i + \dfrac{2(C_0 - C_i)}{K(1 + R)} \displaystyle\sum_{n=0}^{\infty} \left(\dfrac{R-1}{R+1} \right)^n \left(\operatorname{erfc} \dfrac{\dfrac{2L - x}{\sqrt{D_2}} + (2n+1) \dfrac{w}{\sqrt{D_1}}}{2\sqrt{t}} + \operatorname{erfc} \dfrac{\dfrac{x}{\sqrt{D_2}} + (2n+1) \dfrac{w}{\sqrt{D_1}}}{2\sqrt{t}} \right)$ $L \gg \left(\dfrac{D_2}{D_1} \right)^{1/2} w$
(e)	Solid of "infinite" thickness. Solute previously deposited as a coating with surface concentration N atoms per unit area. Coating diffuses into base for time $t > 0$. Initial solute concentration zero in base. Figure 7.6-e. Ref. 61.	$C(x, t) = \dfrac{N}{\sqrt{\pi D t}} e^{-\frac{x^2}{4Dt}}$
(f)	Solid of "infinite" thickness. Initial solute concentration C_i. Solute concentration maintained at zero at surface $x = 0$ for $t > 0$. (Out-diffusion into hard vacuum.) Figure 7.6-f. Ref. 62.	$C(x, t) = C_i \left(1 - \operatorname{erfc} \dfrac{x}{2\sqrt{Dt}} \right) = C_i \operatorname{erf} \dfrac{x}{2\sqrt{Dt}}$

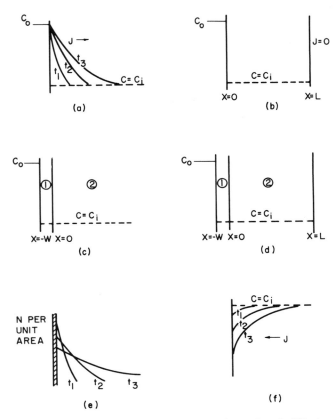

Fig. 7.6. Schematic representation of some one-dimensional diffusion problems (refer to Table 7.5).

quite amenable to a "handbook" solution, provided the mathematical fundamentals are well in mind. Since the conduction of heat is analogous to the diffusion of matter, the work of Carslaw and Jaeger (57) is extremely valuable when unusual boundary-value problems are encountered.

It must be emphasized that the foregoing tabulated diffusion equations should be used with caution. The role of gradients in chemical potential (63) is not fully understood. Not only must one be certain of the boundary conditions, but appropriate diffusion constants must be selected. Bulk diffusion in solids may take place through the crystal lattice (64) or through grain boundaries and free surfaces (65). Each process has its own characteristic diffusivity. One should understand which mechanism(s) is predominant. The temperature dependence and concentration dependence of diffusivity should also be considered. If diffusion through a coating is involved, it should be ascertained if the coating thickness is constant or changing due to oxidation or sublimation processes.

The diffusivity is usually expressible as an exponential function of temperature, that is,

$$D = D_0 e^{-\frac{Q}{RT}},$$

where D_o is a constant, Q is an activation energy, and R is the universal gas constant. Peterson (66) has made an excellent compilation of the diffusivities of elements in the refractory metals.

The diffusivity is known to be dependent upon solute concentration (67) in metal systems, particularly for high concentration. Even the activation energy Q can be a function of concentration (64). Jose (68), Wells (69), and Hoffman (70) discuss various ways of interpreting diffusion data with consideration of concentration dependence.

REFERENCES

1. Lauchner, J. H., and Bennett, D. G., *J. Am. Ceram. Soc.*, **42**, 146 (1959).
2. Kingery, W. D., *J. Am. Ceram. Soc.*, **38**, 3 (1955).
3. Worthing, A. G., "Temperature, Its Measurement and Control in Science and Industry," pp. 1164-1187, New York, Reinhold Publishing Corp., 1941.
4. Gardon, R., *J. Am. Ceram. Soc.*, **39**, 278 (1956).
5. Clauss, F. J., Ed., "First Symposium on Surface Effects on Spacecraft Materials," New York, John Wiley & Sons, Inc., 1960.
6. Thomas, A. R., *et al.*, *Rev. Sci. Instr.*, **29**, 1045 (1958).
7. Olson, O. H., and Morris, J. D., WADC TR 56-222, Part II, Supp. 1, April, 1958.
8. Fieldhouse, I. B., *et al.*, WADC TR 59-744, Part IV, October, 1960.
9. Richmond, J. C., "Coatings for Space Vehicles," pp. 92-112, in Ref. 5.
10. Richmond, J. C., and Harrison, W. N., *Am. Ceram. Soc. Bull.*, **39**, 668 (1960).
11. Burgess, D. G., *et al.*, WADD TR 60-317.
12. Wade, W. R., NASA Memo 1-20-59L, January, 1959.
13. Olson, O. H., and Morris, J. C., WADC TR 56-222, Part III, 1960.
14. Anthony, F. M., and Pearl, H. A., WADC TR 59-744, Vol. III, July, 1960.
15. Dull, R. L., Republic Aviation Corp., Contract AF 33(600)-38042, July 15, 1959.
16. Dushman, S., "Scientific Foundations of Vacuum Technique," p. 20, New York, John Wiley & Sons, 1949.
17. Nicholas, M. G., *et al.*, "The Analysis of the Basic Factors Involved in the Protection of Tungsten Against Oxidation," ASD-TDR-62-205, December, 1961.
18. Steinitz, R., and Resnick, R., Paper Presented at Fifth Refractory Composites Working Group Meeting, Dallas, Texas, August, 1961.
19. Johnson, R. D., *J. Am. Ceram. Soc.*, **33**, 168 (1950).
20. Kingery, W. D., and Economos, G., *J. Am. Ceram. Soc.*, **36**, 403 (1953).
21. Freden, S. C., and White, R. S., *Phys. Rev. Letters*, **3**, 9 (1959).
22. Fan, C. Y., *et al.*, "Space Research," pp. 951-966, H. Kallmann Bijl, Ed., Amsterdam, North-Holland Publishing Co.

23. Van Allen, J. A., *J. Geophys. Research,* **64**, 1683 (1959).
24. Arnoldy, R. L., *et al., J. Geophys. Research,* **65**, 1361 (1960).
25. Dessler, A. J., "Satellite Environment Handbook," pp. 49-74, F. J. Johnson, Ed., Standford, California, Stanford University Press, 1961.
26. Peters, B., *J. Geophys. Research,* **64**, 155 (1959).
27. Wacholder, B. V., and Fayer, E., *Proc. Inst. Environmental Sci.,* 19 (1960).
28. Aukerman, L. W., "Proton and Electron Damage to Solar Cells," Radiation Effects Information Center Report No. 23, Battelle Memorial Institute, April 1, 1962.
29. Redmond, R. F., "Space Radiation and Its Effects on Materials," Radiation Effects Information Center Report Memo 21, Battelle Memorial Institute, June 30, 1961.
30. Gulbransen, E. A., and Andrew, K. F., *J. Electrochem. Soc.,* **98**, 241 (1951).
31. Dunn, J. S., *J. Chem. Soc.,* 1149 (1929).
32. Wagner, C., and Grunewald, K., *J. Phys. Chem.,* B40, 455 (1938).
33. Lustman, B., and Mehl, R. F., *Trans. Amer. Inst. Min (Metall) Engrs.,* **143**, 246 (1941).
34. Gulbransen, E. A., and Wysong, W. S., *Trans. Am. Inst. Mining Met. Engrs.,* **175**, No. 611, 628 (1948).
35. Lustman, B., *Metal Progr.,* **57**, 629 (1960).
36. Kubaschewski, O., and Schneider, A., *J. Inst. Metals,* **75**, 403 (1949).
37. Kubaschewski, O., and Schneider, A., *J. Inst. Metals,* **75**, 403 (1949).
38. Gulbransen, E. A., and Andrew, K. F., *J. Electrochem. Soc.,* **99**, 402 (1952).
39. Barth, V. D., and Rengstorff, G. W. P., DMIC Report 155, July 17, 1961.
40. Krier, C. A., DMIC Report 162, November 24, 1961.
41. Samsonov, G. V., *et al.,* Ogneupory, WPAFB Foreing Technology Division Translation 61-74, No. 7, 335, 1961.
42. Bridges, D. W., and Fassell, W. M., Jr., *J. Electrochem. Soc.,* **103**, 326 (1956).
43. Gulbransen, E. A., and Andrew, K. F., *J. Electrochem. Soc.,* **105**, 4 (1958).
44. Brady, J. F., and Ong, J. N., Jr., "Oxidation Rate of Columbium as a Function of Temperature and Pressure," pp. 719-737, in "Columbium Metallurgy," D. L. Douglass, and F. W. Kunz, Eds., New York, Interscience Publishers, 1961.
45. Inouye, H., "The Oxidation of Columbium at Low Oxygen Pressures," pp. 649-664, in "Columbium Metallurgy," D. L. Douglass, and F. W. Kunz, Eds., New York, Interscience Publishers, 1961.
46. Syre, R., "Niobium, Molybdenum, Tantalum and Tungsten," AGARDOGRAPH 50, Paris, North Atlantic Treaty Organization, 1961.
47. Hukagawa, S., and Namba, J., *ET. F., Tokyo,* **5**, 27 (1941).
48. Fast, J. D., *Foote Prints,* **13**, 22 (1940).
49. Ehrke, L. F., and Slack, C. M., *J. Appl. Phys.,* **11**, 129 (1940).
50. Gulbransen, E. A., and Andrew, K. F., *Trans AIME (Metallurgy),* **185**, 515 (1949).
51. Cubicciotti, D., *J. Am. Chem. Soc.,* **72**, 4138 (1950).
52. Cubicciotti, D., *J. Am. Chem. Soc.,* **73**, 2032 (1951).
53. Hayes, E. T., and Roberson, A. H., *Trans. Electrochem. Soc.,* **96**, 142 (1949).
54. Hickman, J. E., and Gulbransen, E. A., *Analytical Chemistry,* **20**, 158 (1948).
55. Fick, A., *Pogg. Ann.,* **94**, 59 (1855).
56. Tsang, T., *J. Appl. Phys.,* **32**, 1518 (1961).
57. Carslaw and Jaeger, "Conduction of Heat in Solids," 2nd Ed., Oxford, Clarendon Press, 1959.
58. *Ibid,* p. 60.
59. *Ibid,* p. 309 (To conform with the present configuration, the quantity $-x + L$ should be substituted for x in Carslaw and Jaeger's expression).
60. *Ibid,* p. 321.
61. *Ibid,* pp. 50-51.

62. *Ibid,* p. 59.
63. Lazarus, D., "Diffusion in Metals," pp. 71-126, in "Solid State Physics," Vol. 10, New York, Academic Press, 1960.
64. Birchenall, C. E., "Volume Diffusion - An Empirical Survey," pp. 112-128, in "Atom Movements," Cleveland, ASM, 1951.
65. Turnbull, D., "Grain Boundary and Surface Diffusion," pp. 129-152, in "Atom Movements," Cleveland, ASM, 1951.
66. Peterson, N. L., "Diffusion in Refractory Metals," WADD TR 60-793, March, 1961.
67. Mehl, R. F., *J. Appl. Phys.,* **8,** 174 (1937).
68. Jost, W., "Diffusion," pp. 31-32, New York, Academic Press, 1952.
69. Wells, C., "Chemical Techniques and Analysis of Diffusion Data," pp. 26-50, in "Atom Movements," Cleveland, ASM, 1951.
70. Hoffman, R. E., "Tracer and Other Techniques of Diffusion Measurements," pp. 51-68, in "Atom Movements," Cleveland, ASM, 1951.

APPENDIX A

DIFFUSION THROUGH A COATING INTO A BASE OF FINITE THICKNESS

The problem of diffusion through a coating is outlined in Figure A-1. A solute is maintained at concentration C_0 at the surface of the coating for time t greater than zero. The initial concentration is assumed to be C_i throughout the coating and the base. The coating thickness is w and the base thickness is L. The origin of the system is taken at the coating-base interface. Subscripts 1 and 2 refer respectively to the coating and the base. Since this writer is not aware of a detailed solution in the literature, it is felt that a treatment of this problem is important to show the techniques of the Laplace transformation method which so often can be successfully applied to diffusion problems. Laplace transform pairs which are readily available in handbooks are used.

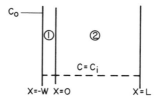

Fig. A-1

We have, in the two regions, the basic relations

$$\frac{\partial C_1}{\partial t} = D_1 \frac{\partial^2 C_1}{\partial x^2} \qquad (-w < x < 0) \tag{1}$$

$$\frac{\partial C_2}{\partial t} = D_2 \frac{\partial^2 C_2}{\partial x^2} \qquad (0 < x < L). \tag{2}$$

The initial conditions are

$$C_1(x, 0) = C_i = C_2(x, 0). \tag{3}$$

The four boundary conditions are

$$C_1(-w, t) = C_0 \qquad\qquad \text{(surface concentration} \tag{4}$$
$$\text{maintained constant)}$$

$$J = -D_2 \frac{\partial C_2}{\partial x}\bigg|_{x=L} = 0 \qquad\qquad \text{(no flux across} \tag{5}$$
$$\text{boundary } x = L)$$

$$C_1(0, t) - C_i = K(C_2(0, t) - C_i), \tag{6}$$

where K is a segregation constant at the coating-base interface, and finally

$$D_1 \frac{\partial C_1(0, t)}{\partial x} = D_2 \frac{\partial C_2(0, t)}{\partial x}. \qquad \text{(continuity of flux} \tag{7}$$
$$\text{across interface).}$$

Taking the Laplace transform of Eqs. (1) through (7) yields, with initial condition (3),

$$s\overline{C}_1 = D_1 \frac{d^2\overline{C}_1}{dx^2} + C_i \tag{1'}$$

$$s\overline{C}_2 = D_2 \frac{d^2\overline{C}_2}{dx^2} + C_i \tag{2'}$$

$$\overline{C}_1(-w, s) = \frac{C_0}{s} \tag{4'}$$

$$-D_2 \frac{d\overline{C}_2}{dx}\bigg|_{x=L} = 0 \tag{5'}$$

$$\overline{C}_1(0, s) - \frac{C_i}{s} = K\left(\overline{C}_2(0, s) - \frac{C_i}{s}\right) \tag{6'}$$

$$D_1 \frac{d\overline{C}_1}{dx}(0, s) = D_2 \frac{d\overline{C}_2}{dx}(0, s), \tag{7'}$$

where $\overline{C}(x, s)$ is the Laplace transformation of $C(x, t)$ and s is the Laplace variable.

A solution of Eq. (1)' is

$$\overline{C}_1(x, s) = A \cosh q_1(x + w) + B \sinh q_1(x + w) + \frac{C_i}{s}, \tag{8}$$

where $q_1 = \sqrt{\dfrac{s}{D_1}}$. Applying boundary condition (4)' yields

$$A = \frac{C_0 - C_i}{s}. \tag{9}$$

A solution of (2)' is

$$\overline{C}_2(x, s) = E \cosh q_2(L - x) + F \sinh q_2(L - x) + \frac{C_i}{s}, \tag{10}$$

where $q_2 = \sqrt{\dfrac{s}{D_2}}$. Applying boundary condition (5)′ yields $F = 0$. Using condition (6)′, we have

$$A \cosh q_1 w = K E \cosh q_2 L. \tag{11}$$

From condition (7)′

$$D_1(A q_1 \sinh q_1 w + B q_1 \cosh q_1 w) = -D_2 E q_2 \sinh q_2 L. \tag{12}$$

Solving (11) and (12 simultaneously for B and E and using (9) yields

$$E = \frac{C_0 - C_i}{Ks} \frac{1}{\cosh q_2 L \cosh q_1 w + R \sinh q_1 w \sinh q_2 L}, \tag{13}$$

where $R = \dfrac{1}{K} \sqrt{\dfrac{D_2}{D_1}}$.

We consider only the solution for the concentration in the base metal. Combining (13) and (10) yields

$$\bar{C}_2(x, s) = \frac{C_0 - C_i}{Ks} \frac{\cosh q_2 (L - x)}{\cosh q_2 L \cosh q_1 w + R \sinh q_2 L \sinh q_1 w} + \frac{C_i}{s}. \tag{14}$$

Eq. (14) can be expressed in a form which is found in tables of the Laplace transform. The identities $\cosh u = \frac{1}{2}(e^u + e^{-u})$ and $\sinh u = \frac{1}{2}(e^u - e^{-u})$ are used to obtain, after some manipulation

$$\bar{C}_2(x, s) = 2 \frac{(C_0 - C_i)}{Ks(1 + R)} \frac{e^{-q_2(L-x)} + e^{q_2(L-x)}}{e^{q_2 L + q_1 w} + \beta e^{q_2 L - q_1 w}} + \frac{C_i}{s}, \tag{15}$$

where $\beta = \dfrac{1 - R}{1 + R}$. It is also assumed that

$$L \gg \sqrt{\frac{D_2}{D_1}} \, w. \tag{16}$$

Dividing numerator and denominator of (15) by $e^{q_2 L + q_1 w}$, we obtain

$$\bar{C}_2(x, s) = \frac{2(C_0 - C_i)}{Ks(1 + R)} \frac{e^{-q_2(2L - x) - q_1 w} + e^{-q_2 x - q_1 w}}{1 + \beta e^{-2q_1 w}} + \frac{C_i}{s}. \tag{17}$$

Since the absolute magnitude of $\beta e^{-q_1 w}$ is always less than unity, we make use of the relation $\dfrac{1}{1 + y} = 1 - y + y^2 - y^3 + \ldots$ for ($|y| < 1$), and obtain

$$\bar{C}_2(x, s) = \frac{2(C_0 - C_i)}{K(1 + R)} \frac{e^{-q_2(2L - x) - q_1 w} + e^{-q_2 x - q_1 w}}{s} \times$$

$$(1 - \beta e^{-2q_1 w} + \beta^2 e^{-4q_1 w} + \ldots) + \frac{C_i}{s}$$

or

$$C_2(x, s) = \frac{2(C_0 - C_i)}{K(1 + R)} \sum_{n=0}^{\infty} (-\beta)^n \times$$

$$\frac{e^{-q_2 \left[2L - x + (2n + 1)w \sqrt{\frac{D_2}{D_1}} \right]} + e^{-q_2 \left[x + (2n + 1)w \sqrt{\frac{D_2}{D_1}} \right]}}{s} + \frac{C_i}{s}. \qquad (18)$$

Making use of Laplace transform pair 83 in "Handbook of Chemistry and Physics,"[1] we have finally

$$C_2(x, t) = C_i + \frac{2(C_0 - C_i)}{K(1 + R)} \sum_{n=0}^{\infty} (-\beta)^n \times$$

$$\left(\text{erfc} \frac{\dfrac{2L - x}{\sqrt{D_2}} + \dfrac{(2n + 1)w}{\sqrt{D_1}}}{2\sqrt{t}} + \text{erfc} \frac{\dfrac{x}{\sqrt{D_2}} + (2n + 1)\dfrac{w}{\sqrt{D_1}}}{2\sqrt{t}} \right). \qquad (19)$$

The series solution (Eq. 19) usually converges rapidly so that only a few terms in the series are significant.

[1] "Handbook of Chemistry and Physics," 36th Ed., Cleveland, Ohio, Chemical Publishing Co., 1954-55.

8

FUTURE OUTLOOK

JOHN HUMINIK, JR.

Vice President and Senior Scientist
Value Engineering
Alexandria, Virginia

AND

JOSEPH L. PENTECOST

Head, Materials Section
Melpar, Inc.
Falls Church, Virginia

In the preceding chapters the characteristics of current coating systems have been discussed, the methods of applying and testing these coatings reviewed briefly, and their use in various high temperature applications presented. For a material to be useful as a temperature resistant coating, it has been shown that it must possess certain physical characteristics and have unusual qualities that are difficult to outline. These qualities include reproducibility, low cost, and high reliability.

The chapters of this book have emphasized the need for studying environments which were formerly unknown or of only academic interest. Because of the rapid advances that have been made in all of the sciences and because of the further advances that have shown to be feasible from the chemistry and physics standpoint, it has become extremely urgent that we learn to cope with these environments.

In many respects, science and technology are advancing at a more rapid rate than our ability to apply our new knowledge productively. In the area of materials in general and in high temperature coatings in particular, however, this is not true. Progress in the recent past in support of the rocket and missile programs especially has been remarkable. Demands for higher melting points, better impact resistance and more erosion resistance will increase, while across-the-board efforts to reduce costs will become a constant target. With the government sponsoring the majority of the high temperature coating research and development, this fast pace will no doubt continue for some time since the capabilities we possess represent first generation developments which are considerably removed from the anticipated goals of efficiency and reliability. A solid technological base on which to develop improved coatings and method of applying them is being formed today with the aid of the government support to over 100 scientific and industrial corporations. In addition, many universities are investigating basic high temperature materials phenomena.

Graphite Coatings Still Required

Now, more than ever before, graphite is being used as a construction material for all manner of high temperature equipment from furnaces to rocket motors. Oxidation and erosion resistant coatings are constantly being sought for this material so that its low cost and machining ease can be utilized in more applications.

One of the areas which should be carefully studied is the utilizing of *in situ* carbide or boride formations on the working surfaces of the finished product. This method of developing a coating is accomplished by depositing materials such as tungsten, chromium, or titanium onto the surface to be treated. These materials can be deposited by electrodeposition, spraying, or slurry coating. The deposit is heated to a temperature which will diffuse the material into the carbon to a predetermined depth. The temperature is then elevated to a point where a reaction will occur between the carbon and the deposited materials thus forming *in situ* carbides. Also, the method of application for the materials that will ultimately form the carbide coating must be accurately understood and controlled. Perhaps the most important and interesting facet of this research will be the study of the solid state reactions (transport of the chemicals to the reaction zone and the chemical reactions themselves) necessary to form the carbides. Before advances can be made in this field, one must realize the variety of transformations and reactions involving the graphite; phase changes in elements and chemical compounds, formation of metastable phases, and oxidation or decomposition possibilities.

The same general type of research approach can be applied to boride, silicide, nitride, and oxide *in situ* coatings. Perhaps the future will see the same type of *in situ* coating research being performed also on tungsten, columbium, molybdenum, and tantalum. Mixed carbides and carbide-boride or boride-silicide combinations appear to warrant study.

Paints for High Temperature Can Be Expected

A new heat resisting paint has been recently announced* which is applied by brush or spray, dries quickly, and is said to be usable over 2000°F. It is reported that an oxygen lance, coated inside and out, had its life extended two to three times. Tubes for exhausting hot air and gases showed virtually no effect, and fiber and paper products were made fire resistant by the paint. Other paints will be developed that can operate up to 2000°F for several hundred hours. Many of these will be based on the phosphates, silicates, and other coating systems described throughout the book.

Substrate Materials and Coating Reliability

Coatings for the refractory metals currently receive widespread attention because of the difficulty in measuring the reliability and reproducibility of the coating system. Though often studied comparatively, various coatings seldom are rated similarly by all investigators. Usually the lack of agreement between tests is blamed on slight differences in the testing procedures.

If one considers the current difficulty in obtaining high-quality, structural, refractory metal sheet, rod or bar stock, and views the 40 to 60 per cent (or more) scrap material from a single ingot, the *absolute* quality of the remainder becomes questionable. The relative quality may be superior to the scrap, but flaws can and do still exist. Perhaps what is measured in many coating programs represents the flaws remaining. If it is argued that this is only proper, since we cannot eliminate *all* flaws in stock material, perhaps the entire development of coatings should be closely reviewed.

Most current coatings have been developed for use on alloys which were developed according to their strength characteristics in a non-oxidizing atmosphere, formability, or fabricability. Since these alloys are useless in oxidizing atmospheres and their strength uncoated is meaningless, perhaps it would be better to start with the development of alloys with improved coating characteristics. This is a more complex approach, but it may represent the only way to improve the "reliability" of current coatings. This philosophy is supported by the early difficulties in porcelain enameling iron sheet. Improvements were made in enameling practice, but the greatest change (and rapid improvement) came when specific sheet material was marketed for enameling.

Minor additives to the coating system, such as chromium, aluminum, or boron in silicide coatings, usually result in quite different, and often improved, performance. Many of these minor constituents should be tried as additions to the refractory metal alloys in an attempt to improve their "coatability."

---

*Fuken Industrial Co. Ltd., Tokyo.

Electrodeposition of Refractory Metals

Refractory metals have been used as coating materials themselves, though their use may be as "sacrificial" coatings. Successful processes must be developed to electrodeposit these metals economically.

Of all the metallic elements in the periodic chart, only about 1/3 have been successfully and economically electrodeposited. Many metals which have not been electrodeposited would have useful applications if they could be made available as smooth, ductile, and adherent coatings.

Those metals which exhibit exceptional corrosion resistance such as titanium and tantalum and also those metals which possess high melting points such as molybdenum, zirconium, and tungsten should be the focal point for such investigations. Metals such as beryllium, aluminum, zirconium, columbium, molybdenum, titanium, tantalum, and tungsten would be very desirable as coatings on less expensive metals or metals that possessed the bulk properties required. For example, the corrosion resistant characteristics of tantalum may be very desirable if used on pipe or pressure vessel shapes for handling of liquid rocket fuels or high temperature nuclear coolants. Also, the use of tungsten electrodeposits for rocket nozzle throats would greatly reduce the weight and cost of present design.

The deposition methods developed should be workable at temperatures under 500°F, since electrodeposition at higher temperatures would pose more difficult handling problems. Many organometallic compounds show promise as the major component of the solutions. Examples of the organometallic compounds which become candidates for yielding metals are the metal alkoxides used as molten salts, π Dicyclopentadienyl compounds of tungsten, molybdenum, titanium, cobalt and other metals.

Immediate laboratory experiments should be conducted with these compounds while a basic study is made to discover which other compounds will lend themselves to electrodeposition processes. Frequently this type of complex research problem is held in the literature search-and-study stage for too long a period, and relatively little laboratory work is performed. Therefore, it should be stressed that immediate deposition attempts are needed to give the investigator the proper perspective of his work.

Another system of electrodeposition uses a bath consisting of a pyridinium halide and a halide of the metal being deposited. Aluminum has been deposited by using ethylpyridinium bromide and aluminum chloride. Zirconium has also been deposited by using ethylpyridinium bromide and zirconium chloride at 300°F. By suitable modification of the pyridinium portion of these compounds, a satisfactorily low melting point could be achieved.

The use of molten inorganic salt baths for electrodeposition of many refractory metals and difficult-to-deposit metals is currently feasible. The temperatures required to keep the baths molten and possible oxidation reactions at the bath surface present some processing problems, but by careful study, salt baths melting at lower temperatures and equipment for maintaining inert atmospheres should eliminate these problems. Even rather complex process equipment could be justified for many coating applications where the alternative coating or cladding processes are unreliable or expensive.

Ductility Test Needed

The ductility of high temperature materials and coatings has always been a property desired, but methods of determining this property have been limited to the cup tests. Specifically, the Erickson cup test which has been used for years to determine the drawability or stampability of the more common metals has been modified slightly to determine the bendability and drawability of the refractory metals. Coated refractory metals usually do not pass the test since nearly all coatings are brittle at the lower temperatures. When the test is performed on heated coated sheet, it can serve as a rough measure of ductility providing the coating is in a plastic state at the test temperature.

Although the cup test has proven to be a valuable tool in the fabrication industry, it does not offer the high temperature researcher much in the way of meaningful data. Too many variables enter the picture when the variety of high temperature materials today are tested. For example, the degree of friction between the dies and the coating will vary with the material or expansion differences between the coating and base material may be exaggerated during the test. A new test for ductility is definitely needed. In the future, precoated sheets will no doubt become available, and before production forming of such material can be done, much laboratory work will be required. Minimum bend radii will need to be established along with data on stamping and drilling before the fabrication industry could intelligently use pre-coated sheet for high temperature hardware.

Adherence and Adherence Tests

Although seldom seriously considered, coating adherence mechanisms are not well understood and current techniques for measuring adherence usually fail to measure the property sought or even yield misleading data. Impact and bending tests which are usually used for measuring adherence actually confuse the *cohesive* strength of the coating material with the *adhesive* strength of the interface. Frequently a coating is deemed to have "excellent" adhesion when the test only confirms that the *adhesive* strength at the interface exceeds the *cohesive* strength of the coating material. Actual adhesive strength is rarely subject to direct measurement and is important when adherence mechanisms are considered.

As the compositions of coatings vary widely, the adherence mechanisms can also vary widely. To understand the possible modes of failure or to improve coating reliability, the interface bonding mechanisms must be well understood. Further work in this area is indicated.

Coating Compositions

Several approaches are popular for refractory metal coatings. These include the formation of intermetallic compounds; interstitial compounds such as the carbides, silicides (hard metals); the use of pure metal or alloy coatings; and the use of oxidic coatings. The intermetallic compounds and particularly the silicides have shown promise; however, ultimate coating performance depends on the outer oxide layer and the kinetics of its formation in most cases. Any materials which form stable refractory oxides as reaction products then become candidates as coating materials. Our inability to explain the kinetics of oxidation in many simple binary metal alloys or compounds at high temperature currently limits our selection of coating materials. Since studies have shown that the presence of a liquid phase at the surface may improve the oxide layer or the kinetics of oxidation, researchers should no longer be inhibited in trying compounds which have a melting point near (or below) the service temperature. Compounds or intermetallics which yield Zr, Hf, Ce, Cr, Th, and other elements with very stable oxides, represent the best choices for the temperature range above 3000°F. For lower temperatures a much wider range of elements is presented.

Most investigators feel that the coating compositions which will have adequate protection at the highest temperatures will not be optimum at low or intermediate temperatures. While this may present a problem for severe cyclic heating, where severe transient heating of short duration occurs, this may not be undesirable.

Basic Science— Severely Needed

Much progress in coatings depends on a better understanding of high temperature reaction rates, diffusion rates in complex systems, phase equilibrium, mass transport, actual reaction products and equilibrium constants, and many other factors. Only recently has the increased attack of silicide coatings at reduced oxygen pressures been confirmed, yet this could have been easily predicted if adequate thermodynamics data had been available. Many coatings have been tried which were doomed to failure and the failure could have been predicted with adequate theoretical studies. This is not to say, however, that all coating problems can be solved by application of reasonable theoretical approaches. Many systems, such as complex alloys with complex coatings, will defy an analysis as to even reaction products. In these cases and for final optimization in nearly all coating systems, an empirical approach based on experience and best approximations will be required.

Much labor could be eliminated through more careful attention to currently available information and through analysis of the information *needed*. While the demands of hardware production frequently evoke the trial-and-error approach to a rapid solution, experience has shown this to be of limited value in many coating development programs. There has been little basic information uncovered which indicates impossibility or impracticality in developing adequate protective coatings for use about 3000°F; however, much experimentation has failed to show rapid progress. A close examination of our basic understanding in coatings systems is in order for all coatings in the temperature range above 2800°F. Current coating development programs should be parallel with the basic studies which will improve high temperature data (not simply compile old, questionable data).

As a summary for this chapter and this book, we can say that many problems remain unsolved and as the current research and development programs progress, new problems will come to light. All of the problems must be attacked by active research efforts, with courage to investigate the new ideas and approaches, and determination to understand the complex systems that most coatings present. Rapid progress has occurred in the past few years, and much basic information has been provided for progress in the next few years.

The present status of high-temperature coatings must at best be termed as one of predominantly research and development, even in view of many widely used commercial coating systems. Therefore, all who are actively engaged in studying coating materials and coating techniques can look forward to the many new developments which will result from our understanding the reactions, the materials, and the environments as this research progresses.

INDEX